ETHICS FOR ENVIRONMENTAL POLICY

An Integrated, Life-Centered Approach

By Berry Crawford
Western Washington University

Bassim Hamadeh, CEO and Publisher
Michael Simpson, Vice President of Acquisitions
Jamie Giganti, Managing Editor
Jess Busch, Senior Graphic Designer
Becky Smith, Executive Editor
Monika Dziamka, Project Editor
Stephanie Sandler, Licensing Associate
Mandy Licata, Interior Designer

First published in the United States of America in 2013 by Cognella, Inc.

Trademark Notice: Product or corporate names may be trademarks or registered trademarks, and are used only for identification and explanation without intent to infringe.

Cover image adapted by Jon Estrella from the following sources: © 2012 Depositphotos/ Iryna Sosnytska; © 2012 Depositphotos/Dmytro Tolokonov; and © 2012 Depositphotos/Anna Subbotina
Interior image copyright © 2010 Depositphotos/aluha123

Printed in the United States of America

ISBN: 978-1-62131-728-9 (pbk) / 978-1-62131-729-6 (br)

www.cognella.com   800-200-3908

CONTENTS

Chapter 2. Moral Standing: Toward a Broader Concept of Moral Community   61

Chapter 3. Animal and Biocentric Ethics

A. Animal Ethics

    1. Overview of the Animal Welfare Movement

        a. Formative Philosophical Views

Chapter 4. Environmental Ethics and Resource Management 133

Chapter 5. Life-Centered Ethical Virtues   163

Chapter 6. Applied Life-Centered Ethical Principles 193

F. Model Uses

G. Toward Reconciliation in Human, Animal, and Environmental Ethics

Dedication

This book is dedicated to my wife, Leticia, whose insight and unwavering love and support see me through; to my son, Berry, whose creative imagination is expressed in diverse and surprising ways; to my son, Charles, for whom nature is a sanctuary and source of contentment; and to my daughter, Georgina, a veterinarian, whose care for animals is practiced with skill and compassion.

Acknowledgments

Many thanks go to Cognella Academic Publishing for its superb teamwork and efficiency in guiding this book to publication. Special thanks go to Monika Dziamka, Project Editor, for her patience, cheerfulness, and helpful suggestions.

INTRODUCTION

S everal aims guided the writing of this book: presenting a convincing rationale for the recognition of the moral standing of biotic entities other than humans, formulating an integrated set of life-centered ethical principles and virtues bearing on the rightful treatment of non-human life and life systems, and working out approaches and methodologies for the application of the proposed principles and the cultivation of supporting virtues. The views of many writers in animal and environmental ethics are critically reviewed and incorporated in the organization and arguments of the book. Because many, perhaps most, issues in the field are addressed, and a serious attempt is made to present positions on these issues in a balanced manner, it is hoped that the book will be viewed as a comprehensive introduction to animal and environmental ethics. It is hoped as well that it will be viewed as an attempt to build on the thinking of others and as advancing the discussion.

Chapter 1 ("Toward an Attitude of Respect for Nature") begins with a review of how nature has been conceived by various commentators in various cultural traditions and examines how strands of these diverse views are amalgamated in what is termed the "modern view." An overarching theme of this chapter is that the "modern view" urgently needs to be supplanted by an "attitude of respect." The centrality of attitudinal orientation in discussions about ethics is elaborated in this context. The focus of the latter two-thirds of the chapter is on what the author considers to be primary formative elements of a respectful attitude toward nature, organized under the headings Rekindling Felt Connections, Telling Life's Epic Story, Understanding Complex Systems, Taking Stock of Nature's Manifold

Value, Recoiling at the Destruction, and Cultivating Life-Centered Virtues. This discussion incorporates the writings of numerous authors concerned with how humans see or ought to see themselves in relation to the broader natural order.

Chapter 2 ("Moral Standing: Toward a Broader Concept of Moral Community") addresses the question of whether biotic entities other than humans can reasonably be thought to have moral standing: to be morally considerable in their own right. A definition of "moral standing" is provided that leaves the question of non-human moral considerability an open question. The definition draws a distinction between the concepts of moral standing and moral significance and clarifies how the two are related but oftentimes conflated. The discussion then turns to a critical review of how the question of moral standing has been posed and answered in the philosophical literature over the past half century, including positions commonly labeled as "anthropocentric," "vertebracentric," "biocentric," and "ecocentric." Attention is given to the debate over the ontological status of species: whether they are simply labels used in biological classification or whether they refer to distinct biological entities. Following this protracted examination of arguments over who or what has moral standing, it is concluded that not only humans but also non-human vertebrates, non-vertebrate organisms, their genomic kinds (species), and the ecosystems they inhabit should be recognized as morally considerable in their own right. More precisely, it is concluded that the question of the moral permissibility of significant harm to populations of any one of these biotic entity types is a relevant moral question, whether or not any human is benefited or harmed thereby, and a question that ought to be raised. The nature of this "ought"—that of giving consideration to the moral permissibility of human-induced harm—is examined, with the contention that it has both an affective component (the "ought" of concerned care, emanating from attitudinal orientation) and a theoretical component (an "ought" of moral obligation, defined in moral theory).

Chapter 3 ("Animal and Biocentric Ethics") addresses the question of what is morally right and wrong in regard to the human treatment of animals, other living beings, and their kinds (species). The discussion begins with a review of the animal welfare movement: its beginnings in eighteenth and nineteenth century philosophical views concerning the moral status of animals, its landmark legal reforms, and its activism. In regard to the rightful treatment of sentient animals, the theories and substantive conclusions of Peter Singer, Tom Regan, and David DeGrazia are reviewed. In regard to the human treatment of the broader panorama of living beings, the biocentric principles developed by Paul Taylor and James Sterba are then examined, noting criticisms that have been directed toward these principles and their application. The chapter concludes with a review of institutional arrangements that have been put in place to protect endangered species in the US and other countries.

Chapter 4 ("Environmental Ethics and Resource Management") begins with a discussion of Aldo Leopold's Land Ethic, including how the development of his ecosystem-oriented thinking reflected developments in the emerging science of ecology and how disagreements have arisen among Leopold's interpreters and critics. The discussion then turns to a review of the sharp debates that have been waged in the US over the past century between "conservationists" and "preservationists." These debates, focusing initially on wilderness protection and set-asides, have broadened to include the theoretical meaning and practical implications of sustainable resource use, the moral imperative of giving consideration to the needs of future generations, and the roles that scientific experts, markets, and government should play in environmental protection and resource management. Various positions on opposing sides of these issues are reviewed. With the objective of putting these debates in broader societal perspective, the chapter concludes with overview accounts of developments in two loosely connected social movements: the preservation/conservation movement and bioregionalism.

Chapter 5 ("Life-Centered Ethical Virtues") begins with a review of the philosophical literature dealing with environmental virtue. It then revisits the contention that virtuous dispositions are one among other important formative elements of attitudinal orientation. In regard to attitudinal orientation toward nature *writ large*, the virtues of respect, humility, gratitude, and responsibility, introduced in Chapter 1 as primary environmental virtues, are discussed in relation to other virtues emphasized in the literature and are more fully defined. The chapter concludes with a discussion of how these virtues can and should be cultivated in education, in media news reporting, and in religious practice, with discussions of how environmental education and religious concern about environmental problems have reached movement proportions.

Chapter 6 ("Applied Life-Centered Ethical Principles") formulates four life-centered ethical principles: the principle of moral consideration, the principle of moral permissibility, the principle of restitution, and the principle of care. These principles are compared to other decision principles, including the principle of precaution and the principle of utility and its common linkage in policy contexts with cost–benefit analysis. The need for a no-rights-violation qualification to the principle of permissibility is addressed, along with a discussion of how the concept of non-human rights needs to understood in the context of an ethic that recognizes the moral standing of biotic entities with very large populations and that rejects the contention that a principle of distributive justice has a constructive role to play. The balance of Chapter 6 is devoted to the development of a model for evaluating the moral permissibility of policies and projects portending serious and far-reaching human and non-human harm. The chapter concludes with a discussion of how the life-centered ethical principles and the proposed application methodologies are thought to resolve some of the long-standing antagonisms among proponents of anthropocentric, vertebracentric, biocentric, and ecocentric perspectives.

The structure of the model involves the designation of aggregate biotic entity types (e.g., humans, vertebrate animals, invertebrate animals, plants, other organisms, endangered species, at-risk ecosystems) potentially impacted by the policy or project (P) evaluated; the representation of P's predicted positive impacts ("benefits") as not-P lost opportunity harms and its predicted negative impacts ("costs") as not-P avoided harms, thus facilitating the use of harm terminology in evaluations involving multiple morally considerable entity types; six defined harm types (physical damage, resource deprivation, functional impairment, physical pain, emotional distress, and life termination) to characterize the respects in which predicted negative impacts (represented as not-P avoided harms) are harmful; six defined complements of these harm types (physical integrity, resource availability, functional capability, physical pleasure, emotional well-being, and life continuation) to indicate how predicted positive impacts (represented as not-P lost opportunity harms) are harmful; and six defined parameters of harm (extent, onset, duration, proliferation, controllability, and remediability) in terms of which the magnitude of harm associated with predicted impacts can be scaled. The magnitude of harm associated with each predicted impact is represented in the model as the sum of the degree-of-harm scalars assigned to each relevant harm parameter, and risk is represented as harm magnitude multiplied by the scalar assigned to estimate probability. Given probability and parameter estimates for each predicted impact, the model computes a number of policy-relevant indices used to determine the moral permissibility or impermissibility of a proposed policy or project. Because the reliability of the computed indices depends on the reliability of model inputs, a suggested approach to developing impact predictions and associated probability and degree-of-harm estimates is discussed in detail: an approach that elicits and refines judgments in multiple rounds of inquiry utilizing structured questionnaires and round-to-round feedback. The discussion then takes up issues related to value weighting and the use of the model to compute value-weighted harm indices. In this regard, an approach to value weighting is proposed that avoids what is argued to be morally unacceptable inter-species bias.

A few comments about the distinguishing features of the book and reasons why it might be an attractive adoption in college courses may be helpful and not too presumptuous. Because most of the issues in contemporary environmental ethics are included in the book's coverage, it might be used as a primary text in the field, perhaps supplemented by materials associated with topics that instructors may choose to give greater emphasis. Each chapter includes a summary account of relevant material covered in depth in other chapters, and can, thus, can be read more or less independently. For courses that have an applied focus and utilize case studies, the book's emphasis on application methodology may make it a particularly attractive choice. To facilitate use of the model in a classroom setting, the book's Appendix provides a detailed case (The Alaskan Native Wildlife Refuge), the evaluation model, and forms for developing and validating model inputs as part of the structured iterative process of inquiry presented in Chapter 6.

Further, because the book incorporates accounts of developments in various sciences (including complex systems theory, molecular genetics, and ecology) and devotes considerable attention to the description of social movements shaping public attitudes and policy (including the feminist, animal welfare, preservation/ conservation, bioregional, and religious environmental movements), the book may be an attractive supplement in conservation biology or ecology courses that emphasize policy issues and their relation to ethics. Because the book's coverage includes developments in science and social responses to environmental problems, it may also be a good choice for environmental studies courses having an issues-related and/or historical orientation. The book will hopefully be of interest as well to readers outside academia who are concerned with the serious environmental problems facing us all.

The book is available from Cognella Academic Publishing as a bound soft-cover volume or as an e-book. Individual chapters are also available in electronic form.

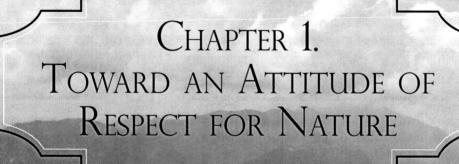

CHAPTER 1.
TOWARD AN ATTITUDE OF RESPECT FOR NATURE

T his introductory chapter has several objectives: to survey how nature has been conceived by various cultures and by various writers who have sought to articulate the meaning of the term "nature;" how these perspectives have shaped what is termed the "modern view" held by many people living in the US and other industrialized and urbanized countries; and to develop the outlines of what is termed an "attitude of respect." It is argued that an individual's and a society's attitudinal orientation toward nature has far-reaching practical implications and that the "modern view" is in serious need of revision.

A. VIEWS OF NATURE

Nature has been conceived in many different ways: as a world in which spirits animate plants and animals and the places they inhabit; as a world created by God, an abode where humans are able to work out individual salvation; as an interconnected and constantly changing network of opposing yin-yang forces naturally tending toward balance and harmony; as a material order governed by physical laws and shaped over vast periods of time by evolutionary processes in which only the fittest survive; as untamed wilderness that impedes civilization and must be brought under control; as a storehouse of raw materials for the production of goods that make human life more secure and enjoyable; as pristine wilderness, where harried urban dwellers are able to retreat for recreation, contemplation, and aesthetic enjoyment; as a world of things-in-themselves that cannot be apprehended save through mind-imposed forms of perception and understanding; and what life was and might again be like if human interventions are radically scaled back. These are but a few of the images that have been entertained by people living in different cultures at various times in human history.

The dominant view held by many people living in contemporary industrialized and urbanized countries has been termed the "modern view." In this view, nature is associated with the good it provides for human beings: land, food, water, energy, raw materials, resources for recreation, and the like. Science and technology are relied upon to keep nature at bay and to increase margins of safety, convenience, and comfort within human-themed environments. Excursions into the wild are enjoyed by some, but generally in small doses and in controlled circumstances. Many see "things human" and "things non-human" as constituting different orders of reality, where the human order—soul, mind, intellect, culture—is regarded as superior to the natural order, and the latter—plants, animals, the land—is regarded as having value to the extent it serves, or is made to serve, human ends. The idea of evolution has challenged the view that human superiority is a divine endowment, but is replaced in the thinking of many by the belief that humankind, standing at the top of the evolutionary ladder, is life's crowning achievement.

This characterization of how nature is conceived by many, perhaps most, contemporary urbanites, is obviously a generalization and an admixture of beliefs shaped by various intellectual and religious traditions. Views of nature of particular importance in shaping the "modern view" are reviewed in broad outline below under the following headings: Nature as Divine Creation, Nature as Antithesis of Mind and Civilization, Nature as Evolutionary Product and Process, Nature as Human Artifact, Nature as Cultural Construct, and Nature as Wilderness.

1. Nature as Divine Creation

Diverse views of nature are found in the Judeo-Christian tradition. Beliefs and doctrines that cast nature in a less than positive light include the view that nature is an abode over which humans have been given mastery and dominion, efforts by Israelite prophets to rid religious thinking of nature gods to ensure that undivided allegiance is given to the one true God, accounts that see nature as the domain of hostile energies where the faith and fortitude of the faithful are put to the test, and the belief that divine creation is hierarchically ordered with humans at the top, superior in value and being.

The early Semites worshipped nature-gods, chief among them Baal, variously characterized as the god of fertility, the protector of crops and livestock, the god of the thunderstorm, and a mighty warrior god. The Old Testament prophets saw Baal as the enemy of the God of the Israelites, and, in their attempts to extirpate these false gods, played a role in desacralizing nature. For the Neo-Platonist theologian, Origen, "The world of flesh is the world of demons. Gross matter ... is the domain of Satan." For St. Bonaventure, the created world is not wretched but a place in which flesh and desire fetter humans and must be overcome and transcended. For Martin Luther, nature is a symbol of God's wrath and certainly not anything to admire or commune with. It is, Luther wrote, the "domain of hostile energies ... which motivate the despairing soul to seek out and cling to 'the right hand of God.'" "And what of thorns, thistles, water, fire, caterpillars, flies, fleas, and bedbugs?" he asked. "Collectively and individually, are not all of them messengers who preach to us concerning sin and God's wrath?"

Passages in Genesis of the Old Testament proclaim that mankind has been given dominion over nature. In Genesis 1:26–29, God said, "Let us make man in our image, after our likeness; and let them have dominion over the fish of the sea, and over the birds of the air, and over the cattle, and over all the earth." In Genesis 9:1–3 God blessed Noah and his sons, and said to them, "Be fruitful and multiply, and fill the earth. The fear of you and the dread of you shall be upon every beast of the earth, and upon every bird of the air, upon everything that creeps on the ground and all the fish of the sea; into your hand they are delivered. ... I give you everything."

The idea that nature is hierarchically ordered is prominent in the theology of St. Thomas Aquinas, who portrayed the created world as an order in which humans are above animals, animals above plants, and plants above minerals, with the whole of the created world below God. For Aquinas, the created world is populated by beings variously distant from God's perfection. He gave this summation: We conclude, then, that lifeless beings exist for living beings, plants for animals, and the latter for man. The whole of material nature exists for man, inasmuch as he is a rational animal." The Aristotelian influence is unmistakable: rational capacity is the defining form, the essence, of human being and is distinguishable in the order of being from animal appetites, the lesser capabilities of plants, and inanimate matter.

But positive images of nature and the mandate to be responsible stewards of God's creation are prominent in Judeo-Christian scripture and theology as well. After creating the world, "God saw that it was good" (Genesis 1:22). Psalms 19:1 tells how the heavens and firmament proclaim God's gory, as does Isaiah

6:3: "Holy, holy, holy is the Lord of hosts; the whole earth is full of his glory." In Matthew 25:14–3 of the New Testament, mankind's stewardship responsibility is made explicit and emphasized: "We who are entrusted with God's property are expected to care for God's property and to distribute God's bounty justly; we will be held accountable for these stewardship responsibilities." St. Augustine extols values found in nature itself: "They [people who disdain nature] do not consider how admirable these things are in their own places, how excellent in their own natures, how beautifully adjusted to the rest of creation, and how much grace they contribute to the universe by their own contributions, as to a commonwealth." St. Francis of Assisi marveled at nature's beauty and order and expressed gratitude and respect for fellow animals and plants, all members of God's creation. In his Canticle of the Sun, he proclaimed "Be praised, my Lord, with all your creatures. … Be praised, my Lord, for our Sister Mother Earth, Who nourishes and governs us, and produces various fruits with many-colored flowers and herbs … Praise and bless the Lord, and give thanks and serve him with great humility."

Not surprisingly, diverse images of nature are found in the theistic beliefs and practices of Judaism and Christianity over the centuries and are variously incorporated in contemporary attitudes toward nature. As discussed in Chapter 5, many interpretations and reinterpretations are found in what today has become a religious environmental movement.

2. Nature as Antithesis of Mind and Civilization

The "modern view" is also heavily shaped by Enlightenment ideology, articulated in its fundamentals by Rene Descartes and Francis Bacon. Descartes maintained that there are two irreducibly different kinds of reality: mind (res cogitans) and matter (res extensa). Bacon formulated the rudiments of the scientific method and saw the new science as an indispensable tool for controlling wild nature for the benefit of mankind. From Descartes, nature came to be seen by people living in Western societies as the dumb and machine-like "other." From Bacon, nature came to be seen as inimical to civilization and needing to be harnessed and brought under human control through scientific understanding. As these ideas were assimilated and augmented by advances in Newtonian science, nature was viewed as a machine capable of being fully understood and controlled. Darwinian images of nature as "red in tooth and claw" (Tennyson's phrase) were later introduced to the public mind, reinforcing the Baconian view of nature as menacing, dangerous, and the antithesis of culture.

The juxtaposition of nature with what was proclaimed to be the nobility of the human mind and human culture had the effect of further desacralizing nature. Viewed as the antithesis of "things human," nature's value was reduced to its use-value for humans, and emerging science was given the mandate to control disease, droughts, dangerous animals, and whatever else there is about nature that was seen to seen to be threatening and menacing to human life and impediments to the progress of civilization. These themes echoed in the new America with the mandate to push back the frontier, cut down the forests for crops and pasture, build railroads and towns, and overcome the resistance of savages.

3. Nature as Evolutionary Product and Process

Charles Darwin's *Origin of the Species*, exuberantly described by Julian Huxley "as the most powerful and the most comprehensive idea that has ever risen on earth," offered a new understanding of human origins. The idea, grounded in Darwin's painstaking research conducted in his five-year voyage on the *Beagle* around coastlines in Africa, Asia, the South Seas, and the Galapagos of South America, challenged the idea that nature is the product of divine creation. Darwin's hypothesis was revolutionary: all species of life have descended over time from common ancestry as the result of an ongoing process of natural selection. In Darwin's words: "As many more individuals of each species are born than can possibly survive; and, as, consequently, there is a frequently recurring struggle for existence, it follows that any being, if it vary however slightly in any manner profitable to itself, under the complex and sometimes varying conditions of life, will have a better chance of surviving, and thus be naturally selected. From the strong principle of inheritance, any selected variety will tend to propagate its new and modified form." Darwin's biological principle of natural selection pre-dated the work of Mendel and later population and molecular genetics, but the basic idea was Darwin's. The theory has since gained broad scientific acceptance and applied in many contexts. Controversial offshoots have been advanced, notably the practice of eugenics to purify selected human gene pools and "social Darwinism" to justify laissez-faire capitalism, but these have been largely discredited as aberrations of Darwin's central scientific insight.

4. Nature as Human Artifact

The modification of landscapes and ecosystems has been occurring for tens of thousands of years as a result of human activities such as gathering, hunting, burning, cutting, grazing, planting, mining, excavating, and building. Since the ramp-up of the Industrial Revolution a scant three centuries ago, human modification of nature has accelerated with mind-numbing speed. In *The End of Nature*, Bill McKibben discusses how humans have transformed not only the land and its communities of life, but also geophysical processes, including the composition of the Earth's atmosphere. Industrial technologies have wrought extensive changes on a macro scale, and more recent advances in genetic engineering and nanotechnology are bringing changes of comparable scope on a micro scale. These developments have led to the claim made by some commentators that nature is fast becoming a human artifact. In the most extreme formulation of the nature-as-artifact thesis, wild nature is said to have been eliminated; nature has become a re-made artifact to suit human purposes. Humans are in control, and little of what was once wild nature remains.

The extreme version of the nature-as-artifact thesis is surely overstated. Human activities have significantly modified the physical environment, but there are still lands and seas relatively undisturbed by humans, including the tundra of North America, northern Europe, and Asia, the coniferous forests south of the tundra, the Amazonian rain forest, the Tibetan Plateau, the Australian Outback, the Sahara and Gobi deserts, and the ocean depths. Conservation International estimates that 45% of the planet's lands are "wildlands," defined as lands retaining 70% of their original vegetation and having a human population of less than five people per kilometer. If the definition of "wildlands" includes areas that are legally protected, the Wildlife Conservation Society estimates that the "last of the wild" comprises about 26% of the planet's land mass.[1] Clearly, also, many disturbed places have the capacity to recover from human intervention, just as life in general has the capacity to adapt to perturbations and to continue to evolve as it has for billions of years. And while technology has extended the ability of humans to protect themselves against non-human agents and events, nature lets us know, sometimes catastrophically, that human control is limited and tenuous. Volcanoes, hurricanes, and other of nature's "reality checks" temper hubris and tell us what we intuitively know anyhow—that the greater natural order establishes the boundary conditions of human thought and action.

---

1   Wildlife Conservation Society, *State of the Wild 2006: A Global Portrait of Wildlife, Wildlands, and Oceans* (Washington, DC: Island Press), pp. 16–17.

5. Nature as Cultural Construct

Rather than seeing nature as a product of human making, postmodernists emphasize that nature is a cultural construct. While this contention has numerous variations, the core assertion is that nature is how it is perceived and understood to be within a particular cultural milieu. Enlightenment thinkers saw nature as the "other": as machine-like, deterministic, inimical to civilization, and utterly devoid of intrinsic value. Romantic writers articulated very different conceptions, seeing nature as reflecting the artistry of God, as having intrinsic value, and as a sanctuary for spiritual renewal. But however nature is or has been represented to be, the postmodernist contention is that nature is just that: a representation. And because any representation is the product of cultural ways of seeing and conceiving, there is no privileged standpoint, no objective truth, no viewpoint that transcends a particular cultural context.

Postmodernists generally contend, moreover, that ideologies are propagated by and reflect the interests of powerful elites within a culture, and that institutions and nations with relatively greater economic and political power have historically imposed their agendas on the less powerful. It is argued in this vein that the view of wilderness enshrined in the Wilderness Act of 1964—"places untrammeled by man without permanent improvement and human habitation, where man himself is a visitor who does not remain"—is one among many conceptions that governments and corporations in the US and other Western countries have sought to impose on undeveloped countries, urging them to preserve natural resources and otherwise forego the kinds of development that have enabled the already-industrialized nations of the West and North to achieve material abundance and high standards of living. Not surprisingly, critiques of this kind are also voiced by critics within the underdeveloped world.[2]

Writers in the ecofeminist tradition have joined postmodernists in rejecting ethnocentric bias in how nature is conceived, focusing more narrowly on male-oriented (androcentric) biases in inherited ideology and their perpetuation in contemporary society. Bacon's characterization of nature as female in character (as wild, dangerous, and reluctant to give up her secrets) and scientific investigation as a fundamentally male enterprise (as requiring an objective, rational, and non-emotional mindset) have been roundly denounced by ecofeminists. Ecofeminist writers have also targeted dualisms associated with the "modern view"—mind/

---

2   A widely read commentary on Anglo-American environmentalism is Ramachandra Gua's "Radical Environmentalism and Wilderness Preservation: A Third World Critique." This widely reprinted article first appeared in *Environmental Ethics*, Vol.1, spring 1989.

body, reason/emotion, abstraction/embodiment, culture/nature—together with the tendency to associate superiority with male attributes (reason, abstraction, etc.) and inferiority with their female counterparts (body, emotion, etc.). Karen Warren characterizes such dualisms as aberrations of "value-hierarchical thinking" and the "logic of domination."[3]

Acknowledging that events, conditions, and processes in the world are disclosed to us through our perceptions of them, and that without such perceptual disclosures humans would have nothing to understand, various writers reject the conclusion that perception and understanding isolate humans utterly and completely from the world they perceive and seek to understand. Without resorting to a "naïve realism"—the view that cognition exactly and precisely discloses an independently existing world as it "really is"—Holmes Rolston articulates a "critical realism" to combat not only naïve realism but also the view that nature is, inescapably, a mental or cultural construct. With reference to scrupulously conducted scientific investigations in evolutionary biology, molecular biology, ecology, and cosmology—investigations in which explanatory hypotheses are developed and tested by observations and in which experiments are designed to confirm or deny those hypotheses—Rolston argues that, over time, we get "nature for real," not merely the cultural construction of nature. What is discovered is bound up with theoretical constructs, but the basic test of truth for scientific knowledge is exacting: a hypothesis stands only as long as its predicted results are corroborated by repeated experimentation, while non-corroborating evidence quickly discredits that hypothesis. Unlike naïve realism, critical realism recognizes the conceptual contribution of the knowing subject in the formation of theories and acknowledges the incomplete, selective, and perspectival character of scientific theories. Although no perfect correspondence exists between scientific hypotheses and reality "out there," the critical realist nevertheless maintains that rigorous science yields, or progressively yields, an accurate and reliable map of physical reality.[4]

Phenomenologists Neil Evernden, Edward Casey, and David Abram emphasize that perception originates in sensory contact with the world and is essentially

---

3   Karen Warren, "The Power and Promise of Ecofeminism," in *Environmental Philosophy: From Animal Rights to Radical Ecology*, Michael E. Zimmerman, et al., eds., (Pearson Prentice Hall, 2005).

4   By his own account, Rolston belongs to the tradition of American pragmatism, and his "critical realism" is closely related to what Charles Sanders Pierce called "warranted assertability." See Rolston's "Nature for Real: Is Nature a Social Construct?" in *The Philosophy of the Environment*, D.J Chappell, ed. (Edinburgh University Press, 1997), pp. 38–64.

participation in the world. "It is misleading," Evernden writes, "to speak of an isolated self surveying a world, for the person is from the start *in* the world, and consciousness is *of* the world."[5] Perception occurs in a body interacting with other bodies in a local environment; perception is corporeal, occurs in a place, and is essentially an interaction between the perceiver and the perceived. In this interaction, the perceiver and the perceived participate in a kind of mutual disclosure; each is "opened up" to the other. In Abram's words, "There is an intimate reciprocity to the senses; as we touch the bark of a tree, we feel the tree touching us; as we lend our ears to the local sounds and ally our nose to the seasonal scents, the terrain gradually tunes us in in turn.[6]

It is misleading to erect a sharp distinction between subject and object, perceiver and perceived, culture and nature, and then to construct a reductive explanation of one in terms of the other. It is as meaningful to speak of a "natural" order as it is to speak of a "cultural" order. In some places (e.g., a university or a library), cultural products and processes predominate; in others (e.g., a rainforest or a coral reef), natural products and processes predominate. Moreover, in maintaining that nature is only a cultural construct while at the same time insisting that all conceptual constructs are relative to particular cultural contexts, postmodernism is said by some writers to trap itself in a contradiction; it inconsistently privileges its own conception of nature as non-relativist truth. As Charlene Spretnak put it, "'Postmodern' is '*most*modern' because its proponents have been socialized and educated in the scientific-humanist world view, which is dedicated to the denial of the power and presence of nature."[7]

6. Nature as Wilderness

The idea of nature as wilderness gained popular appeal through the writings of the European Romanticists (e.g., Shelley, Keats, and Rousseau) and the American Transcendentalists (e.g., Emerson, Thoreau, and Whitman) as well as through grand landscape paintings, photographs of nature's many moods, and the inspiring descriptions of wild places by nature writers. Nature came to be seen as magnificent places where dispirited humans living in controlled urban environments could find escape, liberation, tranquility, and inspiration. The

---

5   Neil Evernden, *The Natural Alien: Humankind and Environment* (University of Toronto Press, 1985), p. 59.
6   David Abram, *The Spell of the Sensuous* (Vintage Books/Random House, 1996), p. 263.
7   Charlene Spretnak, *The Resurgence of the Real: Body, Nature, and Place in a Hypermodern World* (Addison-Wesley, 1997), p. 66.

visions and sentiments expressed in these works played a key role in changing popular attitudes toward nature as hostile and dangerous and in creating a political climate for the establishment of national parks and wilderness areas in the US and elsewhere.

While negative attitudes toward wild places have waned in contemporary western cultures, various writers have sought to debunk what they call the "wilderness myth." Critics point out that there are few places on Earth today that meet the definition of wilderness given in the Wilderness Act, that indigenous peoples occupied and modified the lands that are now designated as wilderness areas in the US and elsewhere, that attempts to set aside wilderness areas and to preserve wilderness conditions require intensive and continuous human management of those areas, and that it dilutes responsibility for protecting areas that are less pristine. Critics have also argued that wilderness preservation as conceived in the Wilderness Act is ethnocentric and flies in the face of the basic fact that change and adaptability to change are basic dynamics in evolving ecosystems, not constancy and uniformity.[8]

There is merit in these critiques, but they, too, run the risk of blurring important distinctions and distorting facts. There are important differences, Holmes Rolston reminds us, between human-inhabited and human-uninhabited regions, between nature and culture, between the generally slow pace of biological change and the increasingly fast pace of social and technological change, and between the modifications made by indigenous peoples of the lands they occupied and those wrought by industrialized societies with bulldozers, large populations, and economies that depend upon natural resources and are remarkably efficient in satisfying voracious wants and desires.[9]

7. Nature Reconsidered

The natural world *has* been transformed to a large extent by ubiquitous human presence and by ever-expanding technological capability to exploit nature's products and processes to serve human ends, but certainly not completely so. Individual and societal views of nature *are* shaped by the beliefs, values, and institutions of the culture in which one lives, but this does not mean that "nature for

---

8   Arguments for and against the "wilderness concept" are presented by the editors and contributing authors to *The Great New Wilderness Debate*, J. Baird Callicott and Michael P. Nelson, eds., (Athens, Ga.: University of Georgia Press, 1998).
9   Holmes Rolston, "The Wilderness Idea Reaffirmed," in *The Environment Professional* 13 (1991), pp. 370–77.

real" cannot be understood through rigorous and continuing scientific inquiry, or that cultural constructs of nature that disadvantage women, people living in Third World countries, and others are immune from moral criticism and reform, or that insidious dualisms should not go unchallenged. Humans and other life *have* evolved by processes of natural selection, but the capacity of systems throughout nature to self-organize, adapt, and create novelty is also part of the story of life's evolution. Religious beliefs *do* give meaning and hope in many people's lives, but religious accounts that reject *ex cathedra* evolutionary and other accounts of the relationship of humans to the broader natural order limit and distort an understanding of the human condition. None of the various conceptions of nature briefly sketched above are adequate by themselves, or for a world in which rapidly growing human populations are transforming landscapes and consuming resources at accelerating rates, regenerative capacities are being diminished, resource shortages are recurring on a global scale with ominous potential for widespread conflict and warfare, human-caused species extinctions are occurring on a scale rivaling the mass extinctions of the distant geological past, and climate changes are occurring as a result of rapidly increasing concentrations of greenhouse gases.

Nature is not only a product, but a vast biosphere in which life-creating and life-sustaining processes occur and have occurred for more than three billion years. The ongoing saga of life is about the capacity of many lives to adapt, survive, and thrive in their environments, about the adaptive and information-based capacity of genomes (the concrete embodiment of species) to orchestrate function at the cellular level, and about the capacity of ecosystems to enable a great diversity of existing kinds to co-exist, co-adapt, and co-evolve in relations of mutual benefit and to generate new kinds of increasing diversity and complexity. Manifestations of these capacities constitute the most basic processes that occur in the planet's biosphere, and themselves are processes through which pro-life tendencies are selected in the natural order.

The distinction between nature as product and nature as process is drawn by various authors.[10] The wilderness concept goes awry when nature is seen as

---

10   For example, Michael Nelson argues that "Wilderness should be reconceived as a process" and that "accordingly, places could be reclaimed and resurrected, based on a standard of "wildness." Nelson points out some of the problems associated with the "received concept of wilderness" as land that is unaffected by humans, a place where humans may be visitors but not residents." See Nelson's article "Rethinking Wilderness: The Need for a New Idea of Wilderness" in *Environmental Ethics: Concepts, Policy, and Theory*, Joseph DesJardins, ed. (Mountain View, CA: Mayfield Publishing Company, 1999), p. 370.

an end product that needs to preserved in a fixed, unchanging state. If the term "wild" is used to refer to processes in the natural world whose operations and products predate human life and whose continuation, while influenced by human activity, are not dependent on human life, the challenge is to preserve wildness, not wilderness. An organism, ecosystem, or bioregion is wild to the extent that its functioning is not disturbed or controlled by human beings, or to the extent that it is capable of recovering from human interference, behaving more or less as it did before. Clearly there are relatively wild places left on Earth, and clearly many disturbed places have the capacity to recover from human interventions.

In his essay "Walking," Thoreau said: "In wildness is the preservation of the world." The term "wildness" in this statement is sometimes interpreted as "wilderness," but Jack Turner insists that this a misrepresentation of what Thoreau meant. Turner points out that Thoreau noted in his Fact-Book that "wild" is the past participle of "to will" and that wildness is "self-willed land."[11] By identifying wildness with fixed conditions in nature rather than self-organizing processes that produce and sustain those conditions, we get a flawed concept of wildness. We also get, according to Jack Turner, wilderness areas that are too small, too accommodating of human recreational interests, too controlled and regulated, and too tamed. In Turner's words, "Thus diminished, wilderness becomes a special unit of property, treated like a historic relic or ruin—a valuable remnant."[12]

In what follows, then, the term "wild" is used to refer to life and life systems whose existence is not dependent on human life and which would continue to function and adapt without human life. The concept of nature-as-wildness legislates against statements such as "Nature is what it is conceived to be" (nature as cultural construct) or "Nature is what humans make of it" (nature as human artifact), or "Everything is natural." At the same time, however, it accommodates basic facts: that humans are part of nature; that culture is situated within and depends on wider natural systems; that wildness can be found in gardens and urban parks as well as set-aside wilderness areas; and that neither culture nor non-human nature refers to unchanging conditions. Like culture, nature is both product and process and constantly undergoes change. Furthermore, it does not presuppose that nature and human culture are inevitably and irreconcilably opposed, or that the human influence on other life is necessarily good or bad. Arguments for the preservation of wilderness and wildlife are examined in subsequent chapters, but the present point is that such arguments should not be settled

---

11   Jack Turner, *The Abstract Wild* (Tucson: The University of Arizona Press, 1996), p. 111.
12   Ibid., pp. 84–86.

in advance by flawed or overly restrictive definitions of the terms "wildness," "wilderness," and "nature."

B. TOWARD AN ATTITUDE OF RESPECT

One's attitude toward anything—toward football, or the outcome of an election, or an aptitude test, or mercy killing—influences what one is likely to say or do with respect to that thing. Attitudes are aggregate expressions of how we think and feel about something, how we regard it, and how we are disposed to deal with it. An attitude toward nature involves these same features, but here the attitude has reference to fundamental conditions of life. One's attitude toward nature reflects how one sees oneself in relation to the natural environment in which one lives and, on the largest scale, to evolving planetary life. An attitude toward nature is a cultural construct, but one that is thoroughly conditioned by the biophysical environments in which cultures arise and change.

As stated at the outset, a central thesis of this work is that an individual's and a society's attitude toward nature has far-reaching consequences, and that the dominant attitude toward nature in the US and other industrialized nations (the "modern view") is in serious need of revision. When levels of human production, consumption, and waste generation exceed the capacity of natural systems to sustain those activities and, worse, degrade nature's regenerative and assimilative capacities; when the dominant economic paradigm ignores, in theory and practice, the costs associated with this inherently unsustainable "using up" of Earth's natural capital; when our dominant ethical traditions deny moral standing to all other species; when environmental problems of unprecedented seriousness face people all around the globe but people and governments are unwilling or unable to take corrective action; when thinking at the frontiers of contemporary science have abandoned dualistic, mechanistic, and reductionist models of explanation—when contemporary life is riddled with these deeply ingrained and far-reaching incongruities—it is time to re-examine fundamental questions related to the relationship of humanity to the broader natural order. It is time for attitude adjustment.

An attitudinal orientation that regards nature as the separate and distinctly different "other," as inferior and inimical to civilization, and as having value only because it yields resources for human needs and aspirations is, not surprisingly, a culture in which sanctions against environmentally and ecologically destructive practices are weak. In contrast, an attitude of respect—an attitude shaped by felt connections to the land and other life; an attitude that draws intellectual support from models of explanation in evolutionary biology, ecology, complexity theory, and other sciences that go beyond mechanistic determinism to focus on relationships, interdependence, and emergent, creative change; an attitude that affirms the value of self-organizing processes throughout the biosphere and recognizes their incalculable instrumental value for human life and culture; an attitude quickened and humbled by direct experience of nature's beauty, wonders, and power; and an attitude aroused and put on "red alert" by growing awareness of the extent to which human activities are putting human life and most other life in serious jeopardy—would, if it took hold in the minds of the general populace, serve as a strong sanction against practices that are inherently unsustainable and massively harmful to non-human life and life systems.

An attitude of respect is an orienting mindset informed by and nourished by numerous dimensions of human experience, pre-conceptual and conceptual, particular and abstract, descriptive and normative, practical and aesthetic. It is an attitudinal complex shaped by numerous dimensions of human experience, including instincts, sensations, feelings, valuations, beliefs, memories, and dispositions. The following presents an overview of what various writers have said about formative elements of an attitude of respect toward nature, summarized under the following headings: Rekindling Felt Connectedness, Telling Life's Story, Understanding Complex Systems, Reassessing Nature's Manifold Value, Recoiling at the Destruction, and Cultivating Life-Centered Virtues. Many of the themes provided in this snapshot are critically examined in subsequent chapters.

1. Rekindling Felt Connections

An ecological attitude of respect depends, in no small part, on the rekindling of felt connections to the land and its communities of life. Indigenous peoples in all cultures have always felt a connection to the land and other life. Writers variously contend that feelings of connectedness to the land and its communities of life initiate at a pre-conceptual level of experience. This awareness is variously said to be encoded in our genes, to engender feelings of care, to be rooted in the structure of perception and heightened when the senses are fully engaged and attuned to the sensorial field, to be associated with the unique qualities of place and the feeling of being at home, to be quickened when one is directly and attentively engaged in activities related to gardening and caring for animals, to be evoked at a primordial level by the "call of the wild," and to be awakened and heightened by aesthetic encounters in nature. World views, lifestyles, and

institutional arrangements that cut one off from these elemental modes of per-
ceiving, living, and adjusting are said to be spiritually impoverishing and to lead
to a host of adverse psychological and social consequences.

a. Biophilia and Care

The celebrated biologist, E.O. Wilson, contends that humans have an "innate
emotional affiliation to other living organisms," which he calls *biophilia* and
associates with genetic predisposition.[13] Stephen Kellert concurs: "During the
long course of human evolution living diversity was valued because of the adaptive benefits it offered us physically, emotionally, and intellectually. ... Buried
within the human species lies a deep and enduring urge to connect with living
diversity."[14] Keller is echoing what Darwin himself noted. Darwin viewed the
feelings of kinship that animal species have with one another and we have with
animals and other members of our own species as adaptive mechanisms acquired
through natural selection. While the sense of connection with other life may be
dimmed in the lives of urbanites cut off from direct contact with the wild, it is
never far from the surface. The loss of songbirds poignantly described by Rachel
Carson in *The Silent Spring* was a loss instantly recognized by readers because it
struck a chord deep within the human psyche.

Many writers have discussed the primacy of sympathetic caring in the human
psyche, variously called empathy, fellow feeling, identification, and compassion,
and see such caring as the wellspring of moral response.[15] Phenomenologist Max
Scheler emphasized the need to re-develop a sympathetic capacity to decode
the symbolic language of nature. "We must," he wrote, "once more look upon
Nature as into the heart of a friend."[16] Albert Schweitzer sought to explain how
the identification of one's own will-to-live with the will-to-live manifest in lives
throughout nature evokes a feeling of compassion.[17] Arne Naess associated one's
identification with other life as a growth of one's sense of self and, with it, a
feeling of sympathetic concern for other life. Naess's interpreter, Warrick Fox,
believes that the recognition of commonality is essential in this process, adding

---

13   E. O. Wilson, *Biophilia* (Cambridge University Press, 1984), p. 31.

14   Stephen R. Kellert, *The Value of Life: Biological Diversity and Human Society* (Island Press,
1996), p. 12.

15   This tradition in ethics is reviewed in Chapter 2.

16   Max Scheler, *The Nature of Sympathy* (Hamden, Conn.: Archon, 1978), p. 105.

17   Albert Schweitzer, *The Teaching of Reverence for Life* (Holt, Rinehart, and Winston, 1965),
p. 26.

that evolutionary biology and ecology play an important role in identifying commonalities that humans share with other life. Holmes Rolston finds manifestations of caring throughout nature, not only in human life and culture.[18] Writers in the feminist tradition view moral response as issuing in feelings of sympathetic care and sincere attempts to imagine the reality of another. "When my caring is directed to living things," Nel Hoddings writes, "I must consider their natures, ways of life, and needs. And although I can never accomplish it entirely, I try to apprehend the reality of the other."[19] Iris Murdock elaborates: "The direction of attention is outward, away from the self, which reduces all to a false unity, toward the great surprising variety of the world and the ability to so direct attention is love."[20] Ecofeminists emphasize generally that such care arises naturally and spontaneously when one realizes how profoundly life is interconnected and interdependent.

b. Attachment to Place and Feeling at Home

Caring for the land and its life is closely related to identification with place. The German phenomenologist Martin Heidegger characterizes human being as being-in-place. For Heidegger, to live authentically is to "dwell in place" and to be "guardians of place." Inauthentic living is alienation from place, a condition that Heidegger calls "homelessness." Homelessness is an existential condition that Heidegger believes is the bane of people living in modern urbanized society. People are alienated from place and experience the anxiety accompanying this alienation. Such alienation is tragic, Heidegger continues, because people are increasingly powerless to do anything about it.

For Edward Casey, place is where one's sensing body integrates with the environment in which it finds itself situated. "Far from being an inert support for egoic mind," Casey writes, "the lived body takes us out of our skin into the world's

---

18   For further elaboration of what Rolston sees as manifestations of care in the biotic order, see his "Care on Earth: Generating Informed Concern," in *From Physics to Metaphysics*, Paul Davies and Niels Henrick, eds. (Cambridge: Cambridge University Press, 2010). See also the discussion of Rolston's views on care in Chapter 5.

19   Nel Hoddings, *Caring: A Feminine Approach to Ethics and Moral Education* (Berkeley: University of California press, 1984), p. 16.

20   Josephine Donovan, "Attention to Suffering: Sympathy as a Basis for Ethical Treatment of Animals," in *Animal Rights*, Josephine Donovan & Carol J. Adams, eds. (New York: Continuum, 1994), p. 150.

flesh, back into *place*."[21] It is through sensation that we come into direct contact with the place we inhabit, and it is through sensation that the sensible and the sentient interact in mutual disclosure.

Casey's student, David Abram, recounts how direct sensuous contact and intimate relations with the land is reflected and preserved in the oral stories and songs of indigenous peoples and how, for oral peoples, language "arose not only as a means of attunement between persons, but also between persons and the animate landscape." He discusses how creation of the alphabet gave humans the ability to interact with written signs in abstraction from the earthly things they represent and how electronic-based communications have blossomed into a vast cognitive realm in which "the senses—once the crucial site of our engagement with animate earth—become mere adjuncts of an isolated and abstract mind bent on overcoming an organic reality that now seems disturbingly aloof and arbitrary." Rather than dwelling in place, we view ourselves as occupying a set of coordinates in space. When we say that we live in the US, or British Columbia, or New Mexico, "we say very little about that earthly place we inhabit, but simply establish our temporary location within a shifting matrix of political, economic, and civilizational forces struggling to maintain themselves." The danger, Abrams believes, is that "we may come to believe that our breathing bodies really inhabit these abstractions, and that we will lend our lives more to consolidating, defending, or bewailing the fate of these ephemeral entities than to nurturing and defending the actual places that physically sustain us." The basic need, Abram believes, is to ground ourselves, once again, in the links between the abstract world and the perceptual terrain that surrounds us. "For it is only at the scale of our direct, sensory interactions with the land around us that we can appropriately notice and respond to the immediate needs of the living world."

Dwelling in place is characterized by Edward Relph as a homeward directed sentiment, one that is comfortable, detailed, diverse, and ambiguous without confusion. To experience this sentiment is to be an "insider": to identify with place, to feel care, concern, and warmth for it, to feel that one belongs there. For Relph, the sense of being "at home" is acquired through communal participation, and is an orientation that individuals experience to a greater or lesser degree. Barry Lopez, too, reminds us that intimate understanding of physical place comes from attending to it with all the senses and with an attitude unaffected by assumptions, expectations, and guile. We must, he says, "Put aside the bird book, the analytic

---

21   Edward Casey, *Getting Back Into Place: Toward a Renewed Understanding of the Place World* (Indiana University Press, 1993, p. 262.

frame of mind, a compulsion to identify and sit still."[22] "The key," he adds, "is to become vulnerable to place. If you open yourself up, you can build intimacy. Out of such intimacy you may come to a sense of belonging."[23] In his essay, "The Stone Horse," Lopez describes how his critical interrogation of an ancient assemblage of stones in the likeness of a horse impeded his appreciation of it—how a process of abstraction drew him away from an intimate and empathetic understanding of its significance. "The land retains an identity of its own," Lopez adds, "still deeper and more subtle than we can know."[24] It is reported that a Native American elder made this comment about settlers and immigrants in the mid-western US: "looks like they are finally beginning to learn how to belong here."

Two early proponents of bioregionalism, Peter Berg and Raymond Dasmann, described "living-in-place" as "becoming native to a place through becoming aware of the particular ecological relationships that operate within and around it. It means understanding activities and evolving social behavior that will enrich the life of that place, restore its life-supporting systems, and establish an ecologically and socially sustainable pattern of existence within it."[25] They emphasize that a bioregion can be determined initially by the use of climatology, physiography, ecology, and other natural sciences, but "The final boundaries of a bioregion are best described by the people Living within it, through human recognition of the realities of Living-in-Place." For these authors and others in the bioregional movement, "home place" is as much cultural as biogeographical.[26]

Mark Sagoff also champions the concept of place in environmental discourse: "It brings together human, environmental, and natural history," he writes, "and is particularly valuable in helping us to understand what we deplore about the human subversion of nature and what we fear about the destruction of the environment."[27] "Unlike the concept of space," Sagoff says, "place refers to land whose significance is not summed up by the consumer preferences of

---

22   Barry Lopez, "A Literature of Place," in *The University of Portland Magazine*, Summer 1997, p. 25
23   Ibid., p. 25
24   Barry Lopez, *Arctic Dreams: Imagination and Desire in a Northern Landscape* (London: Pan, 1987), p. 228.
25   Peter Berg and Raymond Dasmann, "Reinhabiting California," in *The Ecologist* 7 (10), p. 399.
26   An overview of the bioregional movement is provided in Chapter 4, Section H.
27   Mark Sagoff, "Environmental Ethics: An Epitaph," in *Resources*, spring 1993, p. 6. See also Sagoff's "Settling America: The Concept of Place in Environmental Ethics," in *Journal of Energy, Natural Resources and Environmental Law*, 12, pp. 351–418.

individuals; land is far more than delineated space, more than property, more than a commodity."

A large body of nature writing is devoted to the description of the unique features and charms of particular places. Thoreau's observations at Walden Pond and John Muir's colorful descriptions of the High Sierras are classical examples of this large genre of writing.[28]

c. Gardening and Taking Care of Animals

The domestication of animals and the cultivation of crops for human survival, convenience, and enjoyment have a long history and have played an important role in shaping attitudes toward nature. People who work the land, have pets, and care for farm animals know first-hand the necessity of paying attention to the needs of the land, plants, and animals with whom they interact and the importance of heeding nature's time-tested ways.

Michael Pollan has written about what he has learned from years of effort as a gardener.[29] Perhaps the most basic lesson is that successful gardening depends on working in harmony with nature's ways. "The trick is to put her knowledge to our purpose in the garden." Based on his personal and sometimes frustrating experiences, Pollan articulates some of the insights of what he dubs a "garden ethic." This ethic is avowedly an enlightened egoism, but one that shows respect for the wildness that one encounters "right there" in one's soil and plants. The gardener's respect for nature is not abstract and not romantic ("He's seen her ruin his plans too many times for that"), and he feels he has a legitimate quarrel with her weeds, wounds, storms, plagues, rot, and death. He recognizes at the same time, however, that it is a mistake, indeed an impossibility, to reach for outright victory. He does not see nature as a neutral, fixed backdrop but as alive and changing all the time in response to innumerable contingencies, including his own presence. He does not see himself as outside nature, and he doesn't think that his interactions with nature are inherently good or bad. He believes it is possible to make distinctions between kinds and degrees of intervention. He looks for local answers and relies on his skill to make and apply informed distinctions.

---

28   A history of this genre is provided by Thomas J. Lyon in his *This Incomparable Land: A Guide to American Nature Writing*. See also *The Norton Book of Nature Writing*, edited by John Elder (W.W. Norton, 1980).
29   Michael Pollan, *Second Nature: A Gardener's Education* (Grove Press, New York, 1991).

He has learned that nature is, above all, a pragmatist and that the good gardener borrows his methods, and sometimes his goals, from nature herself.

Farmers, ranchers, landscapers, gardeners, and others who interact on a daily basis with the land, its soils, and its non-human inhabitants do not see themselves as outside nature. They look to nature for guidance, and they go about their work with respect for the non-human entities with whom they interact.

d. Call of the Wild

Voices in nature can rekindle vestiges of wildness in our own psyches. The last lines of Gary Snyder's poem, "The Call of the Wild," evoke the realization that the silencing of the last coyote's call is a loss of connection with wildness not only in the world but in our souls as well:

> A war against earth.
> When it's done there'll be
> No place
> A coyote could hide.
>   Envoy
>   I would like to say
>   Coyote is forever
>   Inside you.
> But it's not true.[30]

The howl of a coyote, the melody of a bird, the chorus of voices emanating from a pond at nightfall—these and other sounds from nature evoke the sense of one's connection to life's other voices but, at the same time, trigger the felt realization that one is becoming alienated from wildness in our own psyches. Although many people living in urban environments are losing touch with wildness, it is never far from the surface. In the words of Jack Turner, "The easiest way to experience a bit of what the wild was like is to go into a great forest at night alone. Sit quietly for a while. Something very old will return."[31]

---

30   Gary Snyder, *Turtle Island* (New Dimensions Publishing Corp., 1974), p. 21.
31   Jack Turner, *The Abstract Wild*, Op., cit., p.

e. Aesthetic Encounters: Awe, Beauty, and Wonder

Encounters in the wild have a powerful impact on the human psyche and give rise to aesthetic responses described by many writers. To experience the awesome power of nature, to delight in its beauty, or to find oneself absorbed in wonder about its mysteries and remarkable productions is to find oneself profoundly affected.

Awe and the Sublime

Edmund Burke characterized the sublime in the mid-eighteenth century as an emotion produced in the human mind by what he called "terrible objects," objects whose magnitude or power is so great that they evoke a sense of awe and a peculiar kind of delight. Provided that the terrible "does not press too close"—is not too threatening, too imminent, too dangerous—the encounter produces "the strongest emotion which the mind is capable of feeling."[32] This powerful and strangely pleasing emotion is not sheer terror because it is accompanied by the realization that one is a spectator, not a victim, of the terrible. Once Burke, Immanuel Kant, and other late eighteenth century aestheticians had deciphered this emotion and introduced it to the educated public, it quickly became the rage of Romantic Age adventurers, poets, nature writers, and landscape artists. In 1785 Jean-Jacques Rousseau said "I must have torrents, rocks, pines, dead forest, mountains, rugged paths to go up and down, precipices beside me that frighten me, for the odd thing about my liking precipitous places is that they make me giddy, and I like this giddiness greatly, provided that I am safely placed." Ruskin, Keats, and Shelley expressed similar sentiments in England as did Emerson, Thoreau, and Muir in America. When Keats first beheld the Alps in 1816, he was overwhelmed: "I never knew, I never imagined what mountains were before. The immensity of these aerial summits excited, when they suddenly burst upon the sight, a sentiment of ecstatic wonder, not unallied to madness."[33]

The experience of the sublime produces a sense of awe: one realizes that one is in the presence of forces that transcend the mundane and quickly produce the realization that one's power and place in a larger scheme of things are limited. Diverse encounters produce this felt realization: standing before a range of

---

32   Edmund Burke, *A Philosophical Enquiry into the Origin of our Ideas of the Sublime and the Beautiful*, Adam Phillips, ed. (Oxford: World's Classics, 1990).
33   Percy Bysshe Shelley, *Peacock's Memoirs of Shelley: with Shelley's Letters to Peacock*, H.F.B. Brett-Smith, ed. (London: H. Frowde, 1909).

soaring mountain peaks, being on a lake or ocean during a storm, beholding the countless millions of stars at night, or gazing down a thousand-foot precipice. In one of his remarkable passages, John Muir described a fierce spring storm in the High Sierras. With the wind howling, he chose a sturdy Douglas fir, climbed to the top, lashed himself to its trunk, and reveled as he swung to and fro in the gale. Muir describes how this intense experience was followed by a peaceful calm. "When the storm began to abate, I dismounted and sauntered down through the calming woods. The storm-tones died away, and, turning toward the east, I beheld the countless hosts of the forests hushed and tranquil, towering one above another on the slopes of the hills like a devout audience. The setting sun filled them with amber light, and seemed to say, while they listened, 'My peace I give unto you.'"[34]

Experience of the awesome is attitude-adjusting. One may be terrified, delighted, exhilarated, or humbled by exposure to nature's forces and ever-changing moods, but underlying the emotional response is the realization that one is in the presence of transcendent forces. Confronted with the awesome, ego is scaled back and checked.

Beauty

Mountains, deserts, grassland prairies, rainforests, oceans, rivers, lakes, coral reefs, and many other places in wild nature are places where one can also experience another many-faceted aesthetic emotion: beauty. The beauty of these places is a powerful attraction for people seeking solace or escape from the frenzy of urban life, and for painters, poets, and writers motivated to communicate nature's beauty to others.

Robert MacFarlane comments that there is nothing quite as enchanting as a mountain sunset or sunrise, a meadow carpeted with wildflowers, or the view one gains of canyons, forests, rivers, and valleys from a mountaintop. The beauty of mountains is not competitive, MacFarlane observes, but contemplative and revelatory. Mountains present grand panoramas, offer new perspectives, and enable one to witness an infinite variety of forms, colors, textures, and shades of light. He notes that the plurality of light has probably attracted more comment than any other dimension of mountain beauty. When sunshine is punctuated by falling snowflakes, mountain light flickers and dazzles. During a thunderstorm

---

34   John Muir, *The Mountains of California*, cited in Ann Ronald, *Words for the Wild* (Sierra Club Books, 1987), p. 121.

it flashes with ostentatious splendor, and then may radiate as the most vivid of rainbows. It brightens and dims as shadows are cast by moving clouds. It radiates off snow and ice fields with such intensity on clear days that one cannot look directly without risking snow blindness. When it shines from behind rock ridges and spires, it creates stunning architectural effects. When it shines through stands of aspen or pine, it has a glimmering, impressionist quality. It takes on a tranquil matt-like quality at dusk, unifying the whole landscape with a single texture. And then there is Midas light, the rich yellow light that spills lengthways across the terrain, turning everything it touches to gold.[35]

Wonder

Encounters in nature ignite a sense of wonder. Witnessing the ridges and scoring in rock where a glacier has passed, feeling the soft pelts of moss on rocks and on the lee side of boulders and trees, watching the swirls of water beneath a plate of ice, observing the unique architecture and ephemeral fragility of a snowflake, watching the rapid build-up of nearby storm clouds, hearing a hillside come alive with moving water after a rain shower, watching and being watched by a mother bird protecting her eggs—none of these are trivial experiences. They are the kinds of experiences that inspired Muir, Thoreau, and many other nature writers, and it is their detailed and, at the same time, rapturous accounts that have evoked wonder and rapture in their readers. Nature's creations also ignite wonder about events that unfold in deep time: how the starry heavens came to be and what are their destinies, how continents were formed and reformed, or how fossil and mineral deposits laid down in ocean beds have been transported to mountaintops.

2. Telling Life's Epic Story

An attitude of respect comes from a rekindling of felt connections in the various ways recounted above but, no less, it comes from the telling of life's story. In the words of Stephen Gould, the story of life is the "greatest story ever told."[36] It is the

---

35   Robert MacFarlane, *Mountains of the Mind* (New York: Vintage Books, A Division of Random House, Inc., 2004). MacFarlane provides poignant descriptions of the beauty and allure of mountains and, more generally, discusses the history, psychology, and aesthetics of mountaineering.

36   Stephen Jay Gould, ed., *The Book of Life* (W.W. Norton & Company, 2001). Chapters of *The Book of Life* are written by contributing scientists, included Michael Benton and John Sepkoski

story of the immensity of evolutionary time and the great geophysical forces that have changed climates and have repeatedly reshaped continents and oceans; of the many millions of species that have flourished, sometimes in great bursts of creativity, and then have perished, sometimes in epic mass extinctions; of life's countless adaptations and innovations and the increasing complexity of evolving life forms; of the many paths that have been blazed through the profusely branching Tree of Life, including the branch that has led to "man the wise."

Holmes Rolston, Thomas Berry, and others emphasize the importance of telling life's story and its many sub-narratives, for it is only in so doing that humans will begin to understand their place in the greater natural order. "I cannot," Rolston says, "give you an argument explaining how humans arrived, some logic by which the Earth story eventuates in *Homo sapiens*. … What I can do is invite you as a historical subject to appreciate the objective story that lies in, with and under the Earth we inhabit, to enrich the story by telling it. You can be a microcosm of the macrocosm and enjoy your storied residence here."[37]

Many who contemplate the enormity of life's journey speak of how they are filled with a sense of awe, of how they feel that they are encountering something sacred and are participants in a process that is profoundly significant. Thomas Berry offers this perspective: "Within the solar system, the earth is the immediate context of human existence. … Beyond the sun, however, is our own galaxy, and beyond that is the universal galactic system that emerged some 15 billion years ago through some ineffable mystery. … We suppose that the universe itself is *the* enduring reality and *the* enduring value even while it finds expression in a continuing sequence of transformations. In creating the planet Earth, its living forms, and its human intelligence, the universe has found, so far as we know, the most elaborate manifestation of its deepest mystery. Here, in its human form, the universe is able to reflect on and celebrate itself in a unique mode of conscious self-awareness."[38] Berry calls this the "miracle of mankind." In human beings, the cosmos becomes aware of itself, is able to contemplate itself, and, in this awareness and contemplation, becomes responsible for itself. Chaos-complexity theorist, Stuart Kauffman, is not hesitant to speak in such terms: "We latter-day players are inheritors of almost 4 billion years of biological unfolding. If profound

---

cited in the following notes.

37   Holmes Rolston, "The Human Standing in Nature: Storied Fitness in the Moral Overseer," in *Values and Moral Standing*, W. Summer, D. Dallet & T. Attig, eds. (Bowling Green University Press, 1986), p. 97.

38   Thomas Berry, "The Viable Human," in *Environmental Philosophy: From Animal Rights to Radical Ecology*, Michael Zimmerman et al. eds. (Prentice-Hall, 2001), p. 175.

participation in such a process is not worthy of respect, if it is not sacred, then what might be?"[39]

The immensity of what various writers call "deep time" puts humanity's aspirations and travails in a needed perspective. The time scale of evolving life is depicted by Michael Benton in this way: "In a book of 100,000 words, if life began around 4 billion years ago, each word covers 40,000 years and each letter a period longer than the whole of recorded human history."[40] Another portrayal imagines that life on Earth is compressed into a movie that begins on January 1 and lasts one year. In this movie, the debut of humans would occur late on the last day of the year, about 17 minutes before the movie ends. The appearance of human agricultural communities would occur with about 80 seconds left and the onset of the Industrial Revolution with about three seconds left. If the original script had been written at the outset of the Industrial Revolution but a producer of the movie today decided to add events that transpired between 1750 and the present, the movie's final fraction of a second would have been astonishing to a person living in 1750, so sweeping have been the changes wrought by human population growth, urbanization, and economic growth. Table 1 depicts the

Table 1. Life's Evolution Depicted in a One-Year Time Frame

Evolutionary Milestones	Time of First Appearance (years ago)	Equivalent Calendar Time of First Appearance	First Appearance as Percentage of Age of Earth
Bacteria	4.0 billion	February 16	87.0%
Nucleated Cells	1.4 billion	September 10	30.5%
Multi-cellular Organisms	700 million	November 5	15.2%
Land Plants	435 million	November 26	9.5%
Insects and Reptiles	350 million	December 3	7.6%
Mammals	225 million	December 13	4.9%
Primates	60 million	December 26	1.3%
Humans	150 thousand	11:42:51 p.m., 12/31	0.003%
Agricultural Communities	12 thousand	11:58:37 p.m., 12/31	0.00003%
Industrial Revolution	3 hundred	11:59:57 p.m., 12/31	0.000007%

39   Stuart Kauffman, *At Home in the Universe: The Search for the Laws of Self-Organization and Complexity* (Oxford University Press, 1995), p. 303.
40   Michael Benton, *The Book of Life*, Op. cit., p. 110.

emergence of life forms in evolutionary time and the approximate time each life form would have made its debut in the imaginary one-year movie:

Contemplation of momentous events in life's history and the unfolding of these events in evolutionary time dispel the notion that life is all about humans. Humans are no more at the center of life's history than Earth is the center of our solar system, or our solar system is the center of galaxies that extend beyond. *Homo sapiens* are unique and special in ways that merit special recognition and celebration (Berry's point), but our species is a latecomer and its fate in the continuing unfolding of life's history—measured in geological ages and eons, not centuries and millennia—is hardly certain. Cataclysmic events in the distant past have led to extinctions on a mass scale, and once dominant species have disappeared from the scene. Scientists have found evidence that a super volcano in Indonesia about 70,000 years ago nearly eliminated *Homo sapiens* (survivors in Africa are estimated to have been as few as 3,000 individuals), and have recounted many other examples of how humans have been the hapless victims of volcanoes, earthquakes, hurricanes, climate change, and other of nature's powerful forces since the dawn of civilization.

Reconstruction of Darwin's Tree of Life based on comparisons of molecular sequences in genes that code for ribosomal RNA exhibit three main limbs: bacteria, archaea, and eucharya, with plants and animals forming only small twigs at the top of one branch of the eucharya limb.[41] Bacteria and archaea are microscopic organisms with prokaryotic cell organization (their genome consists of a single strand of DNA on a single chromosome unbounded by a nuclear membrane), and almost all of these organisms are chemosynthesizers that harvest energy from chemical reactions. Eucharya, in contrast, are organisms with eukaryotic cell organization (their genome resides in 2–600 chromosomes, each in a combination of DNA, RNA, and protein within a membrane-bounded nucleus).

The story of life is usually told as stories about humans, dinosaurs, and megafauna, but these are certainly not the only storylines in a much larger narrative. One central narrative recounts how mitochondria came to be incorporated in the cell structure of early eukaryote organisms. While prokaryotic cells exhibit a wide range of metabolic patterns, eukaryotic cells have organelles that support more constant forms of metabolism: in plants, plastids enable anaerobic

---

41   Andrew Knoll, *Life on a Young Planet: The First Three Billion Years of Evolution on Earth* (Princeton University Press, 2003), p. 24. In regard to the contributions made by molecular biology to our understanding of life, Andrew Knoll made this comment: "Experts argue about its details, but all biologists agree that our ability to draw Darwin's great Tree of Life in its entirety constitutes one of the great intellectual achievements of the late twentieth century."

photosynthesis; in animals, mitochondria enable aerobic respiration. As first hypothesized by cell biologist Lynn Margulis in 1967 and confirmed by later molecular biology, neither plastids nor mitochondria are produced directly by the eukaryotic cell itself; rather, they divide by simple fission controlled by their own DNA (mitochondrial and bacterial DNA are closely similar), not the DNA of the host cell. The remarkable incorporation of a mitochondrial "energy factory" in the nucleus of another cell must have occurred sometime after the "oxygen revolution" since mitochondria are oxygen users.[42] Eukaryotic cell structure led to the emergence of organisms with multiple cells and this, in turn, led to the prolific diversification of plant and animal life. As Sepkoski notes, "This was the turning-point that set life expanding out of the microscopic to exploit new resources by building complex structures that would range in size from mosses to sequoias, aphids to dinosaurs. Bacteria often have many-celled bodies, but each cell is almost identical. Only eukaryotes can variegate their cell types into skin, bone, muscle, blood, leaf, bark, and seed, and these into diverse shapes, tissues, and functions."[43]

We humans not only have ancient ancestors, but are constituted, literally, of non-human life. Mitochondria are contained in the trillions of cells that make up the human body, and it is mitochondria that supply energy in all of these cells—just as they have in the cells of all animals for over a billion years. The story of mitochondria is a striking illustration of endosymbiosis. Another illustration is the symbiosis between humans and the 500–1,000 species of microbes that reside on our tongue and eyeballs, in our ears and nose, all over our skin, and in our gut. As Jeffrey Gordon put it, "This is a strategic alliance, a symbiosis between mammals and microbes that goes back millions of years. … We're really

---

42   In the *Book of Life*, Op. cit., contributing scientist John Sepkoski recounts how the "oxygen revolution" was launched by a strain of bacteria (cyanobacteria) that evolved the ability some 2.7 billion years ago to extract hydrogen from water rather than hydrogen sulfide, to combine this hydrogen with carbon dioxide to form carbohydrates, and to transport the waste oxygen molecules outside their cells before damage was done. As Sepkoski explains, "The increasing populations of cyanobacteria on the sunlit bottoms of the new shallow seas relentlessly pumped out free oxygen, and the Earth rusted. From about 2.2 to 1.8 billion years ago, huge volumes of banded iron formations … accumulated in the oceans, rusted, and precipitated to the bottom. Once the reduced iron ran out, there was no other chemical sink big enough to hold the continuing biological surge of oxygen. The buildup of this gas dissolved in water then escaped into the atmosphere." He continues: "With growing concentrations of oxygen, pink skies turned blue, brown seas became azure, and the fumes of methane and hydrogen sulfide given by simple life forms were swept away, thus setting the stage for the emergence of eukarya and the vast profusion of life that followed."

43   John Sepkoski, *The Book of Life*, Op. cit., pp. 44–45.

a composite of species. We have human cells, but we have ten times more microbial cells."[44] The host of organisms within and on our bodies are not invaders, but organisms that have co-evolved with animals over geological ages, working together to advance common causes. Gut microbes, for example, are essential for the digestion of food and the production of vitamins and are defenders against disease.[45]

The roles of bacteria and archaea in regulating basic chemical processes on the planet are storylines that are no less significant. The omnipresence of bacteria is well known, but archaea, too, are widely distributed across the earth and its oceans. Some archaea live in very unusual places: in very hot hydrothermal vents at the bottoms of seas, in waters ten times saltier than the ocean, and in highly acidic mine waters. It is fortunate for plants and animals that microscopic organisms are robust survivors[46] and perform simple tasks well, because eukaryotic life in general would not be possible otherwise. As Andrew Knoll explains, "The cycles of carbon, nitrogen, sulfur, and other elements are linked together into a complex system that controls the biological pulse of the planet, and it is the metabolic pathways of prokaryotes that sustain these cycles. ... Prokaryotic metabolism forms the fundamental ecological circuitry of life. Bacteria, not mammals, underpin the efficient and long-term functioning of the biosphere."[47] When writers refer to the "ecological services" performed by nature, they are talking about the role of bacteria and archaea in maintaining life's "ecological circuitry."

3. Understanding Complex Systems

Cells constitute tissues, organs, and skeletons, and these constitute organisms which themselves are constituent parts of ecosystems and ultimately the whole biosphere. Big or small, each system is a whole comprised of parts: each whole

---

44   Jeffrey Gordon, "Growing on You" in *National Geographic*, November, 2005.
45   Another notable example of endosymbiosis is the association of algae and fungi to produce a single successful organism, where the algal component provides photosynthetic ability and the fungal component contributes structure and nutrient uptake. Another is the harboring of unicellular algae within the tissue of a reef coral, an arrangement in which each derives nutrients from the other.
46   Many prokaryotic organisms have displayed a remarkable resistance to extinction, especially the blue-green algae which have persisted for billions of years with little change. This resistance is attributable to a variety of factors, including immense population sizes and the ability to reproduce quickly, to track and adapt to changing environments with ease, and to persist in a dormant stage when conditions are unfavorable to growth.
47   Knoll, *Life on a Young Planet*, Op. cit., p. 23

has parts and each whole is a constituent element of a larger whole. The following discusses how the mechanistic-reductionist model of parts-whole relationships inherited from Enlightenment science and ideology is being replaced by complex systems models.

a. Models of Explanation

On the mechanistic model, a whole is conceived as an aggregation of discrete parts that act upon each other according to deterministic causal laws. In its Newtonian formulation, indestructible particles of matter are thought to move in accordance with universal laws whose formulations employ linear mathematics. Moreover, the mechanistic model posits that phenomena in a complex system can, in principle, be completely explained in terms of phenomena occurring in constituent, less complex systems. Phenomena in biological systems can be fully explained by the explanation of phenomena in chemical systems, just as phenomena in chemical systems can, in principle, be fully explained in terms of physical phenomena. Psychology is, in principle, reducible to biology, just as biology is reducible to chemistry and chemistry to physics.

Contemporary science is telling a different story: the behavior of sub-atomic quanta do not exhibit definite movements or occupy specific locations, the theoretical possibility of predictive certainty has been abandoned, and systems are said to generate novel and qualitatively unique phenomena that are not amenable to reductive explanation. In chaos-complexity theory, uncertainty and emergent change are applied to systems of all sizes and levels of complexity. New systems of mathematics have been developed to account for the phenomena of complex, dynamic, self-organizing systems.

On the dynamic systems model, the interactions of parts are thought to be capable of causing novel and qualitatively unique properties attributable to the system as a functioning whole. Such properties are thought to emerge from interacting parts, themselves parts of a self-organizing whole. Electrons act together in strong magnetic fields to form new types of particles in atomic structures. Atomic structures and the properties of bulk matter emerge from increasing levels of complexity in physical systems. Chemical auto-catalytic processes allow living systems to self-replicate, to incorporate self-corrective feedback mechanisms, and to adapt to changes in their environments. Evolution creates increasingly complex systems and, with this complexity, novel phenomena and new patterns of relationships. Increasingly complex levels of inner organization, information processing, and awareness of self and environment have emerged and continue to emerge. Human self-consciousness is a phenomenon that emerges from complex interactions in a self-organizing brain. Brain processes generate thoughts and feelings, but the thoughts and feelings are not identical to brain process; something qualitatively unique occurs that cannot be reduced to brain chemistry.

b. Chaos-Complexity Theory

To enable a fuller account of the capacity of dynamic systems to self-organize and generate qualitatively unique phenomena, it is instructive to recount developments in chaos-complexity theory. Developments in this field of science, heralded by many writers as being as important as relativity theory and quantum mechanics, make a fascinating story. Henri Poincare (1854–1912) is regarded as the father of chaos-complexity theory, primarily because he demonstrated that Newton's linear mathematics could not yield predictive certainty when three bodies (earth, moon, and sun) acted upon each other. Using non-linear equations, Poincare showed that small differences in initial conditions produce unpredictable differences in equation solutions. About eighty years later, Edward Lorenz arrived at a similar result in connection with his study of weather systems; using differential equations, he demonstrated that small changes in initial conditions can lead to unpredictable changes in subsequent system behavior. Graphed solutions to the model's three equations revealed a fractal shape that resembled a butterfly. Vitaly Efimov arrived at similar conclusions when he predicted in 1970 that three strongly interacting particles can form an infinite number of different bound states that are spaced geometrically. Recent experiments (one involving ultra-cold atomic gases) have confirmed the "Efimov effect."

Lorenz dubbed the sensitivity of his weather model to initial conditions the "butterfly effect," an image used to emphasize that the flapping of a butterfly's wings in Brazil can lead, unpredictably, to a tornado in Texas. Each butterfly-looking solution curve tended to occur in the same area, cycled around randomly an indefinite number of times without ever crossing itself, and displayed self-similarity at any scale.[48] Lorenz called this resulting fractal shape a "strange

---

48 An attractor is characterized as a state or set of states to which a complex system is attracted, where the attraction comes from complex interactions within the system itself. Several types of attractors have been identified in complexity theory: a *point attractor*, where a system moves to a single state (e.g., death); *cyclic or periodic attractors*, where the system settles at a single point within a cycle (e.g., a point within a predator-prey fitness landscape); and *strange attractors*,

attractor" and emphasized how it appears to act on the system as a whole, functioning as a "collector of trajectories of perturbation."

The work of another pioneer, Ilya Prigogine, showed that far-from-equilibrium conditions in dissipative systems lead to behavior very different from what would be expected from the second law of thermodynamics; rather than entropic degradation and chaotic dissipation, order and more complex structures emerge from simpler ones. Prigione observed that the more complex a system is, the more vulnerable it is to perturbations and the more energy it requires to maintain stability and coherence. When a complex system becomes highly unstable (aperiodic), small disturbances can lead to abrupt and unpredictable changes. But, Prigogine adds, "We know now that nonequilibrium, the flow of matter and energy, may be a source of order."[49] With Prigogine, the focus of investigation in chaos theory shifted to an understanding of the dynamics of complex systems displaying the capacity for *self-organization*. On another front, Mitchell Feigenbaum formulated ratios that describe the critical state at which a system either dissipates or transitions from chaos to order.[50] These ratios are used to predict the onset of turbulence in systems of many kinds.

A rich vocabulary has evolved to characterize the capacity of complex systems to self-organize and continuously renew themselves, including self-production (autopoiesis), self-reflexivity (autognosis), and self-regulation (autonomics). The phenomenon of self-organization involves energy and information exchange and is variously characterized as patterning, networking, coupling, synchronization, synergy, and conservation of what works. An objective of this burgeoning body of research is to formulate laws that account for order in complex systems, ranging from the metabolism of cells, a beating heart, the propagation of nerve impulses, a neural network, an evolutionary ecosystem, an economy, and the Internet. Mitchell Waldrop gave this layman's account of how complex systems are being conceived as a result of research into the behavior of complex systems:

---

where states of a system are never exactly replicated but remain within ranges if the system maintains stability and does not dissipate into chaos (e.g., a weather system, a market-economy, and the Internet).

49   Ilya Prigogine and Isabele Stengers, *Order out of Chaos: Man's New Dialogue with Nature* (Bantam Books, 1984), p. xxvii. With Prigogine, the focus of investigation in chaos theory shifted to an understanding of the dynamics of *complex* systems displaying the capacity for *self-organization*.

50   Feigenbaum's work built on the study of noise interference by Benoit Mandelbrot in the 1970s. Mandelbrot discovered distinct ratios between order and disorder on any scale he used. Geometrical graphs of these ratios revealed a self-similar fractal pattern.

[1] Every one of these systems is *complex*, in the sense that a great many independent agents are interacting with each other in a great many ways. Think of the quadrillions of chemically reacting proteins, lipids, and nucleic acids that make up a living cell, or the billions of interconnected neurons that make up the brain. ... [2] In every case, moreover, the very richness of these interactions allows the system as a whole to undergo *spontaneous self-organization*. ... The genes in a developing embryo organize themselves in one way to make a liver cell and in another way to make a muscle cell. Flying birds adapt to the actions of their neighbors, unconsciously organizing themselves into a flock. Organisms constantly adapt to each other through evolution, thereby organizing themselves in an exquisitely tuned ecosystem. ... [3] Furthermore, these complex, self-organizing systems are *adaptive*, in that they don't just passively respond to events. ... They actively try to turn whatever happens to their advantage. Thus, the human brain constantly organizes and reorganizes its billions of neural connections. ... Species evolve for better survival in a changing environment. ... [4] Finally, every one of these complex, self-organizing, adaptive systems possess a kind of dynamism that makes them qualitatively different from static objects such as computer chips and snowflakes, which are merely complicated. Complex systems are more spontaneous, more disorderly, more alive than that. At the same time, however, their peculiar dynamics is also a far cry from the weirdly unpredictable gyrations known as chaos, [which] by itself doesn't explain the structure, the coherence, the self-organizing cohesiveness of a complex system.[51]

Stuart Kauffman, an interpreter of chaos-complexity theory in evolutionary biology, sees more than selectivity for survival and random variation in evolutionary ecosystems. Kaufmann's hypothesis is that self-organization in complex systems is a necessary condition of evolvability; the phenomenon of self-organization generates and sustains the stable and robust structures ("the building blocks of life") that are molded and refined by ongoing processes of natural selection. He cites the bilipid cell membrane and the genomic network orchestrating cellular activity as self-organized systems that are robust enough to be molded and further refined by processes of natural selection. Quoting Kauffmann: "The cell

---

51   M. Mitchell Waldrop, *Complexity: The Emerging Science at the Edge of Order and Chaos* (Simon & Schuster, 1992).

membrane is a bilipid membrane, stable for almost 4 billion years both because it is robust and … readily malleable by natural selection. The genomic network lies in the ordered regime, perhaps near the edge of chaos, because such networks are readily formed, but also because such systems are structurally and dynamically stable, so they adapt on correlated landscapes and are able to be molded for further tasks [by natural selection]."[52] Self-organization in complex systems is also the key, Kaufmann believes, to explaining the reappearance of millions of species following mass extinctions such as the Cambrian and Permian extinctions.

"Evolution left us stuck on earth with no ladder to climb," Kauffman wistfully notes. "Random variation, selection-shifting. Here lies the brooding sense of accident, of historical contingency, of design by elimination."[53] But Kauffman sees more to it than this: "Evolution is surely 'chance caught on the wing,' but it is also the expression of underlying order." This realization enables us feel "at home in the universe."[54] Various complexity theorists have characterized self-organization as the creative potential of nature.

Thomas Berry suggests a similar interpretative framework. In *The Great Work*, he wrote this: "For our sense of reality, three commitments are basic: to observational science, to a developmental universe, to an inner self-organizing universe."[55] He notes that "Our observational sciences presently have moved beyond the mechanistic understanding of a so-called objective world as it was known in the past few centuries of Newtonian physics. If formerly we knew by downward reduction processes that considered the particle as the reality and the wholes as derivative, we now recognize that it is even more important that we integrate upward, because we cannot know particles and their power until we see the wholes that they bring into being. If we know the elements simply in their isolated individual reality we have only minimal knowledge of what they really are. To understand atoms we must see these elements in their central role in molecules, megamolecules, in cellular life, organic life, even in intellectual perception, since atomic structures in a transformed context live and function in the wide display of all the gorgeous plants and animals of the Earth as well as in the most profound intellectual, emotional, and spiritual experiences of the

---

52   Stuart A. Kauffman, *At Home in the Universe: The Search for the Laws of Self-Organization and Complexity* (Oxford University Press, 1995), p. 188.

53   Ibid., p. 7.

54   Ibid., p. 189,

55   Thomas Berry, *The Great Work* (New York: Bell Tower, 1999), p. 24.

human."[56] On this account, "the universe is revealed to us as an irreversible emergent process," in which "there exists at every level a basic tendency toward self-organization." Further, "It seems best to consider that mind and matter are two dimensions of the single reality that comes into being in an immense diversity of expression throughout the universe by some self-organizing process. ... This we find at the physical level, the biological level, and at the level of reflexive-consciousness."[57]

On a planetary scale, James Lovelock hypothesized that Earth is an entity of great complexity that regulates the mix and concentration of gases in the atmosphere in ways that make life possible. After the name given by the ancient Greeks to goddess Earth, Lovelock called this hypothesis the Gaia Hypothesis. In his words, "The entire range of living matter on Earth, from whales to viruses, and from oaks to algae, could be regarded as constituting a single living entity, capable of manipulating the Earth's atmosphere to suit its overall needs and endowed with faculties and powers far beyond those of its constituent parts." [58]

c. Ecosystems and Self-Organization

Donald Worster recounts how recent research in ecology, meteorology, and other disciplines has led to an unraveling of the view of ecosystems set forth in the classical ecological studies of the 1960s, 70s, and 80s. In his words, "Ecology is not the same as it was. A rather drastic change has been going on in this science of late—a radical shifting away from the thinking of Eugene Odum's generation, away from its assumptions of order and predictability, a shifting toward what we might call a new *ecology of chaos*."[59] Worster discusses how recent ecologists have focused on disturbances such as fire, volcanic eruptions, violent wind, invasive species, and the restlessness of climate; how population biologists are seeing "lots of individual species, each doing their own thing," but not an "emergent collectivity nor any strategy to achieve one"; how the view of an ecosystem in equilibrium is being replaced by "a landscape of patches, big and little, patches

---

56   Ibid., p. 25–26.
57   Ibid., p. 26.
58   James Lovelock, *Gaia: A New Look at Life on Earth* (Oxford University Press, 1987), p. 9. Lovelock in some passages refers to Earth as an "organism." Sympathetic critics suggest that the metaphor of a very complex ecosystem (rather than a giant organism) would be a more apt choice to characterize Earth's self-regulating pro-life tendencies.
59   Donald Worster, "The Ecology of Order and Chaos" in *Earth Ethics: Introductory Readings on Animal Rights and Environmental Ethics*, James P. Sterba, ed. (Prentice Hall, 2000), p. 162.

of all textures and colors, a patchwork quilt of living things, changing continually through time and space, responding to an unceasing barrage of perturbations"; how small changes in initial conditions of a systems model can quickly become substantial differences in output; and how social Darwinists, who were always ideologically suspicious of land use prescriptions and proposals for ecosystem preservation and restoration, are back on the scene advocating a libertarian agenda. Worster ends his account with these unsettling questions: "What is there to love or preserve in a universe of chaos? ... If such is the kind of place we inhabit, why not go ahead with all our private ambitions, free of any fear that we may be doing special damage? ... Does the tradition of environmentalism to which Muir belonged, along with so many other nature writers and ecologists of the past—people like Paul Sears, Eugene Odum, Aldo Leopold, and Rachel Carson—make sense any longer?"[60]

Worster's account of the "ecology of chaos" may not engender an attitude of respect, but Worster is recounting a one-sided story. Chaos theory has indeed taken the scientific world by storm, but recent developments in this rapidly evolving field of inquiry reveal self-organized order at the edge of chaos. Like all complex living systems, ecosystems exhibit chaotic behavior or the potential for such behavior, but they also have an ability to self-organize and to produce order. They rarely, if ever, settle into mature and stable equilibria as Odum hypothesized, but forever generate both change and emerging order simultaneously. The ecosystems described by ecologists and summarized by Worster—as random, chaotic, piecemeal, and disorganized—are, to a large extent, a description of the effects of human intervention; many ecosystems do, indeed, show piecemeal patches, random juxtaposition, and disorganized assemblages in which various species, non-native (invasive) as well as native (endemic), jostle for survival and dominance, but to a large extent these conditions disclose the consequences of human-induced changes and serve as reminders that processes of self-organization can be disrupted and that order is always tenuous.[61]

An ecosystem is a self-organizing whole comprised of living flora and fauna, microbial organisms, water, minerals, and decaying organic matter whose dynamics cannot be adequately understood by focusing on any one constituent element or on discrete relationships among subsets of components. An ecosystem is a self-organizing and open-ended system capable of producing new phenomena, new kinds, and new relationships.

---

60   Ibid., p. 167.
61   The development of ecology as a science is briefly reviewed in Chapter 4, Section A.1.

4. Taking Stock of Nature's Manifold Value

a. Nature as Self-Organizing: Inherent Value in Nature

An anthropocentric account of value holds that values originate in human experience, and that valuers and values are associated exclusively with human life and culture. On this account, something is not a value unless it is judged by a human to be a value: unless it is something to which value is ascribed by one or more humans or toward which one or more humans have a pro-attitude. Distinctions are made between intrinsic value (things valued in and of themselves, or things valued for their own sakes) and extrinsic value (things valued because they are instrumental in bringing about other values), but the anthropocentric claim is the same: to say that something has intrinsic or extrinsic value is to say that some human being judges that it has intrinsic or extrinsic value. For the anthropocentrist, a world without humans would be a world without value; valuing and values do not exist apart from human life and culture.

The anthropocentric account of value is rejected in this work as an unsatisfactory account that sees non-human life as devoid of anything resembling intelligence and value awareness. Incorporating insights from various theorists, most notably Holmes Rolston,[62] a number of theses are defended and developed: that values and valuing processes occur throughout the biotic order and are associated with the capacity of biotic entities to self-organize; that the self-organizing capacity of these entities are *of value* to the entities themselves and are, in this sense, inherent values (irrespective of the question of the value of these capacities for humans, which is immense); and that biotic entities possessing inherent value are worthy of moral respect in their own right.

In regard to *organisms*, inherent value is associated with the capacity to self-actualize: the capacity to survive, adapt, thrive, and realize biological potential in oftentimes harsh and perilous environments. The phenomenon of self-actualization is variously characterized. In the language of physical biology, Lawrence Johnson characterized it as the ability of an organism to exist in "a persistent state of low entropy sustained by metabolic processes for accumulating energy [wherein] organic unity and self-identity are maintained in equilibrium by homeostatic feedback processes."[63] In explicit value terms, Paul Taylor characterizes

---

62 Rolston's views are discussed throughout the book, with particular attention given in Chapter 2 to organisms (Section F), species (Section G), and ecosystems (Section H).
63 Lawrence Johnson, "Toward the Moral Considerability of Species and Ecosystems," in *Environmental Ethics* 149, 1992.

an organism as a "teleological center of life, striving to preserve itself and to realize its own good in its own unique way," and as a "unified system of goal-oriented activities directed toward its preservation and well-being."[64] Holmes Rolston contends that "Every organism has a *good-of-its-kind*; it defends its own kind as a *good kind*" and also that "Every organism is "a *valuing* organism, even if the organism is not a sentient valuer, much less a vertebrate, much less a human evaluator."[65] Unlike a machine or a pile of rocks, a living being is *for itself* and, until life ends as a result of disease, predation, or accident, or until entropy finally dissipates the capacity for self-organization, tends toward its own good.

In regard to *species*, value is associated with the dynamic and adaptive capacity of genomes to encode and express information controlling structural and functional development over the lifetimes of living members and their progeny. Various theorists have commented on the remarkable information-processing capacity involved in genomic expression, even in simple organisms. Jonathan Schull said this about plants: "Gene pools in evolving populations acquire, store, transmit, transform, and use vast amounts of fitness-relative information. ... The information-processing capacities of these massively parallel distributed processing systems surpass that of even the most sophisticated man-made systems."[66]

In regard to *ecosystems*, value is associated with their capacity to generate conditions and processes, including natural selection, out of which countless life forms are continuously created and in which a great diversity of existing kinds are able to co-exist and co-evolve in relations of co-adapted fitness and mutual benefit.

Manifestations of the capacity of systems of life in general to self-organize—of organisms to self-actualize in their environments, of genomes to orchestrate development and function over individual lifetimes, and of ecosystems to generate new kinds and enable individuals of many diverse kinds to self-actualize and co-evolve in mutually sustaining relationships—constitute the most fundamental processes that occur in nature. These capacities are interconnected and synchronized in a dynamic and constantly evolving natural order. Their manifestations have value for their possessors; they are values that inhere in entities that possess

---

64 Paul Taylor, "Biocentric Egalitarianism," in *Environmental Ethics: Readings in Theory and Practice*, Louis P. Pojman, ed. (Wadsworth, 2001), p. 107. Taylor's views are discussed in some detail in Chapter 4.

65 Holmes Rolston, "Naturalizing Values: Organisms and Species" in *Environmental Ethics: Readings in Theory and Practice*, Louis P. Pojman, ed. (Wadsworth, 2001), p. 82.

66 Shull is quoted by Holmes Rolston in "Naturalizing Values: Organisms and Species," in *Environmental Ethics: Readings in Theory and Practice*, Louis P. Pojman, ed. (Wadsworth, 2001), p. 83.

or exhibit them. While it may be said that manifestations of these capacities have both intrinsic and extrinsic value for their possessors, other value terms are perhaps more appropriate. Holmes Rolston refers to such goods as "systemic" or "constitutive" values: self-actualization constitutes the good of organisms; genomic expression constitutes the good of species and living members of their kind; co-adaptive fitness constitutes the good of life communities and their many interacting members. Co-adaptation for mutual benefit is a synergy attributable to an ecosystem as a self-organizing whole; it is an emergent phenomenon in a valuing process that occurs objectively in nature. Humans provide explanatory accounts and may safeguard or interfere with this system-generated value, but humans do not create the value. Humans recognize and attribute value to entities in nature, but the attribution does not create the value; it is already there.

It is meaningful to think of values as organizing trajectories of human activity. When values provide meaning and direction in an individual's life, things tend to go well for that individual. Similarly, when shared values in organizations maintain an attractive force and give direction to collective efforts, things tend to go well and to move in the right direction. When individual and social values lose their attractive and cohesive force, things tend to go poorly and disintegration, disorganization, and dissolution set in. Complex systems theory provides a conceptual framework for similarly thinking about the function of values in non-human life as well. Values in both biotic and cultural systems function as "attractors" or "trajectories" of self-organization. When the attraction of a value or value constellation no longer sustains orderly internal self-organization, disorder results; a shift toward chaos occurs, sometimes abruptly. Whether in an organism, a genome, an ecosystem, the brain of a human being, a human organization, or a human-created system (e.g., an economy in which goods and services are freely exchanged, or an "internet" in which information is freely exchanged), the pervasive phenomenon of self-organization generates order and tendency toward well-being.

On this account, humans are not the origin of all value in nature. Only humans are conceptual valuers, but this does not entail the conclusion that only humans are valuers and have a well-being. Self-actualization is a value within and for an organism, just as co-adaptive fitness within an ecosystem is a value within and for a system of life. While human activities may facilitate, hinder, or terminate the capacity for self-organization within biotic systems, the value of self-organization for them does not depend on human existence.

Levels of complexity exist in nature, and so do levels of awareness. Schull was quoted in connection with the ability of plants to process the vast information encoded in their genes, a capacity rivaling that of advanced computers. Such intelligence has a physio-chemical basis, albeit one far removed from the cognitive abilities of a human being equipped with multiple senses and a nervous system controlled by electro-chemical reactions occurring in the billions of cells in a human brain. There is a big difference, but the difference is not that one involves "matter" and the other "mind"; the difference, rather, is one of levels of evolved self-organizing capacity and differentiated function. Rudimentary awareness in simple self-organizing organisms has led to progressively sophisticated awareness in progressively complex self-organizing systems. Over several billion years, countless trillions of organisms have embarked on paths of self-actualization in environments in which self-organizing ecosystems have delineated and sustained mutually advantageous relationships. Countless species have appeared on the scene, including vertebrate organisms in whose lives value is associated with experiences of pleasure and pain and humans in whose lives value is associated as well with reasoning and its cultural creations.

With the appearance of *Homo sapiens*, awareness has itself evolved to the point where the story of life can be told. A forthright telling of the story acknowledges that the capacity to value is not unique to human life and that valuation in human life, as advanced as it is and may yet become, is an evolutionary product of valuation in very many non-human lives over a very long period of time. A theory that altogether denies the reality of valuing process in other organisms and in evolving ecosystems is an anthropocentric myopia lacking current scientific credentials. Members of *Homo sapiens* are the inheritors of capacities found throughout the biotic order. A functioning human brain, the seat of rationality, is a highly complex embodiment of the phenomenon of self-organization and is an inherited capacity many millions of years in the making.

b. Nature as Provident: The Value of Nature

The discussion of value has focused so far on values *in* and *throughout* nature. It now shifts to the value *of* nature—nature's *extrinsic value*—for human need fulfillment. Agriculture, fishing, and forestry harvest resources directly from nature. Plant species domesticated from wild species are the source of most of the calories consumed in diets and a primary source of genetic materials used for the prevention and treatment of disease. A third of all prescription drugs are derived from chemical compounds found in non-human nature and pharmaceutical companies are aggressively "bioprospecting" to find other potentially useful compounds in rainforests and other ecosystems. Biotechnology is yielding an astonishing range of new and useful products, as are efforts to mimic processes in nature (biomimicry) and to miniaturize technologies that replicate processes at the microscopic level (nanotechnology).

In these and other ways, nature provides the wherewithal of human life and is the source of raw materials used to produce the products traded in economies around the world. The value of these inputs are explicitly acknowledged when they are treated as production costs and reflected in market prices. Less acknowledged but more fundamental are the myriad ecological services performed by non-human nature, including nutrient cycling, pollination, air and water purification, climate control, drought and flood control, and regulation of atmospheric chemical composition. These services are commonly referred to as "natural capital" and regarded as "free goods." Such goods are rarely included as line items in accounting systems, nor are the costs associated with the human-caused diminution of nature's capacity to produce these essential services. The price tag imaginatively assigned to natural capital is astronomical. Even if evolving science and technology could one day lead to human substitutes for many of nature's ecological services, the associated cost—conservatively estimated to exceed the total of the world's combined GDPs[67]—would far exceed humanity's ability to pay. The ominous implications of economic systems that fail, theoretically and in practice, to account for the cost of natural capital and are consuming nature's capital at rates far in excess of replenishment rates are further discussed in Chapter 4. Here the intent is simply to acknowledge the incalculable value of nature's resources for human life and to underscore the magnitude of loss potentially associated with the continuing impairment and using up of these resources.

c. Nature as Mentor: Learning from Nature

Our sciences and technologies are based on what we have learned *about* nature, but much of our wisdom is what we learn *from* nature. Albert Einstein told us to "Look deep into nature, and then you will understand everything better." Leonardo de Vinci remarked that "Human subtlety will never devise an invention more beautiful, more simple, or more direct than does Nature, because in her inventions, nothing is lacking and nothing is superfluous." Nature has experimented for billions of years with arrangements that enable diverse life to

---

67   Robert Costanza et al., "The Value of the World's Ecosystem Services and Natural Capital," in *Nature* 387 (1997), p. 253.

survive, co-adapt, and reproduce and only shallow hubris denies that nature is humankind's most experienced and most reliable mentor. Indigenous peoples understood this truth intuitively, as have Taoists and the followers of numerous other cultural and religious traditions that see humans as inseparably linked to "nature's ways." Michael Pollan saw nature as the gardener's most reliable mentor: "If you think of evolution as a three-and-a-half billion-year-long laboratory experiment, and the gene pool as the store of information accumulated during the course of that experiment, you begin to appreciate that nature has far more extensive knowledge about her operations than we do."[68]

While science is practiced to learn about nature as a means of control (the "Baconian Project"), we are well-advised to look to nature for guidance in organizing human affairs. In her book, *Biomimicry*, Janine Benyus explains why humans would do well to pay heed to nature's ways, which she summarizes in a series of observations: nature runs on sunlight, uses only the energy required to meet basic needs, fits form to function, recycles everything and wastes nothing, rewards cooperation, banks on diversity, demands local expertise, and curbs excesses and unsustainability.[69] Many examples can be given of how inventors, designers, and fabricators in numerous fields mimic processes or otherwise incorporate insights derived from nature. In the field of building design, we have McDonough's and Braungart's Hannover Principles, Van der Ryn's and Cowan's Five Principles of Ecological Design, and John and Nancy Todd's Principles of Ecological Design, among others.

5. Recoiling at Destruction

It is not hard to be alarmed by the environmental and ecological devastation that is occurring everywhere in the world, and to be dismayed by the lack of progress being made in addressing some of the most serious problems.

a. Indicators and Drivers of Environmental and Ecological Decline

The signs of environmental and ecological decline are evident on many fronts: forests are shrinking, grasslands are deteriorating, water tables are falling, fisheries are collapsing, soils are eroding, deserts are advancing, biodiversity is declining, greenhouse gases are concentrating, glacial ice is melting, and seas are rising.

---

68 Michael Pollan, *Second Nature: A Gardener's Education*, Op. cit.
69 Janine Benyus, *Biomimicry* (William Morrow and Company, 1997), p. 7.

On top of this, our bodies are loaded with toxins (one study determined that the umbilical cords of Chicago-area newborns contained 190 toxins) and many millions of animals are held in captivity in factory farms, zoos, and laboratories and managed in ways that create untold suffering as well as serious environmental and health problems for humans.

In regard to growing levels of pollution of the air we breathe, the water we drink, and other "sinks" into which pollutants are discharged, Gus Speth provided this characterization:

> *From modest to huge quantities*: Pollutants of all kinds have increased dramatically. Levels of atmospheric emitted CO_2 NO_x SO_2, for example, have increased fivefold, sevenfold, and eightfold, respectively over the past 100 years.

> *From gross insults to microtoxicity*: Earlier concern about smoke and sewers has broadened to include toxic substances and their role in causing cancers and respiratory ailments and, more recently, their adverse effects on reproduction, neurological function, and immune systems.

> *From First World to Third World*: Concern about air and water pollution in urbanized and highly industrialized nations have become painfully evident throughout the world but are often more severe in developing and undeveloped nations, in large measure because major factors contributing to environmental deterioration—poverty, disease, lack of education, and lack of opportunity for women—are found disproportionately in the Third World.

> *From local effects to global effects*: Environmentally and ecologically harmful activities in one area of the world increasingly affect people and ecosystems in other parts of the world, and cumulative totals and concentrations have global effects, affecting humans and non-humans around the world more or less simultaneously (e.g., ozone layer depletion caused by the production of hydro fluorocarbons and global warming resulting from the concentration of heat-trapping gases in the atmosphere) [70]

---

70 See Gus Speth, *Red Sky at Morning* (Yale University Press, 2006) for a more complete discussion of these trends.

Speth gives this account of what he and others see as the primary drivers of environmental and ecological decline:

Population growth: Population rates vary from country to country and decade to decade, but the total number of humans worldwide increased from three to six billion between 1960 and 2000 and today has reached seven billion; by 2050, another 2.3 billion people are likely.[71]

Economic growth: While the world population increased about four-fold during the 20th Century, economic output increased twentyfold; from the dawn of history to 1950, the world economy grew to seven trillion dollars, and now grows by this amount every five to ten years.

Market failure: Market failure to account for all of the costs associated with the production of economic goods, including costs associated with the depletion and degradation of natural capital, means that adverse consequences are ignored in the world's economies and are, wittingly and unwittingly, shifted to distant peoples, future generations, and other life.

Political failure: Market failure is compounded by the failure of national governments and international political institutions to make corrections, control dangerous technology, encourage environmentally benign alternatives, and cooperate in international problem-solving initiatives.

Conservation biologists report that we are living in a period of mass species extinctions. Five other mass extinctions are believed to have occurred in the geological past: the Ordovician (440 mya), Devonian (370 mya), Permian-Triassic

---

71   The projected world population estimate of 9.3 billion comes from the *State of the World 2011* report published by the United Nations Population Fund. According to this report, the world population will exceed ten billion by the end of the century. It is estimated that the human population was about 300 million at the time of Christ, and about 500 million by 1750. By 1850, the world population was about one billion. It took one hundred years between 1750 and 1850 to reach a doubling of the human population, compared to the forty-year doubling between 1960 and 2000. The 1960–2000 doubling involved an average growth rate of 4.6%. There has been a slowing of the global population growth rate since 2000, with negative rates in several European countries.

(245 mya), Triassic-Jurassic (200 mya), and Cretaceous (65 mya). The current wave of mass extinctions (the "Holocene") is believed not only to be among the greatest but also unique in the respect that most of the causes are directly attributable human activity. One report estimates that 50% of all species existing in 1950 will have become extinct by 2050.[72] Estimates of the number of species that have gone extinct in recent millennia and those that are threatened vary greatly, but there is little disagreement that, overall, current extinction rates greatly exceed natural background rates. There is also broad agreement that mammals, birds, and amphibians are among the vertebrates most threatened. The International Union for Conservation of Nature estimates that 23% of all mammals and 12% of all birds are threatened with extinction, and that amphibians are declining on a global scale faster than any other vertebrate group, with over 32% of all amphibian species threatened.[73] For amphibians, the extinction rate is estimated to be between 25,000–45,000 times greater than the background rate. It is also reported that 90% of all open ocean tuna, billfishes, and sharks are gone, and that numerous other fish groups are headed toward extinction.[74] Global assessments of coral reefs are no more heartening. By 2000, 27% of the world's coral reef ecosystems had effectively collapsed, and it is predicted that coral reefs will go extinct in the next century. The situation is also bleak in regard to many insect, plant, and fungal taxonomic groups. The vast majority of biodiversity is represented in plant communities and some of these, notably tropical rainforests, are in rapid decline.[75]

Numerous studies and statistics could be cited to document the host of environmental and ecological problems that beset us.[76] The problems are serious, suffice it to say, and are likely to get much more serious in the not-too-far-distant future unless individuals and nations own up to the seriousness of the problems and corrective action is taken. We are on unsustainable paths as measured by various indices. One widely used index is the size of a population's "ecological footprint," a measure of the extent to which consumption patterns in a region depend on resources imported from other regions of the world. Vancouver, BC, is estimated by William Rees to have an ecological footprint twelve times greater

---

72   Koch et al., "Species Coextinctions and the Biodiversity Crisis," in *Science* 305.
73   See http://www.iucnredlist.org.
74   J.B. Jackson, "Ecological Extinction and Evolution in the Brave New Ocean," in *Proceedings of the National Academies of Science*, 105: 11458–65.
75   Efforts in the US and other countries to slow the pace of species extinctions are reviewed in Chapter 3 (Section C) and Chapter 4 (Section G).
76   Good general sources of information are the annual editions of the Worldwatch Institute's *Vital Signs* and *State of the World*, published by W.W. Norton.

than the territory it occupies; having overused or overdrawn local natural capital stocks, the people of this region are heavily dependent on temporary surpluses elsewhere.[77] This phenomenon is occurring in urban centers around the world.

Another revealing index is a measure of net primary production (NPP): the energy produced by photosynthesizing organisms in excess of what they require for their own growth. An ever-increasing proportion of the biosphere's NPP goes to support human life, diminishing available NPP for other life and the stock of NPP producers. Whatever measures are used, the recurring conclusion is that production and consumption levels in many areas of human activity exceed sustainable levels. On a global scale, the World Wide Fund for Nature estimates that the bio-regenerative capacity of the planet has already been exceeded: that 1.5 Earths are required to support current demands on natural resources.[78]

b. An Attitude of Respect: Needed Counter-Driver

If an attitude of respect toward nature—constituted of the formative elements sketched in the foregoing—were to take hold in the public mind in the US and other nations, we would have another much-needed driver, one capable of countervailing the seemingly unstoppable forces that have gotten us into the predicament we are in. The "modern view" provides validation for the failure of markets to fully account for environmental costs, for the trust placed in the technological imperative and society's vast technological enterprises, for the faith that an "invisible hand" operates in unregulated markets to promote the greatest good for the greatest number, and for the widespread acceptance of moral frameworks that deny moral standing to non-human life and life systems. These beliefs are widely and firmly held in Western society and are spreading throughout the world, and will likely not be seriously challenged unless and until an attitudinal change begins to take hold in the minds of many. Without groundswells of public sentiment, the initiatives needed to effectively address environmental and ecological problems will likely remain piecemeal and easily derailed by powerful interests motivated to maintain the status quo. Absent a paradigm shift in how humans view themselves in relation to non-human life and the systems in nature that support and sustain all life, it is hard to see how catastrophic consequences can be averted. Many express faith in the capacity of

77 William E. Rees, "Consuming the Earth: The Biophysics of Sustainability," in Earth Ethics, James P. Sterba, ed. (Upper Saddle River, NJ: Prentice Hall, 2000), pp. 382–386.
78 Reported in "Living Planet Report" at http://www.panda.org/news facts/publications/.

technology to see us through: that the inventive and creative mind of humans will find technological solutions to whatever problems are looming on the horizon.[79] The problem with this position is that technology is captive of the "modern view" and, more narrowly, national and corporate interests.

The great irony is that there are solutions to the long list of ecological and environmental problems we face. As Lester Brown sees it, "All the problems we face can be dealt with using existing technologies. And almost everything we need to do to move the world economy onto an environmentally sustainable path has been done in one or more countries."[80] The problem is that the majority of those making decisions in economic and governmental institutions around the globe are unwilling or unable to implement at-hand solutions. A groundswell of public outcry throughout the world is perhaps capable of bringing needed change. But absent a fundamental change in the attitude of many people toward nature, fundamental and enduring change is doubtful.

6. Cultivating Life-Centered Ethical Virtues

An aphorism in ethics states: principles without dispositions are impotent, and dispositions without principle are blind. The first half of this aphorism emphasizes that right choice and right doing depend on dispositions to think and to act in right ways. Without dispositions backing exhortations, we get only exhortations, not right action. But dispositions alone are not enough. Principles grounded in concepts of value are needed to determine what dispositions are indeed virtues deserving cultivation and to provide guidance for resolving the endless situations in which human and non-human interests are at odds.

The work of contemporary philosophers in the field of environmental virtue ethics is surveyed in Chapter 5. This discussion explores how dispositions are rooted in attitudinal orientation and how needed virtuous dispositions might be more effectively cultivated by educators, media news reporting, and religious organizations. Pending that discussion, four primary virtues are singled out in this overview account: respect, responsibility, humility, and gratitude.

---

79   Julian Simon is perhaps the most influential of writers who sees no population, pollution, or resource problem that is incapable of being resolved in contemporary science and economics. He insists that all aspects of life and environment are constantly improving and that environmentalists are "doomsayers" in the midst of ever-increasing abundance. Simon's views are developed in *The Ultimate Resource* (Princeton, NJ: Princeton University Press, 1981).
80   Lester Brown, *Plan B 2.0: Rescuing a Planet Under Stress and a Civilization in Trouble* (W. W. Norton & Company, 2006), p. 17.

a. Respect

Unless one cares about something, one does not have respect for it. The object of respect can be any number of things: oneself (self-respect), certain people (admirable role models), institutional arrangements (democratic governance), one's country, or symbols (a national flag). Every culture singles out "things" toward which members of that culture are expected to have and show respect, and regards such respect as a matter of high importance. In Confucianism, having and showing respect toward elders and ancestors is a key virtue. In Islam, respect for Allah is the foundation of faith and is shown by diligent practice of the Five Pillars of faith.

It has been emphasized that respect for nature in all its variety and diversity is formed by many elements of experience. Felt connections and the direct experience of nature in the wild engender care, and with care, respect. But more than instinct, feeling, and affective response, respect or the lack thereof grows out of what we are taught and learn. If one is taught that the value of non-human life consists entirely in its value for humans or that humans are inherently superior to other life, the learner will likely have and show little respect for things non-human. If, on the other hand, one learns and develops an appreciative understanding of the fundamental respects in which human life is rooted and shares commonalities with other life past and present, of the fundamental ways in which human life is dependent on biodiversity and healthy ecosystem functioning, of valuing processes occurring in non-human life and life systems, of the many scientific and practical insights that derive from heeding nature's ways, and of the ways in which human as well as non-human life is being put in jeopardy, care and respect is engendered. When products and processes in nature are thought to be put at risk, care becomes a concerned care; one feels "obliged" to safeguard those things and to accept responsibility for doing so.

b. Responsibility

The term "responsibility" has several meanings. In one sense, it is used as a synonym for "obligation": to have a responsibility is to have an obligation. In another sense, it is used to convey that one is appropriately subject to praise or blame, or reward or punishment, for compliance or non-compliance with one's obligations; its meaning conveys that one is accountable for one's actions. In a third sense, the term is used to refer to one's taking or accepting responsibility. A responsible person is a person who takes responsibility (third sense) and is inclined to act in responsible ways (first sense). He or she is also a person who thinks and feels that it is appropriate to hold oneself and others accountable (second sense) for irresponsible acts. The "ought" implicit in taking responsibility has a theoretical component (defined in a theory of obligation), but it has an affective and motivational component as well (emanating from attitudinal orientation).

Absent accountability systems and mechanisms for compelling people to act in certain ways, one's actually doing so and expecting others to do so as well would be little more than an accident unless people are disposed to act in those ways. Accountability systems and enforcement mechanisms are in place and function with varying degrees of effectiveness in virtually all areas of human association, but institutionalized accountability is generally lacking in regard to the human treatment of non-human life. Until this institutional void begins to be filled, the indispensable fallback is a heightened sense of responsibility for the rightful treatment of life's non-human participants. This will occur to the extent that there is growing respect for non-human life and life systems and growing realization that human well-being depends on more respectful treatment. If non-human biotic entities are not respected and not regarded as morally considerable in their own right, continuing mistreatment will likely continue unabated and little momentum will be generated to fill the institutional void.

The next chapter critically examines the question of moral standing and, more particularly, whether any non-human entity can reasonably be regarded as morally considerable in its own right. The conclusion reached is that all living organisms, their kinds, and the biotic communities they inhabit are all *worthy* of moral consideration in their own right by virtue of the inherent value they possess and exhibit. Worthiness of moral consideration implies, at a minimum, that the question of the moral permissibility of human-inflicted harm is a *relevant* moral question, whether or not any human is also benefited or harmed thereby. Without dispositional respect rooted in caring, there is little inclination to pose the question of the permissibility of the harm that humans inflict on non-human life: to recognize the "ought" of doing so. There is much in nature to find admirable and worthy of one's respect: much to which a respectful attitude can meaningfully be attached and directed. But this requires a quickening of felt connections, educational practices that affirm the value of nature itself, and an owning up to the environmental and ecological devastation that is occurring.

c. Humility

Many cultures have extolled the importance of humility. Confucius said that "humility is the solid foundation of all the virtues." Jesus taught the central importance of humility as have Christians throughout the centuries. Richard Rohr offers this perspective: "I don't believe Jesus gave us a plan of what the perfect society is supposed to look like. It's not evident from the New Testament anyway. Instead Jesus gave us a process, a way of being, a way to look behind things and to press forward to the truth. It is humility." In the fourth century, Archbishop Chrysostom said that "Humility is the root, mother, nurse, foundation, and bond of all virtue," and in the early thirteenth century St. Francis of Assisi professed that one cannot but be humbled when one beholds the wonders and beauties of God's creations in nature. "Praise and bless the Lord," St. Francis said, "and give thanks and serve him with great humility." Thoreau saw humility as revelatory: "Humility, like darkness, reveals the heavenly lights." Benjamin Franklin warned that when humility (defined in his autobiography as "imitating Jesus and Socrates") is not habituated through practice, prideful ego takes over: "In reality," Franklin wrote, "there is perhaps not one of our natural passions so hard to subdue as pride. Disguise it, struggle with it, beat it down, stifle it, mortify it as much as one pleases, it is still alive, and every now and then it peeps out and shows itself. ... For even if I could conceive that I had completely overcome it, I would probably be proud of my humility."

In regard to one's attitudinal orientation toward nature, humility comes from the realization that nature's powers and achievements transcend our powers and achievements, and that its history transcends our history. This realization tempers hubris. To be gripped by this realization is to experience awe and to be gripped by a sense of humility. One does not exaggerate one's power or significance when one is immersed in wild nature, when one encounters wonders one cannot decipher, or when one stands before forces one cannot control. Humility is a feeling, sometimes an aesthetic feeling, associated with the realization that there are powers that exceed human powers. Humility is induced by the direct experience of nature's many faces and moods and the powerful emotions they produce, by contemplation of the great achievements and failures of life in its three-billion-year-long evolutionary history, and by the realization that the deepest mysteries of the cosmos elude human understanding. One cannot but feel humility when one comes face-to-face with the transcendent. Deeply religious people have always felt and said this. And so have scientists who seek to unravel the mysteries of the cosmos.

Robert MacFarlane said this about humility: "Most of us exist for most of the time in worlds which are humanly arranged, themed, and controlled. One forgets that there are environments which do not respond to the flick of a switch or the twist of a dial, and which have their own rhythms and orders of existence. Mountains correct this amnesia. By speaking of greater forces than we can possibly invoke, and by confronting us with greater spans of time than we can possibly envisage, mountains refute our excessive trust in the man-made. They pose profound questions about our durability and the importance of our schemes. They induce, I suppose, modesty in us."[81]

Books are written about the "end of nature" and about how technology has enabled *Homo sapiens* to free itself from evolutionary process and to control the evolution of other life forms, but this kind of thinking is prideful and reckless. Stephen Gould agrees: "I suggest that we execute a pact with our planet [to treat her as we would want her to treat us]. She holds all the cards and has immense power over us—so such a compact, which we desperately need but she does not at her own time scale, would be a blessing for us, and an indulgence for her. We had better sign the papers while she is still willing to make a deal. If we treat her nicely, she will keep us going for a while. If we scratch her, she will bleed, kick us out, bandage up, and go about her business at her planetary scale."[82]

d. Gratitude

Historically, gratitude as a virtue has been closely linked with religious traditions. In Judaism, all good things come from God, and it is essential that worshipers show gratitude and give thanks for their many blessings. Psalms 30:12 says "O lord my God, I will give thanks to you forever." The Jewish prayer book begins with a simple appreciation for being alive: "Thank you, God, for returning soul to my body." A similar emphasis on expressions of gratitude for God's blessings also permeates Christian teachings and formal religious practice. The medieval mystic Meister Eckhart suggested that "If the only prayer you said in your whole life was 'thank you,' that would suffice." Martin Luther called gratitude "the basic Christian attitude." In Islam, thanks is given to God in each of five prayers made

---

81   Robert MacFarlane, *Mountains of the Mind* (New York: Vintage Books, A Division of Random House, Inc., 2004), pp. 275–76.
82   Stephen J. Gould, "The Golden Rule—A Proper Scale for Our Environmental Crisis," in *Reflections on Nature*, Lori Gruen & Dale Jamieson, eds. (New York: Oxford University Press), p. 39.

daily by the faithful and fasting during the month of Ramadan is intended to strengthen the resolve of believers to submit to God and to put believers in a state of gratitude for the abundance that God provides.

Although gratitude may be less commonplace in today's secular world, it has experienced somewhat of a comeback with the rise of the positive psychology movement. Studies indicate that gratitude has one of the strongest links with mental health of any personality trait. In one study, participants were randomly assigned to one of six therapeutic interventions designed to improve perceived overall quality of life. One intervention involved having participants write and deliver a letter of gratitude to someone in their lives. Results showed a rise in happiness scores by 10% and a significant fall in depression scores, results that lasted up to one month. Comparable but longer lasting effects were found to be associated with the keeping of "gratitude journals" in which participants wrote down three things they were grateful for every day.[83] Other studies provide evidence that the expression of gratitude may be a uniquely important contributor to one's sense of well-being. They also show that short-lived feelings can acquire a degree of permanence as personality traits. It is good that psychology provides this insight because, as Aldous Huxley put it, "Most human beings have an almost infinite capacity for taking things for granted."

We have very good reasons for being grateful for nature's contributions to our lives individually and collectively, including not only the manufactured goods and services that make their way to us as food and conveniences for living, but also nature's value as mentor, its value as provider of venues for recreational and aesthetic opportunities, its value in sustaining the biological structures and functions that compose our bodies and make us what we are, and its value in providing essential ecological services ranging from nutrient cycling and pollination to regulation of the chemical composition of the oceans and atmosphere. Indigenous peoples everywhere expressed gratitude for nature's bounty, but relatively few moderns do so today. Most people living in urban environments are largely unaware where their food, energy, clothing, and other of life's essentials come from and are not disposed to care unless breakdowns occur in production and distribution systems. When gratitude is perfunctorily expressed on a day of thanksgiving or voiced at family mealtimes, it is generally directed to a divine provider, where divinity is conceived as agency and nature is conceived as an instrument of God's providence.

---

83 M. Seligman, T. Steen, A. Park, & C. Peterson, "Positive Psychology Progress: Empirical Validation of Interventions," in *American Psychologist*, 60, 410–421.

Gratitude for all that nature provides goes hand in hand with the inclination of people to respect nature, to take responsibility for actions detrimental to nature's products and processes, and to realize with some degree of humility that human capabilities are limited and that, as E. O. Wilson put it, "nature holds the trump cards." These themes are further explored in Chapter 5.

CHAPTER 2.
MORAL STANDING: TOWARD A BROADER CONCEPT OF MORAL COMMUNITY

The question of moral standing[1] is a basic question in animal and environmental ethics. Anthropocentric theorists argue that only human beings have moral standing and insist, accordingly, that the question of the moral permissibility of harm to a non-human biotic entity—a vertebrate animal, a non-vertebrate animal, an animal or plant species, an ecosystem, a bioregion, ongoing evolutionary life as a whole—is answered by considering human interests exclusively. Vertebracentric theorists extend moral standing to animals capable of experiencing pleasure and pain and any emotional distress that may accompany the experience of pain. Biocentric theorists advance arguments for recognition of the independent moral standing of all living beings. Many biocentrists argue that the moral standing of discrete biological kinds (species) should be recognized as well. Ecocentric theorists argue in support of the moral standing of ecosystems, with some arguing, more broadly, that moral considerability should be extended to planetary life as ongoing dynamic whole.

This chapter provides a definition of "moral standing" that does not (it is maintained) presuppose whether any biotic entity other than humans is morally considerable in its own right. Using this definition, arguments supporting and opposing recognition of the moral standing of various non-human life forms are critically examined. It is concluded that all organisms, their biological kinds, ecosystems, and nature as totality have moral standing.

---

1   The predicate "has moral standing" is used interchangeably with "counts morally in its own right," "is morally considerable in its own right," and "is worthy of moral consideration in its own right" throughout the chapter.

A. NEW QUESTIONS, DIVERGENT ANSWERS

Beginning in the second half of the twentieth century, the new and burgeoning field of environmental ethics asked new questions and posed old questions in a new way. Some of these questions are:

Non-Human Value: Does the value of non-human life consist entirely of its value for human beings? Would a world without humans be a world without value? Do any non-human entities have a well-being or good of their own? Can any non-human entity be said to have value awareness in a way meaningfully comparable to value awareness in humans? Is intelligence or purposefulness involved, even though it may not be cognitive or conceptual?

Non-Human Moral Standing: What makes an entity worthy of moral consideration in its own right? If it is meaningful to speak of the well-being of a non-human biotic entity, does its well-being matter morally, even though human well-being is not affected in any significant way? Is any non-human entity the kind of entity to which obligations could meaningfully be said to be directly owed or rights directly ascribed?

Non-Human Moral Significance: If it is acknowledged that biotic entities have well-being of their own and are morally considerable in their own right, what is the moral significance of this well-being compared to that of humans? Is the well-being of one non-human entity any more or less significant morally than that of any other non-human entity? When a policy or project designed to secure human well-being is harmful to non-human life, how should the moral permissibility of that policy or project be decided? What relative weights should be assigned to the well-being of diversely impacted biotic entities in such situations?

Not surprisingly, the theoretical and practical answers given to these questions diverge sharply. The focus in this chapter is on the concept of moral standing and the respects in which questions of value and moral significance are raised in this context. Broader questions of moral significance are explored in subsequent chapters and are touched on only tangentially in this chapter.

B. "Moral Standing" Defined

Three criteria of moral standing are proposed: (1) the entity in question must have structural and functional parts that enable it to persist in an environment as a unified self-regulating whole; (2) it must be capable of being harmed, and (3) it must possess capacities or characteristics by virtue of which it can be considered to be worthy of moral consideration in its own right.

1. Self-Regulation

The first criterion of moral standing states that the entity in question must have structural and functional parts that enable it to persist in an environment as a unified self-regulating whole. A pile of rocks is not internally regulated; there is no coherent structure or function to the assemblage, much less self-regulation that permits persistence over time. A spider is a unified self-regulated entity, but a spider web (a product) or spider leg (a functioning part) is not. A spider web has a structure that can be physically damaged and a spider leg can be functionally impaired, but neither is self-regulating. A landscape painting may be said to be an entity that has structural components comprising a unified whole, but it does not have functioning parts that are internally self-regulated. If a sculpture has functioning components arranged as a unified whole (perhaps a battery-operated moving component is part of the arrangement), it is still not a harmable entity on the above criterion because the function (movement) is artist-imposed. In general, an entity cannot reasonably be considered to be morally considerable in its own right if it does not have internally regulated structural and functional components: if its coherence as a unified entity persisting through time cannot be characterized as a self-regulated adaptation in an environment.[2]

---

2   An interesting test case is a robot that self-corrects for functional inadequacies. Such a robot is a unified entity with structure and functional components, but can the robot be said to be self-regulating? The answer proffered here is "no," because the robot has been programmed to re-program if certain performance requirements (specified in the original program) are not met. Another test case arises in connection with the contention that all organisms have been "programmed" by natural selection to self-regulate in the way they do. As suggested in the previous chapter, natural selection is regarded by complexity theorists working in the field of evolutionary biology as inseparably linked to the capacity of biotic systems to self-organize. If so, an explanation incorporating the theory of natural selection requires reference to self-regulation. This thesis is revisited in Sections F and G below.

2. Harmability

A morally considerable entity must, moreover, be capable of being harmed. Section D below explores various ways in which vertebrate animals can be harmed. In regard to the question of how non-vertebrate organisms and systems of life (as well as vertebrates) can be harmed, six general types of harm are delineated and defined in Chapter 6: physical damage, resource deprivation, functional impairment, physical pain, emotional distress, and terminal harm in the form of death (individual organisms), extinction (species), or total destruction (ecosystems).[3] While not all self-regulating biotic entities can be harmed in all of these ways (clearly, this not the case), candidacy for moral standing requires the capacity to be harmed in one of combination of these ways.

To be considered harmable (in general), an entity must be capable of being made better or worse off with respect to something that is of value to, or a value for, that entity. A harmable entity is one whose well-being can meaningfully be said to be diminished, where well-being is defined with reference to something that is of value to, or a value for, the entity in question.

3. Worthiness

The third criterion states that there must be something about a harmable self-regulating entity that makes it *worthy* of moral consideration *in its own right*. To make this criterion clear, two stipulative definitions are required to answer two questions: What does it *mean* to say that an entity is *morally considerable*? What does it *mean* to say that an entity is morally considerable *in its own right*?

To say that an entity is *morally considerable* means that human-caused harm to that entity legitimizes the question of the moral permissibility of the harm; it is to say that the *question* of the moral permissibility of the harm is a *relevant* moral question.

To say that an entity is morally considerable *in its own right* means that the question of the moral permissibility of human-caused harm is a relevant question *whether or not* the harm in question is harmful or beneficial to any human being. It is also to say that any obligation owed to that entity is an obligation owed *directly* to the morally considerable entity *whether or not* any associated

---

3   A harm assessment methodology is developed in Chapter 6 for determining the moral permissibility of proposed policies and projects that portend far-reaching harm for both human and non-human biotic entities. The six types of harm are defined in this context, along with the identification of parameters in terms of which harm magnitude can be gauged.

obligation is owed to any human who may have an interest in that entity and the harm involved. If one has an obligation to consider the moral permissibility of harming Sue's dog, the obligation is owed both to Sue's dog and to Sue. If, upon deliberation, it is judged that the harm is morally impermissible, the obligation not to harm would be owed to both Sue and her dog.

The concept of inherent value is employed to clarify what there is about an entity that makes it worthy of moral consideration in its own right. When inherent value is ascribed to an entity, the reference is to something that "inheres" in that entity. Some theorists associate this "something" with intrinsic value.[4] Holmes Rolston suggests that other value terminology—constitutive, systemic, or synergistic value—is more appropriate. But however the value is characterized and defined, inherent value refers to something that is of value to, or a value for, the entity in question, whether or not it is of value to, or a value for, a human or any other entity.

C. MORAL STANDING AND MORAL SIGNIFICANCE

The concepts of moral standing and moral significance are distinct concepts, but not entirely unrelated. "Worthiness of moral consideration" *means* that the question of the moral permissibility of human-inflicted harm is a morally *relevant* question. Whether one feels obliged or is motivated at an affective level to raise the permissibility question, or whether one acknowledges at a reflective level that one is obligated to raise it are separate questions. As suggested in Chapter 1, respect for something and one's sense of responsibility toward it are integral components of attitudinal orientation, and are as much normative as descriptive and as much pre-conceptual as conceptual. One would not be disposed to recognize the "ought" of raising the question of the moral permissibility of harm if one does not care about and respect the entity in question or if the harm in question were not thought to be "serious enough" in magnitude or value significance. These themes are addressed throughout this work, but the point to be made here is that advocates for the recognition of the moral

---

4   Intrinsic value is commonly contrasted with extrinsic value, where the former is associated with things that are valuable in and of themselves and the latter is associated with things that are means to other valued things. Otherwise stated, an extrinsic value is said to have instrumental or means value and to require reference to some other value, while an intrinsic value is said to be something valuable or good for its own sake, to be an end or terminal value, and to require no further reference to any other value. Something can have both intrinsic and extrinsic value, of course.

standing of non-human biotic entities have the burden of explaining how moral relevance is connected with moral obligation. The connection should not be built into a definition of "moral standing" and settled by definition, but should, rather, be addressed within an accompanying moral psychology and theory of obligation.

If the definition of an entity's "worthiness of moral consideration" is understood to imply an obligation to consider the moral permissibility of human-caused harm to that entity, it is important to emphasize that it does not imply anything more about the entity's moral significance than this; it does assume that harm to the entity in question has greater or less moral significance than comparable harm to any other morally considerable entity, or that greater weight should be given to certain types of harm or certain types of harmable entities in moral permissibility determinations. Such questions of moral significance are important in the consideration of how moral permissibility deliberations and justificatory arguments should be structured. But such questions go beyond simply asking whom or what has moral standing.

The combined effect of the several criteria of moral standing—that an entity must be a self-regulating entity capable of being harmed and the possessor of something of value that makes *it* worthy of moral consideration—are not contrary to common sense. They are presumably framed in a theoretically neutral manner that leaves the question of non-human moral standing an open question. They are also criteria that presumably eliminate counter-intuitive claims about who or what has moral standing.

D. ANTHROPOCENTRISM: ONLY HUMANS COUNT MORALLY

1. Anthropocentric Arguments

Most moral theorists begin with the premise that humans have moral standing: of course humans are morally considerable; of course the harm that humans inflict on other humans raises the question of the moral permissibility of that harm. Some theorists have contended that only *some* humans count morally on the grounds that they are inherently superior to other humans. However, such claims have been denounced as morally unacceptable bias and prejudice. Social movements have been mobilized to defeat prejudice and discrimination of this sort and laws have been enacted to eliminate it.

Theorists who contend that *all* and *only* humans have moral standing are labeled "anthropocentrists" or "humanists." The argument is as old as Plato and Aristotle, was reiterated by Kant, and is made by numerous contemporary moral philosophers. The core argument is that only humans have moral standing because only humans are capable of rationality, and that this unique capability deserves moral respect. Rationality is variously defined, including the unique ability of humans to communicate symbolically, to discover truth, to act on principles of right action and to take responsibility for their actions (moral agency), to create and appreciate works of art, to solve problems with advanced technologies, and to live in cultural milieus that expand human rational capacities and opportunities. These are admirable capabilities that few theorists deny are worthy of respect, even though humans fall short of realizing their potentialities as rational moral agents and living up to the ideals associated with rationality. Rationality is viewed, moreover, as an inherent (intrinsic) value that "commands" that all humans be treated respectfully. At a minimum, respectful treatment requires that humans be regarded as morally considerable and, beyond this, that they be treated as ends-in-themselves equally deserving of the basic rights that all humans deserve by virtue of their being rational beings.

An anthropocentrist argues that it is unnecessary and counterproductive to ascribe moral standing to non-human life and to base claims of non-human standing on claims that non-human biotic entities have inherent value. A humanist does not deny that we have obligations not to mistreat animals, not to pollute the land, air, and water, not to drive endangered species to extinction, not to destroy ecosystems, and not to consume renewable resources in excess of replenishment rates. But, for a humanist, such obligations derive from considerations of what is prudent and necessary to protect and benefit human life, including future generations of humans. Disagreement exists over specific obligations in specific cases, but there is no disagreement among humanists that obligations are owed to humans, not to non-human forms of life. If some of these obligations imply correlative rights, they are human rights, not the rights of non-humans.

The common denominator in all these reasons is that they are *human* reasons for securing and safeguarding *human* well-being. William Godfrey-Smith neatly summarized four lines of argument used by anthropocentrists to make the case that human well-being depends on responsible stewardship of nature's resources: the *cathedral argument,* highlighting the opportunities that wilderness areas afford for spiritual renewal and aesthetic delight; the *laboratory argument*, reminding us that the opportunity to study nature in all its diversity enables us not only to discover biological laws the transgression of which puts human life in peril, but also to derive the compounds needed to make pharmaceuticals that prevent, treat, and cure human disease; the *silo argument*, reminding us that good things come from nature, including food, water, energy, and backup stockpiles of genetic diversity in case something goes suddenly wrong with monoculture agriculture; and the *gymnasium argument*, focusing on the many athletic and recreational opportunities that nature provides.[5] Richard Watson summarized the argument in simple and blunt terms: "There is very good reason for thinking ecologically, and for encouraging human beings to act in such a way as to preserve a rich and balanced planetary ecology: human survival depends on it."[6]

The distinction has been drawn between "weak" and "strong" anthropocentrism, where the latter is associated with the claim that humans are superior to non-humans in some morally relevant respect and the former with the claim that there is no need, theoretically and practically, to appeal to values outside human life and culture. "Weak" anthropocentrism calls for an "enlightened" perspective: one that shows moral respect for all humans and one that focuses on what is necessary to secure and safeguard human well-being in the long term. If this occurs, non-renewable resources essential for the well-being of current and future generations will not be thoughtlessly depleted, renewal resources will continue to be generated in quantity and quality sufficient to meet basic human needs, the ecological services on which humans depend will not be jeopardized, and life will continue to evolve and diversify.

Bryan Norton has perhaps best stated the case for "weak" anthropocentrism. He argues that sound environmental and ecological policies and practices can be formulated from an anthropocentric perspective, provided that future generations of humans are taken into account and that nature's value for humans is not reduced to economic value. He advanced what he calls the "convergence hypothesis": that an informed and morally adequate anthropocentrism yields the same resource management policies and practices as would a non-anthropocentric framework if it were fully and adequately worked out. In his words: "At least in the important area of moral obligations regarding

---

5   Geoffrey-Smith himself thought that anthropocentric reasons for protecting and preserving wilderness, while compelling, were not enough; also needed, he thought, were reasons based on the intrinsic value of processes and products in nature.

6   Richard Watson, "A Critique of Anti-Anthropocentric Ethics," in *Environmental Ethics: Readings in Theory and Application*, Louis P. Pojman, ed. (Wadsworth, 2000), p. 167.

fauna and flora, the policy implications of a broadly formulated and farsighted anthropocentrism and non-anthropocentrism will be identical."[7]

Norton was a participant in the heated exchanges among animal rights advocates, environmentalists, and anthropocentrists during the latter half of the twentieth century and sought to develop a practically useful framework that avoided counter-productive vitriol. In his article, "Why I am not a Nonanthropocentrist," he characterized his position as follows:

> Rather than *reducing* pluralistic principles by relating them to an underlying value theory that recognizes only economic preferences or 'inherent' value as the ontological stuff that unifies all moral judgments, I have sought integration of multiple values on three irreducible scales of human concern and valuation [individual, community, and global], choosing pluralism over monism, attempting to integrate values within an ecologically informed, multi-scalar model of human habitat. ... If the problem of environmentalism is the need to support rationally the goals of environmental protection—the problem that Callicott misconceived as the need for a realist moral ontology to establish the 'objectivity' of environmental goals—then I endorse the broadly Darwinian approach to both epistemology and morals proposed by the American pragmatists. ... We humans will understand our moral responsibilities only if we understand the consequences of our actions as they unfold on multiple scales, and the human community will only survive to further evolve and adapt if we learn to achieve individual welfare and justice in the present in ways that are less disruptive of the processes, evolving on larger spatio-temporal scales, essential to human and ecological communities."[8]

Norton's later writings have focused on clarifying the obligations that current generations owe to future generations, how "sustainability" should be interpreted in this context, and how planning and resources management can effectively integrate economic, environmental, and local values.

---

7 Bryan G. Norton, "Environmental Ethics and Weak Anthropocentrism," in *Environmental Ethics*, 6, 131–148.
8 Bryan Norton, "Why I am not a Non-anthropocentrist," in *Environmental Ethics* Vol. 17. This article is reprinted and lightly edited under the title "Integration or Reduction: Two Approaches to Environmental Values," in *The Environmental Ethics & Policy Book* (Thomson Wadsworth, 2003). Pp. 240–259.

2. Critique of Anthropocentrism

Many of the criticisms of anthropocentrism have been directed at the "strong" version that asserts human *superiority*. Claims of superiority are usually associated with the unique ability of humans to reason, but other reasons are given: because only humans are created in the image of God, or have a mind, or are the crowning achievement of an evolving natural order. If the claim is based on the theological belief that only humans are created in the image of God, a common objection is that this view is crudely anthropomorphic or that it boils down to the claim that humans, like God, are rational beings. If the explanation is that only humans have a mind, a common objection is that it presupposes a mind-body dualism that has been widely rejected in contemporary science and philosophy. Various writers have observed that the mind-body dualism was not a Judeo-Christian concept until Platonic metaphysics was incorporated in neo-Platonic theologies and Aristotelian metaphysics was incorporated in the theology of Thomas Aquinas, only later to regain primarily philosophical status in the writings of Descartes. The rationality criterion is generally taken by most anthropocentrists today to be the only acceptable criterion of moral standing, and philosophical discussions in this context are generally decoupled from claims of superiority rooted a mind-body dualism or theological explanations.

Various critics have been quick to point out that the claim that humans are superior simply because they are humans or belong to the species *Homo sapiens* is no less baseless and discriminatory that the claim that are men are superior to women because they belong to the class of males, or whites are superior to non-whites because they belong to the Caucasian race; class membership does not establish superiority. But the discrimination does not have to be this blatant. Authors in feminist tradition have been especially critical not only of the mind-body dichotomy but other dualisms as well—reason–emotion, masculine–feminine, human–non-human, culture–nature—where the first-mentioned characteristics in each of these pairs (mind, reason, masculinity, human, culture) is regarded as superior to each of their complements (body, emotion, femininity, non-human, and nature). They strongly oppose the use of spurious claims of superiority and inferiority to justify the domination of men over women and humans over nature. Karen Warren put it this way: "Ecofeminists insist that the sort of logic of domination used to justify the domination of humans by gender, racial, ethnic, or class status is also used to justify the domination of nature."[9] Ecofeminists contend that species discrimination is as deeply embedded in society as gender and racial discrimination, and their aim is to expose and weed it out.

Biocentric and ecocentric theorists contend that non-human organisms, species, and ecosystems have goods of their own kind: that it is no less meaningful to say that certain things are good for and about non-humans than to say that certain things are good for and about humans. Given this contention, it is argued that claims of human superiority *beg the question*. These claims select a characteristic that is good for or about humans, a characteristic that non-humans do not have or lack, and use this characteristic (good) to posit human superiority and/or exclusive moral standing. But, as Paul Taylor notes, "To use standards based on human values is already to commit oneself to holding that humans are superior to non-humans, which is the point in question."[10] James Sterba makes the same point in his observation that humans have characteristics or capacities (valuable to humans) that plants and animals lack, but animals and plants also have characteristics or capacities (valuable to them) that humans lack.[11] Humans are uniquely able to formulate and solve complex mathematical equations, but they lack the homing ability of a pigeon, the speed of a cheetah, the scent of a wolf, the visual acuity of an eagle, and the photosynthetic power of a plant. Mathematical problem solving is good for humans, but not for cheetahs and pigeons. Photosynthesis is good for plants, but not for humans and wolves. To take what is good for or about humans as a basis for asserting human superiority and exclusive moral standing is circular reasoning. The argument presupposes the conclusion that it purports to establish.

Arguing that considerations other than rationality make an entity morally considerable, Peter Singer's criticism of anthropocentrism is that it violates a fundamental principle of human justice: "If a being suffers, there can be no basis for refusing to take that suffering into consideration ... The principle of equality requires that its suffering be counted equally with like suffering of any other being." As discussed subsequently, vertebracentrist Tom Regan makes a similar

---

9   Karen J. Warren, "The Power and Promise of Ecological Feminism," in *Environmental Ethics: Readings in Theory and Application*, ed. Louis Pojman (Belmont, CA Wadsworth, 2001), p. 192.
10   Paul Taylor, "Biocentric Egalitarianism," in *Environmental Ethics: Readings in Theory and Application*, ed. Louis Pojman (Wadsworth: Belmont, CA, 2001), p.108. Taylor's biocentric ethical theory is examined in some detail in the next chapter.
11   James Sterba, "Environmental Justice: Reconciling Anthropocentric and Non-anthropocentric Environmental Ethics," in *Environmental Ethics: Readings in Theory and Application*, ed. Louis Pojman (Belmont, CA: Wadsworth, 2001), p. 179.

justice-based argument based on his more restrictive subject-of-a-life criterion, as does biocentrist Paul Taylor using a much broader teleological criterion.

The charge of species discrimination in these various versions is particularly unpalatable to the humanist who strenuously opposes any criterion that limits the scope of moral considerability to a subset of human beings. Humanists insist that moral standing should not be based on gender, race, nationality, or any other criterion that gives special moral status to *some* human beings. These beliefs have inspired activist movements that have liberated slaves, women, and other historically marginalized groups. In view of these achievements, there is a startling irony in the charge that humanism is another form of discrimination: that the "speciesism" implicit in a claim of special moral status for human beings is no more justified than sexism, racism, or any other "ism" that claims special status for a subgroup of humans. The humanist insistence that *all* humans have moral standing has been a boon to humankind. The claim that *only* humans have moral standing has opened a floodgate of criticism from biocentrists and animal welfare/rights theorists.

Another frequently made criticism of anthropocentrism is that its defenders cannot come up with a version of the rationality criterion that includes all humans but excludes all non-humans. As Peter Singer, Tom Regan, and others have argued, a criterion that excludes animals also excludes infants, elderly persons with dementia or Alzheimer's disease, imbeciles, and persons who have suffered brain injuries. Exclusion of these members of the human population is morally objectionable to all ethicists. But any adjustment of the rationality criterion to extend moral standing to the very old, the very young, and the mentally disabled has the effect of extending moral standing to "higher animals" as well. The mother chimpanzee's ability to learn a sign language and teach it to her baby chimp, an elephant's mourning of the death of a fellow elephant and treating its remains with respect, and the ability of spiders to construct elaborate insect-trapping webs are examples of intellectual, moral, and technical capabilities that exceed those of very young, very old, and brain-impaired humans. Various writers attempt to get around this problem by saying that all humans have rational potential, but humans with Alzheimer's disease or who are severely mentally retarded or have suffered irreversible brain damage do not have even the potentiality of rational thought and action.[12]

---

12   Carl Cohen replies that brain-damaged humans are appropriately regarded as morally considerable even though they lack the capacity to make moral judgments. His argument is that the test for moral judgment "is not a test to be administered to humans one by one, but applied to the capacity of members of the species in general." See Carl Cohen, "The case for the use of Animals

As noted earlier, Norton and other anthropocentrists argue that, from a practical standpoint, non-anthropocentric perspectives are unnecessary: that an "enlightened" anthropocentrism is all that is needed for adequate environmental and ecological protection. Critics question this assertion and the optimism it embodies, arguing that the reduction of non-human value to human value and the denial of the non-human moral standing have led and will continue to lead to environmental and ecological decline to the detriment of all planetary life. The thrust of this line of criticism is that an anthropocentric mindset is incapable of sustaining an "enlightened" humanism. Norton calls for a pluralistic value theory that recognizes the full extent of nature's extrinsic value for humans and does not reduce aesthetic, educational, and other "quality of life" values to economic and monetary value, but critics question whether this is enough to engender respect for the broader natural world of which humanity is a part. Katie McShane, for example, wrote this: "Many recent critical discussions of anthropocentrism have focused on Bryan Norton's 'convergence hypothesis': the claim that both anthropocentric and non-anthropocentric ethics will recommend the same environmentally responsible behaviors and policies. I argue that even if we grant the truth of Norton's convergence hypothesis, there is still good reasons to worry about anthropocentric ethics. Ethics legitimately raises questions about how to feel, not just about which actions to take or which policies to adopt. From the point of view of norms for feeling, anthropocentrism has very different practical implications from non-anthropocentrism; it undermines some of the common attitudes—love, respect, awe—that people think it appropriate to take toward the natural world."[13] McShane and other critics agree with Norton that value should not be reduced to economic value, but they are concerned about a more insidious reduction: the reduction of all value to human value. An attitude toward nature that has this reduction as its centerpiece will, critics believe, perpetuate continuing environmental and ecological decline.

When policy deliberations start with the premise that only humans count morally, or that value does not exist apart from human life and culture, harm to non-human life and life systems is easily overlooked or dismissed. When non-human harm is taken into account, the evaluation models used by policy makers ignore or trivialize such harm. In cost–benefit analysis, for example, harms to

---

in Biomedical Research," in *New England Journal of Medicine*, vol. 315, issue 14, October 1986, pp. 865–870.

13   Katie McShane, "Anthropocentrism vs. Non-anthropocentrism: Why Should We Care," in *Environmental Values* 16(2), pp. 169–85.

non-human entities are assigned monetary values based on willingness to pay or other proxy measurements when market values cannot be derived, and often the assigned values are discounted in the analysis when effects are expected to occur in the future. Numerous writers have pointed out the inadequacies of cost–benefit analysis when monetary values are assigned to human life, health, safety, and other basic human values. The inadequacies are no less glaring when monetary values are assigned to things like biodiversity loss and disappearing coral reefs. Direct market values do not exist for these kinds of things, so proxy values are sought. The value significance of biodiversity loss becomes what people would be willing to pay to avoid the loss. But however monetary values are derived, the anthropocentrist contends that it is the interests and well-being of people that matter morally, not the well-being of animals, plants, species, and biotic communities.

It is not unreasonable for decision makers to ask whether the monetary benefits of a proposal exceed its costs or for them to want to get the "greatest bang for their buck." What non-anthropocentrists find troubling is the reduction of the value of non-human life to its value for human beings. In the many situations in modern life where development proposals benefit human parties but harm non-human life, and preservation is considered as an alternative to development, the development option generally prevails. If the preservation option does prevail, the justificatory rationale is that the human benefits of preservation outweigh the human costs of development. Preservationist options rarely win in such contests, particularly when the benefits and costs are defined in monetary terms.

3. Remarks/Conclusions

Notwithstanding the problems associated with anthropocentrism in environmental ethics, it must be acknowledged that humanistic reasons for protecting the environment are compelling reasons, and that these reasons have carried the day on many notable occasions. Important environmental protection and conservation initiatives have been adopted because international bodies, governments, non-governmental organizations, corporations, and ordinary citizens have sought, above all, to protect the general public and promote general human welfare. At the international level, a notable achievement was the 1985 Vienna Convention on the Protection of the Ozone Layer and its 1987 Montreal Protocol, ratified by many nations (including the US) and major corporate interests (including DuPont). There are also important international initiatives (discussed in Chapters 3 and 4) to conserve wild places and protect endangered species. In the US, there are the 1964 Wilderness Act, the 1969 National Environmental Policy Act, the 1970 Clean Air Act, the 1972 Clean Water Act, the 1973 Endangered Species Act, and the 1990 Environmental Protection Act.

But there have also been notable setbacks. At the international level, there have been failures to reach protocol agreements on climate change, desertification, deforestation, biodiversity loss, population control, freshwater resources, marine environmental deterioration, toxification, and acid rain. In the US, the aforementioned environmental legislation has been repeatedly amended, in many cases (not all) to relax requirements at the behest of powerful business lobbies. Meanwhile, many (not all) indicators of environmental and ecological health have continued to decline.

It is the conclusion here that the strong version of anthropocentrism that regards humans as inherently superior to other biotic entities does not stand up. Some of the objections to this position have been noted and are further developed in this chapter and throughout the book. But the most basic problem with anthropocentrism, even in its most enlightened form, is that value in nature is reduced to its value for human beings. Holmes Rolston and other biocentric and ecocentric writers construct arguments for the moral standing of non-human entities based on the contention that values and valuing processes operate in the natural order. Ecofeminists and other writers contend that anthropocentrism ignores the fundamental respects in which a caring attitude is the wellspring of moral response, and that the belief that nature is devoid of value undercuts the kind of concern that motivates people to take responsible action. It is argued along these lines that the virtue of respect and responsibility are undermined by the belief that nature is value-less, and that the cultivation of both respect and responsibility as virtuous dispositions depend on deep-seated caring about the well-being of non-human biotic entities.

E. VERTEBRACENTRISM: SENTIENT ANIMALS COUNT MORALLY

Vertebrate animals are sentient beings: they have the sensory capacity to see, hear, smell, taste, and touch objects in their environments and to feel pleasure and pain in response to visual, auditory, olfactory, and tactile stimuli. Mammals also have at least the rudiments of such mental capacities as emotion, memory, belief, desire, intentional action, a sense of the future, and self-awareness. In view of these capacities, various moral philosophers have sought to extend moral standing to "higher animals." Three main lines of argument have been used for such an extension: the hedonistic utilitarian approach of Peter Singer, the deontological rights-based approach of Tom Regan, and the approach that emphasizes sympathetic identification.

1. Peter Singer: Pain and Suffering Matter

Singer's argument for the moral standing of sentient animals involves several premises: (1) that "pain and suffering are in themselves are intrinsically 'bad,'" (2) that the most fundamental interest a sentient being has is not being subjected to pain and suffering, (3) that this fundamental interest is alike for humans and other animals capable of feeling pleasure and pain, and (4) that like interests should be given like consideration in determinations of what is morally right. Singer makes it clear that proposition (1) and (4) are not statements of fact; proposition (1) is a value statement and (4) is an ought statement. People are not like animals in many respects, but all are alike in one fundamental morally relevant respect: they have a like interest in not suffering and not being in pain. Proposition (3)—that humans and other sentient animals are alike in their interest to not be in pain and to not suffer—is defended by Singer at some length. We know our own pain and "nearly all the external signs that lead us to infer pain in other humans can be seen in other species, [including] writhing, facial contortions, moaning, yelping or other forms of calling, attempts to avoid the source of the pain, appearance of fear at the prospect of its repetition, and so on." And "although human beings have a more developed cerebral cortex than other animals, this part of the brain is concerned with thinking functions rather than with basic impulses, emotions, and feelings … located in the diencephalon, which is well developed in many other species of animals, especially mammals and birds." He notes that "the overwhelming majority of scientists who have addressed themselves to this question agree." He argues that linguistic ability is not an indicator that only humans suffer: "Human infants and young children are unable to use language. Are we to deny that a year-old child can suffer? If not, language cannot be crucial." "So to conclude: there are no good reasons, scientific or philosophical, for denying that animals feel pain.

If we do not doubt that others feel pain we should not doubt that other animals do so too. ... Animals can feel pain."[14]

In regard to the question of moral standing, Singer defends Bentham's contention that "The question is not Whether animals can think? nor Can they talk? but Can they suffer?" Singer frames the question in terms of interests because interests reflect how sentient beings are related to the world. Stones do not have interests but sentient beings do. "It would be nonsense to say that it was not in the interests of a stone to be kicked along the road. ... A stone has no interests because it cannot suffer. Unlike a stone, "A mouse has an interest in not being kicked along the road because it will suffer if it is." The capacity for suffering and enjoyment is, Singer maintains, not only a necessary but also a sufficient for us to say that a being has interests.

Because humans and other sentient animals have a like interest in not suffering, there is no moral basis, Singer argues, for not giving equal consideration to the suffering of humans and vertebrates. "If a being suffers," he says, "there can be no moral justification for refusing to take that suffering into consideration. No matter what the nature of the being, the principle of equality requires that its suffering be counted equally with the like suffering—insofar as rough comparisons can be made—of any other being. So the limit of sentience is the only defensive boundary of concern for the interests of others." He continues: "To mark this boundary by some other characteristic like intelligence or rationality would be to mark it in an arbitrary manner. Why not choose some other characteristic, like skin color?" Also: "Racists violate the principle of equality by giving greater weight to the interests of members of their own race when there is a clash between their interests and the interests of those of another race. Sexists violate the principle of equality by favoring the interests of their own sex. Similarly, speciesists allow the interests of their own species to override the greater interests of members of other species. The pattern is identical in each case."

As discussed in the next chapter, Singer invokes the principles of utility and equal consideration to argue for what he takes to be morally permissible and morally required behavior toward animals in factory farms, zoos, research laboratories, and sexual relations. The relevant point in regard to the question of moral standing is that Singer's equality principle requires equal consideration of equal interests, not equal treatment.

---

14   The quotations related to proposition (3) above are excerpted from Singer's *Animal Liberation* (New York: Avon Books, 1990, Second Edition), pp. 10–15.

2. Tom Regan: Being a Subject-of-a-Life Matters

Tom Regan proposes a different criterion of moral standing: the capacity to be an experiencing subject-of-a-life. Mammals feel pleasure and pain, but, more than this, they remember, anticipate events, form social bonds, have a sense of self, and have emotions. Their mental lives do not include the full range of cognitive components found in human lives, but they are subjects of life concerned about their lives, and there can be little doubt that they are capable of suffering in ways comparable to humans.[15] Regan's criterion includes all normal mature mammals and is less inclusive than Singer's criterion: the capacity to feel pleasure and pain.

For Regan, value inheres in animals that can meaningfully be said to be a subject-of-a -life; they have, he says, *inherent value* and *ought* to be respected by human beings for this reason. He argues that such respect entails the exceptionless right of subjects-of-a-life not to be harmed by human beings: not to be kept in zoos, eaten, experimented upon, shot for sport and pleasure, or otherwise used as means to human ends. He insists on the kind of treatment for mammals which Kant reserves for humans; subjects-of-a-life ought to be regarded as ends-in-themselves having an absolute right not to be treated merely as means. Unlike Singer, Regan insists that equal consideration entails equal rights and equal treatment.

Regan rejects Singer's account on the grounds that it excludes recognition of the inherent worth of beings that can be said to be a subject-of-a-life. In his words, "Utilitarianism has no room for the equal moral rights of different individuals because it has no room for their equal inherent value or worth. What has value for the utilitarian is the satisfaction of an individual's interests, not the individual whose interests they are."

Like Singer, Regan also criticizes anthropocentrism on the grounds that it violates the principle of equal consideration. Mammals and humans are equal in the morally relevant respect that they are subjects-of-a-life. Since morally relevant equals ought to be given equal consideration, it is wrong not to give equal consideration to mammals.

Mary Ann Warren criticizes Regan for not providing an adequate explanation of why experiencing subjects-of-a-life have inherent value. In her words, "Regan says that it is a postulate that subjects-of-a-life have inherent value, a postulate justified by the fact that it avoids certain absurdities which he

---

15   16 See Regan's *The Case for Animal Rights* (University of California Press: Berkeley, 1983) for his description of characteristics attributable to an experiencing subject-of-a-life.

thinks follow from a purely utilitarian theory. But why is it a postulate that subjects-of-a-life have inherent value? … If the reason is that subjects-of-a-life have an existence which can go better or worse for them, then why isn't the appropriate conclusion that all sentient beings have inherent value, since they would all seem to meet that condition? … If inherent value is based on some natural property, then why not try to identify that property and explain its moral significance."

3. Care-Based Approaches: Sympathetic Caring Matters

Lord Shaftesbury, David Hume, and Adam Smith claimed in the late eighteenth and early nineteenth centuries that humans have a "natural sympathy implanted in our nature" (Hume's phrase). Schopenhauer argued a century later that innate natural sympathy extends beyond human communities, noting that "the *animals* are also taken under its protection." Baird Callicott is a contemporary champion of this tradition in ethics. Noting that Singer "heaped scorn on 'sentimental appeals to sympathy' … and avowed that his animal welfare ethic was grounded exclusively in 'basic moral principles' … based in reason, not emotion," Callicott alludes to the alternative course taken by Hume, who "regarded altruistic feeling and sentiment as the edifice upon which ethics is erected," and by Darwin, "who explained how we came to have such feelings … by appeal to the evolutionary principle of natural selection."[16] Callicott discusses how this sympathy has enlarged historically to encompass progressively larger communities, ranging from family to the global human community, and from domesticated animals to the all-encompassing biotic community.[17]

In addition to or in place of a justice approach, ecofeminists see *sympathetic care* as a sound basis for thinking about human responsibilities toward animals. Sympathetic caring is described in feminist literature as attentiveness to another's reality and as a sincere attempt to imagine how another feels. Moral imagination of this sort involves taking another's point of view and is said to be

---

16   Baird Callicott, "Environmental Liberation and Environmental Ethics: Back Together Again," in *Environmental Philosophy: From Animal Rights to Radical Ecology*, Michael Zimmerman et al., eds. (Upper Saddle River, NJ: Prentice Hall, 2005), p. 134.

17   Callicott focuses on this enlarging sense of sympathetic identification as the key to bridging the chasm between animal rights and environmental ethics and these with anthropocentrism. He suggests that the "concentric rings" of what we care about spread outward, that each ring carries its own set of obligations, and that, generally, obligations associated with inner and more intimate rings outweigh obligations corresponding to the outer more global and inclusive rings.

more than imagining how one would feel if one were in another's place; more than this, it requires imagining how the other feels. Iris Murdoch uses the term "attentive love" to describe what is needed to sympathetically identify with another. In her words, "The direction of attention is outward, away from the self, which reduces all to a false unity, toward the great surprising variety of the world, and the ability to so direct attention is love."[18] Ecofeminists generally maintain, moreover, that sympathetic identification experientially and logically precedes justice—that sympathy initially dictates who are to be counted as falling under the umbrella of justice. Accordingly, the focus for ecofeminists is on needs, not rights and justice.

Many ecofeminists also emphasize that ethics exist in a political context. As Josephine Donovan puts it, "People exercising attentive love see the tree, but they also see the logging industry. They see the downed cow in the slaughterhouse pen, but they also see the farming and dairy industry. They see the Silver Spring monkey, but they also see the drug corporations and university collaboration."[19] "Like many other feminists," Donovan says, "I contend that the dominant strain in contemporary ethics reflects a male bias toward rationality, defined as the construction of abstract universals that elide not just the personal, the contextual, and the emotional, but also the political components of an ethical issue. Like other feminists, particularly those in the 'caring' tradition, I believe that an alternative epistemology and ontology may be derived from women's historical, economic, and political practice."[20]

In his article "Justice, Caring, and Animal Liberation," Brian Luke also contends that the justice arguments of Singer and Regan skirt the basic issue. He argues that "direct sympathetic responsiveness to need is more central to animal liberation than concerns about consistency anyway,"[21] and then goes on to discuss the myriad ways that institutions in contemporary society seek to override and undercut our gut-level capacity to respond to the suffering inflicted on animals in laboratories, factory farming, and sport hunting. He concludes with this summary: "The lesson I draw from this analysis is twofold, part heartening and part sobering. Heartening is the realization that the ethical basis of animal

---

18   Iris Murdoch, *The Sovereignty of Good* (1971), p. 66
19   Josephine Donovan, "Attention to Suffering: Sympathy as a Basis for Ethical Treatment of Animals," in *Animal Rights*, Josephine Donovan & Carol J. Adams, eds. (New York: Continuum, 1994), p. 150.
20   Ibid., p. 147.
21   Brian Luke, "Justice, Caring, and Animal Liberation," in *Beyond Animal Rights*, Josephine Donovan & Carol J. Adams, eds. (New York: Continuum, 1994), p. 99.

liberation is very simple and generally moving. A straight-forward presentation of what the animals are like and what is done to them by hunters, vivisectors, and farmers can stir people, especially if the ideologies that block sympathy are simultaneously debunked. But sobering is a grasp of the nature of the social forces allied against a true perception of animals, against an understanding of what is done to them, against the possibility of acting from compassion. The substantial power of institutionalized animal exploitation sustains ignorance, promotes fear, rewards cruelty, and punishes kindness. So, though the ethics of animal liberation are inherently appealing, the obstacles placed in the way of radical social change based on sympathy are daunting."[22]

Max Scheler, regarded as the founder of the phenomenological method in the social sciences, elevates sympathy to a form of knowledge or understanding (*Verstehen*). Seeing the need for a counter-balance to objectification in science, he argued that investigators need to "redevelop a sympathetic capability to decode the symbolic language of nature." "We can, he says, "understand the experience of animals by attending to their behavioral and expressive signs: these have as their referent the animal's emotional and psychological state." A dog's wagging its tail is a "grammar of expression" expressing joy. Similarly, other forms of life have a "grammar of expression" that humans can come to understand. To understand the language of other life, "We must," Scheler believes, "rid ourselves henceforward of our one-sided conception of Nature as a mere instrument of human domination. … We must learn once more 'to look upon Nature as into the heart of a friend.'"[23] Indigenous people know this intuitively. Walking Buffalo, a member of the Stoney Tribe of Canada, reportedly said this about trees: "Did you know that trees talk? Well they do. They talk to each other, and they'll talk to you if you listen. Trouble is, white people don't listen. They never learned to listen to the Indians so I don't suppose they'll listen to the other voices in nature."[24]

4. Remarks/Conclusions

Some of the "intramural" criticisms made within the vertebracentric camp—Regan on Singer, Warren on Regan, ecofeminists and Luke on the centrality of the justice-based argument of Singer—have been noted. The basic objection

---

22   Ibid., p. 99–100.
23   Max Scheler, *The Nature of Sympathy* (Hamden, Conn.: Archon, 1978), p. 105.
24   Quoted in David Hughes, *American Indian Ecology* (El Paso: Texas Western Press, 1983), p. 49.

advanced by biocentrists is that the vertebracentrist does not go far enough: by not identifying what it is that makes all living beings worthy of moral respect, vertebracentrism fails to provide a defense of the moral standing of sentient animals based on their inherent value and fails, for this reason, to acknowledge the moral standing of the vast majority of living beings. It is estimated by Holmes Rolston that vertebrate species comprise only about 4% of all known species and that, since the number of individuals belonging to vertebrate species is typically much smaller than the numbers belonging to invertebrate, plant, and microbial species, total vertebrate animals constitute only a miniscule fraction of all living organisms.

Per the definition of moral standing proposed at the outset of this chapter, vertebrate animals are unified self-regulating entities capable of being harmed by humans. Vertebrates are harmed by being physically injured, deprived of essential resources, and functionally impaired—conditions often involving physical pain and sometimes acute emotional distress. They are also harmed when they are killed and when their kinds are driven to extinction. In regard to the worthiness criterion, ecofeminists contend that sympathetic caring about animals—a caring that encompasses not only their pain and suffering but also their yearnings, strivings, inclinations, and remarkable skills and accomplishments—is all that is needed for the recognition of their worthiness, particularly when such caring is combined with the realization of the commonalities that humans share with animals and how we live in complex relations of interdependency. For the ecofeminist, respect and the imputation of worthiness are mutually reinforcing and inseparable. We do not care about something seen to be worthless, but conversely, when we care, we see worthiness.

Singer's pain criterion is perhaps sufficient to acknowledge the moral standing of vertebrate animals. The experience of pain is intrinsically bad, even though it has evolutionary origins and plays an instrumentally valuable role in pain avoidance and survivability. Coupled with the justice argument and the ability of humans to sympathetically identify with sentient animals, it is concluded here that the case for acknowledging the moral considerability of vertebrates is strong. It can be made stronger, biocentrists maintain, if it is recognized that vertebrates, like all living beings, have inherent value.

F. Biocentrism: All Organisms Count Morally

1. Albert Schweitzer and Kenneth Goodpaster: Beyond Humans and Vertebrates

Albert Schweitzer argued in the first half of the Twentieth Century that an ethics of reverence for life is rooted in the intuition that "I am life that wills to live in the midst of life that wills to live." For Schweitzer, to will something is to value it; willing to live is a valuing of life. A human intuitively knows that he or she wills to live, that one is *for* one's life, *for* one's existence and flourishing. This intuition is unmistakably vivid when one's life is in peril: when one realizes that a misstep in a dangerous situation can lead to death, or when one realizes that infirmity or dying means the end of unfulfilled hopes and unfinished projects. One is also intuitively aware, Schweitzer believed, that other living beings will to live, that they, too, are *for* their lives. This awareness creates a sense of solidarity with other life; one sees the value of other lives in the same way as one sees the value of one's own life, as life willing to live, as life valuing life.[25]

Kenneth Goodpaster wrote several decades later that "Nothing more than the condition of *being alive* seems to me to be a plausible and non-arbitrary criterion [of moral considerability]."[26] Goodpaster sought to expose flaws in arguments limiting moral standing to humans, primarily by showing how they confound the concepts of moral considerability and moral significance. He associated the condition of being alive with the capacity of living beings to perpetuate their lives through organization informed by homeostatic feedback. "The core of moral concern," he wrote, "lies in respect for self-sustaining organization and integration in the face of pressures toward high entropy."[27] Lawrence Johnson characterized self-actualizing organisms in similar terms "as a persistent state of low entropy sustained by metabolic processes for accumulating energy [wherein] organic unity and self-identity are maintained in equilibrium by homeostatic feedback processes."[28]

---

25 This interpretation of what Schweitzer means by "will to live" is based on discussions that the author had with Dr. Schweitzer in Lambarene, Gabon, in 1964. The quotation is from Albert Schweitzer's *Teaching of Reverence for Life* (Holt, Rinehart, & Winston, 1965), p. 26.

26 Kenneth Goodpaster, "On Being Morally Considerable," in *Journal of Philosophy*, 75. Goodpaster's article is included in *Environmental Ethics: Readings in Theory and Practice*, Louis P. Pojman, ed. (Wadsworth, 2001).

27 Kenneth Goodpaster, "Moral Considerability," in *The Journal of Philosophy*, 75, p. 323.

28 Lawrence Johnson, "Toward the Moral Considerability of Species and Ecosystems," in *Environmental Ethics* 149 1992. See also Johnson's *A Morally Deep World* (New York: Cambridge

2. Paul Taylor: Teleological Centers of Life Count Morally

Every organism is, Taylor wrote, "a teleological center of life, striving to pre-serve itself and to realize its own good in its own unique way."[29] For Taylor, "To say [that an organism] is a teleological center of life is to say that its internal functioning as well as its external activities are all goal-oriented, having the constant tendency to maintain the organism's existence through time and to enable it successfully to perform those biological operations whereby it repro-duces its kind and continually adapts to changing environmental events and conditions. It is the coherence and unity of these functions of an organism, all directed toward the realization of its good, that makes it one teleological center of activity." Further, to say that an organism has a good of its own is to say that its life and the realization of its biological potential are *good for* that organism. He emphasizes that it is *objectively* true that certain things are good for an organism: "Concerning a butterfly, for example, we may hesitate to speak of its interest or preferences, and we would probably deny outright that it values anything in the sense of considering it good or desirable. But once we come to understand its life cycle and know the environmental conditions it needs to survive in a healthy state, we have no difficulty in speaking about what is beneficial to it and what might be harmful to it."[30]

An organism's having a good of its own is regarded by Taylor as a necessary condition of moral standing, but he does not regard it as a sufficient condition. In addition to being a teleological center of activity with a good of its own, an organism must be deemed to have *inherent worth,* to be *worthy* of moral re-spect. For Taylor, an organism's worthiness of moral respect is a judgment made by a person who has adopted what he (Taylor) calls a "biocentric outlook." This outlook is centered around four basic beliefs: that humans are members of Earth's community of life in the same sense and on the same terms as are all other living beings; that humans and all other species-populations co-exist in complex relations of interdependence; that all living beings are teleological centers of life that pursue their own good in their own way; and that humans and human goods are not inherently superior to other living beings and their goods. Persons who adopt these beliefs will readily attribute inherent worth to all entities having a good of their own and will, moreover, regard all such

University Press, 1991).

29   Paul Taylor, "Biocentric Egalitarianism" in *Environmental Ethics: Readings in Theory and Practice*, Louis P. Pojman, ed. (Wadsworth, 2001), p. 107.

30   Paul Taylor, *Respect for Nature* (Princeton, N.J.: Princeton University Press, 1986), p. 80.

beings as having equal inherent worth.[31] For Taylor, inherent *worth* is a value judgment made by a person who adopts the biocentric outlook. As discussed below, this understanding of "inherent worth" is quite different from Holmes Rolston's notion that natural values are found throughout the biotic order and are revealed by knowing nature's ways and telling "life's story" in ways that permit the revelation of these values.

3. Holmes Rolston: Revelation of Value in Life's Storied Evolutions

Rolston's thinking is interdisciplinary and structured by the Darwinian paradigm. Far more than a "universal acid" to be used to discredit beliefs, Darwinian science provides a framework for expanding and integrating knowledge gained from other areas of scientific inquiry. Several basic tenets are developed in Rolston's writings: that evolutionary development reveals adaptive intelligence as well as random variation, self-organization as well as natural selection; that evolving life is creative and has produced a vast profusion of life forms in ever-increasing levels of diversity, complexity, and organization, including the human brain and its creation, culture; that, while very many players have participated in the saga of life's immense journey, only humans are capable of telling the story of their participation; that those who contemplate life's evolutionary journey over more than three billion years, and themselves participate in the telling of the story, cannot but give up the idea that value and moral worthiness are confined to human culture; and that many stories, consistent with the Darwinian story line, are needed to account for all the creativity, innovation, and valuational thrust. Rolston tells life's story as a continuous and ever-expanding display of caring, organization, complexity, diversity, and intelligence on a special planet, but insists that no theory is adequate to account for life's long history, which has eventuated in humanity. "No theory exists from which [humans] follow as conclusions. ... What I can do is invite you as a historical subject to appreciate the objective story that lies in, with, and under the Earth we inhabit, to enrich the story by telling it. You can be a microcosm of the macrocosm and enjoy your storied residence here."[32]

---

31   These four basic beliefs of the "biocentric outlook," together with the substantive moral principles he derives from them and his position on equal inherent worth, are discussed in Chapter 3.
32   Holmes Rolston, "The Human Standing in Nature: Storied Fitness in the Moral Overseer," in Values and Moral Standing, W. Summer, D. Callen, & T. Attig, eds. (Bowling Green University Press, 1986), p. 97.

Whereas Taylor emphasizes that moral respect emanates from a biocentric outlook, Rolston emphasizes that an organism is worthy of moral consideration by virtue of the value that is intrinsic to its being. For him, an organism's intrinsic value is what makes it worthy of moral consideration in its own right, not only one's attitude toward it. While Rolston certainly does not deny that attitudinal orientation toward non-human entities is central to how one is disposed to regard and treat non-human biotic entities, he regards an organism's possession of a good-of-a-kind (an intrinsic value) and its pursuit of its good as both a necessary and sufficient condition of its independent moral standing. For Rolston, nature discloses value; value is already there, awaiting discovery and conceptual articulation by its "telling." Humans confer worth by the telling, but the ground of this worth is objectively occurring natural value.

For Rolston, value permeates nature. It is found in organisms, species, and ecosystems, and it existed before humans arrived on the scene. These values are "displayed" by biotic entities and are "on show" for humans to contemplate and understand. In his words: "Every species is "a 'display' or 'show' … in the natural history book. Their stories are plural, diverse, erratic, but they are not wholly fragmented episodes. The pressures of natural selection pull them into roles in their communities, fit them into niches, give continuity to the stories, and make more unified ecosystemic stories of the many stories. Always there are themes in their settings, characters moving through space and time, problems and their resolution, the plotting of life paths. Exceeding the births and deaths of individual members, species form and life unfolds an intergenerational narrative. What humans are bound to respect in natural history is … the living drama, continuing with all its actors."[33]

In his article "Value in Nature and the Nature of Value,"[34] Rolston describes how value is exhibited in wild animals, plants, species, ecosystems, and planet Earth. In regard to *wild animals*, he says that "There is no better evidence of non-human values and valuers than spontaneous wildlife, born free and on its own. Animals hunt and howl, find shelter, seek out their habitats and mates, care for their young, flee from threats, grow hungry, thirsty, hot, tired, excited,

---

33   Holmes Rolston, "Naturalizing Values: Organisms and Species," in *Environmental Ethics: Readings in Theory and Practice*, Louis J. Pojman, ed. (Wadsworth, 2001), p. 84.
34   Holmes Rolston, "Value in Nature and the Nature of Value," in *Philosophy and the Natural Environment*, Robin Attfield and Andrew Belsey, eds. (Cambridge: Cambridge University Press, 1994), pp. 13–30. The article was presented at the Royal Institute of Philosophy Annual Conference in 1993 and also published in *Institute of Philosophy Supplement: 36*.

sleepy. They suffer injury and lick their wounds. Here we are quite convinced that value is non-anthropogenic, to say nothing of anthropocentric. ... These wild animals defend their own lives because they have a good of their own. There is somebody there behind the fur or feathers. Our gaze is returned by an animal that has a concerned outlook. Here is value right before our eyes, right behind those eyes. Animals are value-able, able to value things in their world." But *plants*, too, have goods of their own: "they repair injuries; they move water, nutrients, and photosythate from cell to cell; they store sugars; they make tannin and other toxins and regulate their levels in defense against grazers; they make nectars and emit pheromones to influence the behavior of pollinating insects and the responses of other plants; they emit allelopathic agents to suppress invaders; they make thorns, trap insects. They can reject genetically incompatible grafts." Moreover, "A plant like any other organism is a spontaneous, self-maintaining system, sustaining and reproducing itself, executing its program, making a way through the world, checking performance by means of responsive capacity with which to measure success. Something more than physical causes ... is operating; there is information superintending the causes; without it the organism would collapse into a sand heap." But what of *species*: "Can a species be value-able all by itself [where] there is no analogue to the nervous hookups or circulatory flows that characterize the organism?" Rolston's answer is that species, too, "run a telic course through the environment, using individuals resourcefully to maintain its course over much longer periods of time. The species is the vital living system, the whole, of which individual organisms are the essential parts. The species defends a particular form of life, pursuing a pathway through the world, resisting death (extinction) by regeneration, maintaining a normative identify over time. ... The value resides in the dynamic form; the individual inherits this, exemplifies it, and passes it on." He continues: "Species are quite real; that there really is a bear-bear-bear sequence is about as certain as anything we believe about the empirical world. Species ... have a kind of unity and integrity. They are able to conserve a biological identity." And what of *ecosystems*? Are they, too, value-able? Indeed they are, Rolston answers: "They are selective systems, as surely as organisms are selective systems. The system selects over the long ranges for individuality, for diversity, for adapted fitness, for quantity and quality of life. ... Organisms defend their continuing survival; ecosystems promote new arrivals. Species increase their kinds, but ecosystems increase kinds, and increase the integration of kinds." And what of planetary *Earth*? Is calling Earth value-able anything more than the *reduction ad absurdum* of valuing dirt? Reflecting on the creativity within the natural system and the values this generates, Rolston characterizes Earth as the "ground of our being, not just the ground under our feet."

In concluding "Values in Nature and the Nature of Value," Rolston revisits the claim, addressed throughout the article, that there can be no value without a valuer. "The problem with [this] axiom," Rolston writes, "is that it is too individualistic; it looks for some centre of value located in a subjective self. ... But that is not the whole account of value in a more holistic, systemic, ecological, global account. Perhaps there can be no doing science without a scientist, no religion without a believer, no tickle without somebody tickled. But there can be law without a lawgiver, history without a historian ... creativity without creators. ... A sentient valuer is not necessary for value." He continues: "It is true that humans are the only evaluators who can reflect what is going on at this global scale, who can deliberate about what they ought to do conserving it. When humans do this, they must set up the scales, and humans are the measurers of things. Animals, organisms, species, ecosystems, Earth, cannot teach us how to do this evaluating. But they can display what it is that is to be valued. The axiological scales we construct do not constitute the value, any more than the scientific scales we erect create what we thereby measure." For Rolston, "The valuing subject in an otherwise valueless world is an insufficient premise for the experienced conclusions of those who value natural history."

In another article, "Care on Earth: Generating Informed Consent,"[35] Rolston argues that care (caring) is pervasive in life's natural history and reveals ever-increasing levels of complexity. "Initially the evolution of caring on Earth requires the generation of complex chemistries, developing into enzymatic self-reproduction, developing into life with self-interest. But caring gets complicated, since selves are implicated. They eat each other, but equally they depend on each other. ... Self-defense requires adapted fit; living things, and hence their cares, are webbed in ecosystems." While caring may be caring for survival limited to self initially, it "is self-contained only up to a point: after that it is caring 'about' relationships, the contacts and processes with which one is networked. It is caring about others: if only a predator caring to catch and eat prey; the prey to escape; both caring for their young. Caring is matrixed and selective within such matrices. Networking requires distinctions, differential concerns. ... In humans, there arise more inclusive forms of caring. Such wider

---

35   Holmes Rolston, "Care on Earth: Generating Informed Consent," in *Information and the Nature of Reality: From Physics to Metaphysics*, Paul Davies & Niels Henrik Gregersen, eds. (Cambridge: Cambridge University press, 2010).

vision requires even more complexity, a complex brain that can evaluate others not only in terms of helps and hurts, but also with concern for their health and integrity. This radically elaborates new levels of cultural information, and caring. Humans care about family, tribe, nation, careers, and ideational causes. ... Ethics shapes caring. In due course, humans alone on the planet can take a transcending overview of the whole—and care for life on Earth."

Rolston acknowledges, indeed emphasizes, the differences between human and non-human life. "Humans superimpose cultures on wild nature out of which they emerged, with radical innovations. Information in wild nature travels intergenerationally on genes; information in culture travels neutrally as people are educated into transmissible cultures."[36] But Rolston refuses to say that awareness and intelligence are unique to human life and culture. These capacities and their manifestations are disclosed throughout nature, present and past—but, again, with notable differences. Awareness in a single-cell organism is simple chemical awareness; in humans, it is self-conscious awareness associated with a highly complex system of electro-chemical neural networks regulated in a brain composed of billions of cells, each with a complex set of human DNA. Intelligence in a single-cell organism is associated with information-processing capability encoded in the DNA of its genome; in humans, intelligence is associated not only with the processing of information encoded in human DNA but with a brain specialized and complex enough to permit the kind of information processing involved in reasoning and symbolic communication and, with these, the creation and transmission of culture.

Rolston believes that it is morally naïve, if not morally perverse, to claim that only one among several million species counts morally. In his words, "Seven billion years of creative toil, several million species of teeming life have been handed over to the care of this late-coming species in which mind has flowered and morals have emerged. Ought not those of this sole moral species to do something less self-interested than count all the produce of an evolutionary ecosystem as rivets in their spaceship, resources in their larder, laboratory materials, recreation for their ride? Such an attitude hardly seems biologically informed, much less ethically adequate. Its logic is too provincial for moral humanity. Or, in a biologist's term, it is ridiculously territorial."[37]

---

36   Holmes Rolston, *Conserving Natural Value* (New York: Columbia University Press, 1994), p. 2.
37   Holmes Rolston, "Duties to Endangered Species," in *Earth Ethics: Introductory Readings in Animal Rights and Environmental Ethics*, James Sterba, ed. (Prentice Hall, 2000, p. 328.

4. Remarks/Conclusions

Many believe that the granting of moral status to invertebrate animals, plants, and microbes flies in the face of common sense. On a planet with millions of species and countless trillions of living organisms, critics say that it is confusing, if not maddening, to be told that all of them ought to be taken into moral consideration. When organisms feed on other organisms throughout nature and when numerous organisms pose threats to human health and safety, it is absurd, they maintain, to suggest that all of these many trillions of organisms deserve moral consideration. Why worry about a virus that makes us sick? Why fuss over snail darters when people need electricity? Questions such as these typically focus on pests, pathogens, or microbes with huge populations as part of a *reduction ad absurdum* strategy to shut down further discussion. Goodpaster was among the first biocentrists to point out that this strategy conflates the concepts of moral standing and moral significance. The recognition of an entity's moral standing is a recognition that harm to the entity is a morally relevant question; it is not a claim that it is always wrong to kill non-human entities and certainly not a blanket claim that the entity is entitled to rights protection. It would, indeed, be absurd to claim that a disease-causing microbe has a moral right not to be harmed when harm to it is unavoidable and of no great consequence for its kind and other organisms and their kinds. If a population of microbes is judged to be a threat to human health and not an essential component of well-being in some greater scheme of life, the obviously morally justifiable course of action would be to eliminate the threat.

Some writers have claimed that Schweitzer's use of the term "will-to-live" or Taylor's use of the term "teleological centers of life" are anthropomorphic and impute human characteristics such as "striving," "desiring," "aiming," and "goal-seeking" to life that lacks the mental or cognitive abilities that these terms connote. But a close reading of the biocentric theorists discussed above suggests that this line of criticism is not plausible. In explaining what self-actualization in an organism involves (not all of them use this term), Goodpaster, Johnson, Taylor, and Rolston provide naturalistic explanations that are not anthropomorphic. As discussed in the previous chapter, complexity theory posits that "attractors" (values) function in complex systems as ordered states and as trajectories of organization toward which the system as a whole tends and without which the system tends toward disintegration and collapse.

Seeing all life in human-like terms needs to be guarded against, and important differences between humans and non-humans need to be recognized. But life is a continuum, and humans share important commonalities with many life forms past and present, the most basic of which is the capacity to self-organize. Even though only humans ask value questions and make value judgments, humans are not the only entities capable of tracking and realizing valued end-states. And even though the cognitive abilities of humans far surpass those of other animals and certainly plants and microbes, non-human life is not "dumb" and utterly devoid of intelligence. The capacity of simple organisms to survive and reproduce in perilous environments is rooted in information-processing intelligence encoded in their DNA. In organisms with brains, this information-processing intelligence surpasses that of the most advanced parallel-operating computers. Computers do not "care," Rolston remarks, but all organisms do.

The capacity to self-actualize—to realize a good-of-a-kind, to progress developmentally toward a valued end-state, to track and realize value, to ac-tualize biological potential, to process vast amounts of information directing life paths, to be value-able in this way—is a capacity deserving human moral respect. Harm to entities possessing and exhibiting this capacity is a relevant moral issue.

Various writers question the biocentric focus on *individual* organisms and note the consequent failure of this perspective to recognize that the good of an individual does not always trump the good of its kind or of the community of which it is a member. This failure leads to an inability, the criticism goes, to make morally significant distinctions between domesticated and wild animals, between abundant and endangered species, and between invasive and endemic members of ecosystems. These are questions of moral significance that expose problems for an ethical perspective that focuses exclusively on the well-being of individual organisms. But such questions do not necessitate the conclusion that individual organisms do not have moral standing. The question they raise is whether species and ecosystems have moral standing as well, and, if so, how questions of moral significance should be settled in contexts where the good of individual organisms, species, and ecosystems do not coincide and trade-off decisions have to be made.

G. BIOCENTRISM EXTENDED: SPECIES COUNT MORALLY

1. Species: Classifications or Concrete Reality?

Taylor argued that living individuals have moral standing, but that species do not. In his view, species are labels that scientists give to individual organisms that share certain common characteristics. While we say that species evolve, split, bud off new species, become endangered, and go extinct, what this means, Taylor maintains, is that changes occur in the populations of the named groups, changes that sometimes result in new names and new biological classifications. We also say that what may be good for the species may not be good for an individual member of that species. For example, predation that culls less fit members of a species benefits the species but not the animals preyed upon. But this assertion can be restated so that only individuals of the named species population are referred to: the elimination of weak or diseased members of a present population ensures that their genes will not be passed on to offspring, thus enhancing overall fitness and prospects for survival in the next generation's population.

Taylor's view of species was held by Darwin: "I look at the term species, as one arbitrarily given for the sake of convenience to a set of individuals closely resembling each other." This also is the view of A. B. Shaw: "The species concept is entirely subjective."[38] But other scientists see species as having objective referents. G. G. Simpson states that species "are real biological entities in the natural world."[39] Viewing species as "interbreeding natural populations that are reproductively isolated from other such groups," E. Mayr states that "species are real units of evolution."[40] Viewing species as "entities that exhibit a pattern of phylogenetic ancestry and descent among units of like kind," Elderedge and Cracraft characterize species as "discrete entities in time as well as space."[41] For

---

38   A. B. Shaw, "Adam and Eve, Paleontology, and the Non-Objective Arts," in *Journal of Paleontology* 43, pp. 1085–1098.
39   G. G. Simpson, *Principles of Animal Taxonomy* (New York: Columbia University Press, 1961), p. 153.
40   E. Mayr, "The Biological Meaning of Species," in the *Biological Journal of the Linnaeus Society* 1, pp. 311–320.
41   N. Eldridge and J. Cracraft, *Phylogenetic Patterns and the Evolutionary Process* (New York: Columbia University Press, 1980), p. 92.

Stephen Gould, too, "Species are nature's objective packages."[42] In his view, evolution is like a bush, not a ladder, and species are like new branches on the bush that emerge quickly in comparison to the millions of years that many species-populations have lived with only minimal change. "The principle of bushes and the speed of branching" reveal that "continuous evolution can and does yield a world in which the vast majority of species are separate from all others and clearly definable at any moment in time."[43]

Holmes Rolston describes a species as "a living historical form, propagated in individual organisms, that flows dynamically over generations" and as "a coherent, ongoing form of life expressed in organisms, encoded in gene flow, and shaped by the environment."[44] Higher order biological classifications—genus, family, order, phylum, and kingdom—do not have objective referents in the way that species do; unlike species, they do not refer to concrete biological entities that maintain an identity over time. In Rolston's words, "The assertion that there are specific forms of life historically maintained in their environments over time seems as certain as anything else we believe about the empirical world."[45] Species names "refer to discrete biological realities" and are "as real as individual plants and animals."

2. Genomes and Moral Standing

To have moral standing, a species must, it has been stipulated, be a self-regulating, harmable entity possessing a characteristic or capacity by virtue of which it is reasonable to conclude that it is worthy of moral consideration in its own right. It is the contention here that a species-genome meets these criteria.

A genome is understood in molecular genetics as the complete set of genes carried by individuals of a species. The human body contains about 100 trillion cells containing more than 50,000 genes carried on twenty-three chromosome pairs.[46] There is a basic division of labor in each cell: genes give instructions for the performance of cellular tasks, and proteins carry out these instructions. Each type of protein is a specialist that performs a single task; if a cell needs to

---

42   Stephen Jay Gould, "What is a Species?" in *The Environmental Ethics & Policy Book*, Donald VanDeVeer and Christine Pierce, eds. (Thomson Wadsworth, 2003), p. 467.
43   Ibid., p. 467.
44   Holmes Rolston, "Duties to Endangered Species," Op. cit., p. 321.
45   Holmes Rolston, "Environmental Ethics: Values in and Duties to the Natural World," Op. cit., p. 74.
46   Mitochondria are dubbed "the powerhouses of cells," but are also thought to be associated with cellular differentiation, cell growth, and cell death.

do something faster or slower, it makes more or less of the protein, or if it needs to perform a new task, it makes a new protein. Each protein is composed of a chain of amino acid molecules (DNA). Each DNA molecule is made up of four types of nucleotides (A, T, G, C).[47] Their base pairings and sequencing along the amino acid chain determine what the protein will do. Genetic instruction (expression) occurs when a gene is "read" by a cell. The process involves transcribing a gene's DNA sequence into a very similar molecule called RNA. The RNA copy is then fed though a structure called a ribosome whose function is to translate the sequence of nucleotides in the RNA into the correct sequence of amino acids and to join these amino acids together to make a complete "folded up" protein chain. A similar process occurs each time a cell divides. Because DNA is made of two strands with paired-up nucleotides holding the two strands together, enzymes "unzip" the old strands, pair up new nucleotide units, and "zip" the strands back together again. The new unit contains one strand from the old DNA and one newly made strand. The process sometimes produces mistakes (e.g. a G or C nucleotide may be paired with A or T), causing a mutation in the gene sequence. Along with natural selection, mutations play an important role in evolutionary development.[48]

Phylogenetic studies in molecular biology reveal how the human genome is related to the genomes of ancestors. The human genome is reported to be approximately 96% identical with that of the chimpanzee (the last common ancestor of humans and chimpanzees lived about five million years ago), and 34% identical with that of a mouse (the last common ancestor of humans and mice lived about seventy-five million years ago).[49] More than thirty genomes have been sequenced to date, including six virus species, six bacteria species, five plant species, five insect species, and two fish species.

A genome is self-regulating entity; it adapts to environmental influences and other epigenetic factors. It is pervasive in the biotic order and of fundamental importance to the ongoing process of life on the planet. What makes a genomic kind (species) morally considerable in its own right is the expressive capacity of its genome to control growth and development over the lifetimes of individuals

---

47   A human's whole genome consists of about three billion nucleotides, but only about 2% of this complex (its "exome") is protein coding; the other 98% of nucleotides are "switches" regulating when and where genes are expressed.
48   According to the National Institutes of Health, about 85% of disease-causing mutations occur in the exome.
49   It is estimated that 99% of mouse genes have analogues in humans and exhibit identical functions. The genetic defect causing cystic fibrosis is reportedly found in both humans and mice.

in which it is imprinted and to enable the transmission of this genetic blueprint intergenerationally. Genomic expression makes self-actualization in an organism possible, just as its intergenerational transmission through reproduction makes species perpetuation possible. Mutations play a role in this process, but as complexity theorist Stuart Kauffman emphasizes, so does an underlying process of self-organization. Genomic expression is a valuing process involving information-processing intelligence. Surely a genome—a self-regulating, adaptive, harmable entity—is something worthy of respect.

Extinction is an ultimate harm. As Holmes Rolston puts it, "Every extinction is a kind of superkilling. It kills forms, beyond individuals. It kills 'essences' beyond 'existences.' ... It kills collectively, not just distributively. ... A shutdown of the life stream is the most destructive event possible." He continues: "If, in this world of uncertain moral convictions, it makes any sense to claim that one ought not to kill individuals, without justification, it makes more sense to claim that one ought not to superkill the species, without justification."[50] If killing a human being matters morally, then doing what could lead to the extinction of *Homo sapiens* certainly matters morally. The same logic applies to non-human life: if killing an animal matters morally, killing the last remaining members of its kind matters morally. A shut-down of a life stream without justification is a heinous act.

Besides extinction, species can be harmed in other ways. Mutations in gene coupling and sequencing can occur randomly and unpredictably, sometimes with negative consequences for an organism's higher-level functioning and survival, but environmental conditions are also part of the story. Apart from considerations of whether genetic engineering is good for humans, gene manipulation may not be good for the species whose genes are modified. For example, while genetic modification of corn may enhance resistance to pesticides and food security for humans, genomic integrity may be comprised, diminishing the prospects for corn-populations to adapt and survive in their environments.

---

50 Holmes Rolston, "Challenges in Environmental Ethics," in *Environmental Philosophy: From Animal Rights to Radical Ecology*, Michael E. Zimmerman, J. Baird Callicott, George Sessions, Karen J. Warren, and John Clark, eds. (Prentice Hall, 2005), p. 136.

H. ECOCENTRISM: ECOSYSTEMS COUNT MORALLY

Ecosystems are made up of air, water, gases, minerals, and decomposing organic matter and are places where living members of species interact. They are places where biological production occurs and where processes of self-organization, mutations, and natural selection take place. They surround us as forests, grasslands, rivers, coastal waters, seas, islands, mountains, and other landscapes. Collectively, they constitute the Earth's biosphere.

1. Holmes Rolston on Ecosystems

Ecosystems are characterized in some quarters as haphazard places exhibiting little order and continuity. As noted in Chapter 1, Donald Worster reports that ecologists are seeing "lots of individual species, each doing their own thing" in their studies of ecosystems but not an "emergent collectivity nor any strategy to achieve one." Rather than seeing ecosystems as communities of life that progress toward stable and mature equilibrium, ecologists are seeing "a landscape of patches ... changing continually through time and space, responding to an unceasing barrage of perturbations."[51] Worster called this an "ecology of chaos."

Taking up and amplifying this theme, Rolston comments that "The plants and animals within an ecosystem have needs, but their interplay can seem simply a matter of distribution and abundance, birth rates and death rates, population densities, parasitism and predation, dispersion, checks and balances, and stochastic process."[52] Furthermore, "Unlike higher animals, ecosystems have no experiences; they do not and cannot care. Unlike a plant, an ecosystem has no organized center, no genome. ... Unlike a species, there is no ongoing telos, no biological identity reinstantiated over time." "In animals the heart, liver, muscles, and brain are tightly integrated, as are the leaves, cambium, and roots in plants. But the so-called ecosystem community is pushing and shoving between rivals, each aggrandizing itself, or else seems to be all indifference and haphazard juxtaposition—nothing to call forth our admiration." An ecosystem seems to be "too low a level of organization to be the direct focus of moral concern."

---

51   Donald Worster, "The Ecology of Order and Chaos," in *Earth Ethics: Introductory Readings on Animal Rights and Environmental Ethics*, James P. Sterba, ed. (Prentice Hall, 2000), p. 162.
52   Holmes Rolston, "Environmental Ethics: Values in and Duties to the Natural World," Op. cit., pp. 78–80.

"But this is to misunderstand ecosystems," Rolston contends, "to make a category mistake … to look at one level for what is appropriate at another." It is the mistake of attempting to understand ecosystems using the metaphor of the organism; to look for characteristics associated with organisms and, not finding them, to conclude that what is being studied is devoid of value significance. "The evolutionary ecosystem spins a bigger story," Rolston continues, "limiting each kind, locking it into the welfare of others, promoting new arrivals, increasing kinds and the integration of kinds." "An ecosystem has no head," he says, "but it heads towards species diversification, support, and richness. Though not a superorganism, it is a kind of vital field." It is a vital field where "order arises spontaneously and systematically as many self-concerned units jostle and seek to fulfill their own programs, each doing its own thing and forced into informed interaction." And rather than viewing an ecosystem as an arena in which participants are locked in mortal struggle and only the fittest survive, the more appropriate model is "co-action in adapted fit: predator and prey, parasite and host, grazer and grazed, are contending forces in dynamic processes in which the well-being of each is bound up with the other—coordinated as much as heart and liver are coordinated organically."

Rolston further characterizes an ecosystem as "a spontaneously organizing system of interrelated parts, simultaneously persisting and evolving through changes over decades and centuries." It is, he says, "a vital and dynamic collection of organisms each with its capabilities and limits, each species selected over evolutionary history to do rather well in the niche it inhabits, an adapted fit, and with some capacities for adapting to changes in its altering environment."[53] Also: "There are ordered regularities (seasons returning, the hydrologic cycle, acorns making oak trees, squirrels feeding on the acorns) mixed with episodic irregularities (droughts, fires, lightning killing an oak, mutations in the acorns) … And over longer scales there are climate changes, respeciation, new niches generated and occupied."[54]

2. Remarks/Conclusions

Ecosystems cannot be fully understood by isolating individual components and studying these in exacting detail from each of several disciplinary perspectives,

---

53   Holmes Rolston, "The Land Ethic at the Turn of the Millennium," in *Environmental Ethics: Divergence and Convergence*, Richard G. Boltzer and Susan J. Armstrong (McGraw Hill, 1998), p 395.
54   Ibid., p. 395.

nor can relationships between individual components be fully understood apart from the role they play in larger relational contexts. An ecology that relies exclusively on concepts and methodologies derived from the reductionist-mechanistic paradigm is an inadequate, self-limiting science. An ecology that acknowledges that ecosystems (wholes) have systemic characteristics that are not reducible to components (parts) in isolation is better positioned to understand the complex dynamics of ecosystems and the synergies they generate. Holmes Rolston agrees: "In these ecosystems qualities emerge that are corporate or holistic (such as tropic pyramids or tendencies to succession), not the qualities of any individual parts (such as metabolism or death)." The result is the richness of diversity over the geological millennia.

Ecosystems do not have a head or a central nervous system, as Holmes Rolston says, but they are self-organizing entities that generate order and relative stability amidst unceasing internal and external change. Using the terminology of chaos-complexity theory, what functions as a primary attractor or an ordered end-state to which the ecosystem as a whole tends is co-adaptation for mutual benefit. Mutually advantageous relationships among a multitude of organisms are of value to the system as a whole (Aldo Leopold called this value "integrity") and to its inhabitants and participants. The value is system-generated. It inheres in the system (is an inherent value) and is both a product and process whose existence does not depend on humans knowing that it is a value. Processes of self-organization in ecosystems can be disrupted, diminished, or destroyed by exogenous forces, and, when this occurs, ecosystems and their living inhabitants are made less well off. Ecosystems are dynamic places where individual organisms of many kinds self-actualize and where order is established and tenuously maintained in response to unceasing internal and external change.

I. MORAL STANDING OF NATURE AS TOTALITY

The case has been made for the moral standing of vertebrates, non-vertebrate organisms, species as genomes, and ecosystems. What about nature *writ large*, nature as totality?

Nature as a totality encompasses myriad members of myriad species of myriad ecosystems in myriad geophysical environments, where all of these lives, life forms, and communities of life interact with each other and their changing environments, continually adapting and evolving in the fullness of time. New species are created and existing species, many of them with histories dating back millions and tens of millions of years, become extinct. The human species, one of five to fifty million other species (the total number is far from established) is a latecomer but has, in a relatively very short period of time, become a major player in the ongoing evolution of life. It is an exaggeration to say that non-human nature is now under human control and has become a remade artifact of human design, but it is not an overstatement to say that human influence is ubiquitous and continues to expand. Human activities are transforming the land, modifying basic geophysical cycles and the composition of the atmosphere, depleting critical non-renewable resources, utilizing renewable resources in excess of replenishment rates, utilizing growing proportions of life's net primary production of energy, and causing a mass extinction rivaling the major extinctions of the planet's ancient past.

The question of the moral standing of nature as a whole can be answered rhetorically by asking these questions:

- We attribute value to the human communities which sustain and enrich us. Should we not also value the larger biotic community which sustains and enriches us?
- We value the full actualization of potential in human lives and in human institutions that facilitates cooperation and relations of mutual benefit. Should we not also value self-actualization in non-human lives and the mutually beneficial relationships generated by ecosystems?
- We readily attribute intrinsic value to intelligence, beauty, excellence, and well-being in human life. Should we not also value the analogues and precursors of these values in non-human nature?
- We value the wisdom of mentors in human society. Should we not also value nature's wisdom, nature as mentor?
- We view human history with a sense of awe and respect: the epic stories of human travails, tragedies, intrigues, aspirations, achievements, and triumphs. Should we not also regard life's much longer and certainly no less storied history with awe and respect?
- We feel a connection with the places we inhabit and the cultural traditions associated with those places. Do we not have a feeling of connectedness to the broader natural landscapes of which we are a part, and an underlying antipathy to institutional forces that diminish and debunk such feelings of connectedness?

- We are alarmed by the risks posed by the many signs of ecological and environmental decline for human well-being. Should we not also be similarly alarmed about their implications for the well-being of other life?

"Yes" answers to these questions parallel the discussion in Chapter 1 of elements of an attitude of respect for nature. The questions are rhetorical, but summarize previous arguments for concluding that nature as a whole is worthy of moral respect.

J. Summary of Conclusions

Three criteria of moral standing have been stated:

- an entity must be an entity whose structure and function is self-regulated;
- an entity that is harmable by being deprived of conditions essential to its perpetuation and inherent well-being;
- an entity that is worthy of moral consideration in its own right.

It is has been argued that human beings, all other individual living beings, species, ecosystems, and nature as a whole meet these criteria. In regard to all living organisms, inherent value is associated with the capability of individuals to self-actualize: to survive, thrive, and realize their full biological potential in oftentimes perilous environments in which processes of natural selection operate. In regard to species, value is associated with the capacity of distinct genomes to impart information (intelligence) controlling structural and functional development over the lifetimes of living members and their progeny, thus making individual self-actualization and species preservation possible.

In regard to ecosystems, inherent value is associated with the capacity of biotic communities to self-organize in ways that generate new kinds and enable a great diversity of existing kinds and their living members to co-exist and co-evolve in relations of mutual benefit. Manifestations of these capacities in individual living beings, their kinds, and the biotic communities they inhabit constitute the most basic processes that occur in Earth's biosphere. All of them are self-organizing processes involving modes of awareness (conscious or not) and intelligence (cognitive or not). Entities exhibiting these capacities tend toward end states of value to the entities that possess them. Value inheres in the manifestation of these capacities, and entities possessing these capacities are worthy of respect in their own right, irrespective of their extrinsic value (or disvalue) for humans. Although it takes human cognition to call conceptual attention to these self-organizing processes and the value they exhibit and embody, their existence does not depend on human existence.

Because humans are *in* nature and *of* nature, it is not surprising that processes of self-organization operate in human life and culture, constituting the foundation of human well-being: self-actualizing human lives and institutional arrangements that create relations of mutual benefit among participants, including democratic forms of governance, free market economies, and the Internet, all regulated to the extent necessary to prevent force, fraud, and monopolization and to safeguard health and safety.

CHAPTER 3.
ANIMAL AND BIOCENTRIC ETHICS

T his chapter examines substantive issues related to the human treatment of "higher animals," other living organisms, and their kinds. The focus is on action-guiding theories and on the institutional context in which activists have effected reform. Section A provides an overview of the animal welfare/rights movement. Section B examines the theories developed by Peter Singer, Tom Regan, and David DeGrazia and what these prominent writers in the field of animal ethics argue is right and wrong in regard to how we treat sentient animals. Section C examines the biocentric ethics of Paul Taylor and James Sterba. Section D reviews efforts in the US and other countries to protect plants and animals whose species are believed to be in danger of extinction.

A. ANIMAL ETHICS

1. Overview of the Animal Welfare Movement

a. Formative Philosophical Views

The question of the moral status of animals was not ignored entirely by earlier European philosophers. Rene Descartes argued in the mid-seventeenth century that animals are automatons with no souls or minds, and that, while they exhibit responses to external stimuli, are unable to suffer or feel pain. John Locke argued in the late seventeenth century that animals do have feelings, and he opposed cruel treatment on the grounds that "the custom of tormenting and killing of beasts will, by degrees, harden their minds even toward men."[1] Immanuel Kant reiterated a similar view in the mid-eighteenth century, stating that "cruelty to animals is contrary to man's duty to himself, because it deadens in him the feeling of sympathy for their sufferings, ... [whereby] natural tendency that is very useful to morality in relation to other humans is weakened."[2] For Kant, "Animals are there merely as a means to an end. That end is man."[3] At about the same time, Rousseau linked the treatment of animals to natural law: "[Here] we put an end to the time-honoured disputes concerning the participation of animals in natural law: for it is clear that, being destitute of intelligence and liberty, they cannot recognize that law; as they partake, however, in some measure of our nature, in consequence of the sensibility with which they are endowed, they ought to partake of natural right; so that mankind is subjected to a kind of obligation even toward the brutes."[4] At the end of the seventeenth century, Bentham called talk of natural rights "nonsense on stilts," but insisted that the relevant moral question is not whether animals can think or talk but rather whether they can suffer. In the mid-nineteenth century, Arthur Schopenhauer wrote that Europeans are "awakening more and more to a sense that beasts have rights" and applauded the English as "the first people who have, in downright earnest, extended the protecting arm of the law to animals," while chiding the Kantian view and Christian morality for "leaving animals out of account." [5]

More recently, a group of intellectuals at the University of Oxford collaborated in the late 1960s to promote the concept of animal rights. Inspired by an article ("The Rights of Animals") written by novelist Brigid Brophy for the *Sunday Times*, Oxford clinical psychologist Richard Ryder took up the cause. He collaborated with Brophy and Oxford philosophers Stanley and Roslind Godlovitch and John Harris in publishing *Animals, Men, and Morals: An Inquiry into the Maltreatment of Non-humans*. Ryder coined the phrase "speciesism," which term was adopted by Singer in his 1975 *Animal Liberation*.

---

1   John Locke, *Some Thoughts Concerning Education* (1693), Ruth Weissbourd Grant & Nathan Tarcov, eds., Hackett Publishing, 1996), p. 91.
2   Immanuel Kant, *The Metaphysics of Morals*, part II, Para 16.
3   Immanuel Kant, *Lecture on Ethics* (Harper Torchbooks, 1963), p. 239.
4   Jean-Jacques Rousseau, *Discourse on Inequality*, 1754, preface.
5   Arthur Schopenhauer, *On the Basis of Morality*, Part III, chap 8.

b. Legal Reform

Oliver Cromwell's government in England adopted an ordinance prohibiting such blood sports as cockfighting, cock throwing, dog fighting, and bull running, seeing these as particularly odious violations of the obligation of humans to be responsible stewards of God's creation.[6] Before the nineteenth century, there were prosecutions for the unlawful treatment of animals in England, but only on the grounds that property was damaged. Bills were unsuccessfully introduced after 1800 to protect animals themselves, but it was not until 1822 that the first major animal protection legislation, *An Act to Prevent the Cruel and Improper Treatment of Cattle*, was adopted, imposing fines up to five pounds or two months imprisonment for persons who "beat, abuse, or ill-treat any horse, mare, gelding, mule, ass, ox, cow, heifer, steer, sheep or other cattle." The champion of this Act in the House of Commons was Colonel Richard Martin, and it was Martin who brought the first prosecution.[7] The 1822 Act was amended in 1835 to bring cockfighting, baiting, and dog fighting under its jurisdiction, renaming it the *Cruelty to Animals Act*. In France, *Loi Grammont* was passed in 1850, outlawing cruelty to domestic animals.

The first legal code protecting animals in North America was *The Body of Liberties*, endorsed by the Massachusetts Bay Colony in 1641. Rite 92 of this code states that "No man shall exercise any Tirrany or Cueltie toward any bruite Creature which are usuallie kept for man's use." New York courts ruled over the ensuing years that wanton cruelty to animals was a misdemeanor at common law. State animal protection laws were adopted in Washington in 1859, New York in 1866, California in 1868, and Florida in 1889. In contemporary American legal circles, the idea of conferring rights to animals has been advocated by Christopher Stone and has the support of Alan Dershowitz and Laurence Tribe of Harvard Law School. Animal law is reportedly taught at 135 laws schools in the US and Canada. Toronto lawyer Clayton Ruby wrote in 2008 that the movement to expand rights protections for animals had reached the stage the gay rights movement was at twenty-five years earlier.

In Germany, several animal protection laws were passed during Hitler's Third Reich. In announcing the first of these, Hitler announced that "In the new Reich, no moral animal cruelty will be allowed." Ensuing laws prohibited hunting and

---

6   See Kathleen Kete, "Animals and Ideology: The Politics of Animal Protection in Europe," in *Representing Animals*, Rothfels & Nigel, eds. (Indiana University Press, 2002), pp. 19–20.

7   See Debbi Legge & Simon Brooman, *Law Relating to Animals* (Cavendish Publishing, 1997), p. 40.

animal transport by car and train, with instructions even on the least painful way to shoe a horse and to cook lobsters without boiling them alive. Vivisection was banned as "Jewish science" and "internationalist medicine." The ban was later modified to permit institutionalized animal research, with the explanation that "It is a law of every community that, when necessary, single individuals are sacrificed in the interests of the entire body." Medical experiments were conducted on Jews and Romani children, particularly in Auschwitz by Dr. Josef Mengele. Suspecting that experiments involving Jews were unreliable, animal testing was conducted as a follow-up. It is reported that Hitler, Rudolf Hess, Joseph Goebbels, and Heinrich Himmler adopted some form of vegetarianism.

c. Advocacy and Activism

On the activist front, the Society for the Prevention of Cruelty to Animals (SPCA) was formed by Richard Martin and other members of Parliament in 1824 to monitor compliance with the 1822 Act. The SPCA sent inspectors to livestock markets, slaughterhouses, and the stables of coachmen. A royal charter was conferred to the Society in 1840 by Queen Victoria, who herself strongly opposed vivisection. A youth section of the SPCA, the Bands of Mercy, was established by Catherine Smithies in 1824. Originally intended to encourage the love of animals, this group became known for its direct engagement with hunters. Irish feminist Frances Power Cobbe founded the Society for the Protection of Animals Liable to Vivisection in 1875, which became the National Anti-Vivisection Society. She also spearheaded the establishment of the British Union for the Abolition of Vivisection and led campaigns against the use of dogs in research. The Band of Mercy was reenergized in 1972 when activists promoted guerrilla tactics against hunters.

The first animal protection group in the US was the American Society for the Prevention of Cruelty to Animals (ASCPA), founded by Henry Bergh in 1866. Bergh authored the "Declaration of the Rights of Animals" and persuaded the New York state legislature to grant to ASPCA the authority to enforce the prohibitions of this declaration. In 1976, some of the Bands of Mercy activists, principally Ronnie Lee and Cliff Goodman, founded the Animal Liberation Front, identifying itself to the press as a "nonviolent guerilla organization dedicated to the liberation of animals from all forms of cruelty and persecution at the hands of mankind."[8] In 1973, the AFL's first act of arson occurred when members set fire to a pharmaceutical laboratory. The AFL is active in numerous countries, operating as a grassroots, leaderless resistance. These activists see themselves as a modern Underground Railroad, removing animals from animal farms and laboratories to sympathetic veterinarians and ultimately to sanctuaries. Threats, intimidation, and arson have significantly eroded public sympathy for the ALF and the US Department of Homeland Security put the organization on its list of domestic terrorist threats in 2005. Undaunted, Ingrid Newkirk believes that "Thinkers may prepare revolutions, but bandits must carry them out."[9]

Activist Henry Spira is a proponent of lawful non-violent change, favoring what he calls "reintegrative shaming." His first campaign in 1976 successfully persuaded the American Museum of Natural History to abandon experimentation on cats. Perhaps his most notable achievement was "shaming" Revlon so that it stopped using animals for cosmetics testing and donated money to help set up the Center for Alternatives to Testing. Spira's approach has been widely adopted by other animal welfare groups, most notably the People for the Ethical Treatment of Animals (PETA). PETA members see themselves as "new welfarists" and "animal protectionists" rather than "animal rights" advocates.

2. Peter Singer's Applied Utilitarianism

Peter Singer has probably played the most influential role among contemporary ethicists in shaping the animal welfare movement in the US. As discussed in the previous chapter, Singer's ethics incorporates two principles: the principle of utility and the principle of equal consideration. The principle of utility states that one morally ought to choose and act on the course of action (among alternatives) that is expected to produce the greatest good for the greatest number of affected parties. The principle of equal consideration states that like interests ought to be given like consideration in utilitarian deliberations. In Singer's words: "One ought to choose and act in a manner that maximizes the interests of all affected parties," where, he adds, "the interests of every being affected by an action are

---

8   Neil Molland, "Thirty Years of Direct Action," in *Terrorists or Freedom Fighters* (Lantern Books, 2004), Best, Steven, Nocella & Anthony, eds., p.70.

9   Ingrid Newkirk, "The ALF: Who, Why, and What?" in *Terrorists or Freedom Fighters*, Best, Steven, Nocella & Anthony, eds. (Lantern Books, 2004), p. 341.

to be taken into account and given the same weight as the like interests of any other being."[10]

Singer argues that not being in pain and not suffering are the most basic of all interests—that, indeed, to have any interest at all, one must be capable of feeling pain and of suffering. He argued that there is no reason for concluding that sentient animals are not capable of experiencing pain and suffering in ways comparable to that experienced by humans. He states that "It is surely unreasonable to suppose that nervous systems that are virtually identical physiologically, have a common origin and a common evolutionary function, and result in similar forms of behavior in similar circumstances should actually operate in an entirely different manner on the level of subjective feelings."[11] Thus, "If a being suffers, there can be no basis for refusing to take that suffering into consideration … If a being is not capable of suffering, or of experiencing enjoyment or happiness, there is nothing to be taken into account."[12] Not taking a sentient animal's pain and suffering into moral account and giving its pain and suffering equal weight to human pain and suffering is, Singer insists, no less a form of unjustified discrimination than racism or sexism.

Singer has applied the principles of utility and equal consideration to formulate his position on a wide variety of issues, including, in addition to animal treatment, abortion, euthanasia, infanticide, and world poverty. In the second edition of *Practical Ethics*, he adopts a "journey model" of life which enables us to think of wrong actions in relation to the degree that they frustrate the goals of a life journey. This model also enables us to make needed distinctions between genuine interests and trivial desires and pleasures, Singer believes. In regard to abortion, he argues that it is not wrong to kill a human fetus, at least up to at least eighteen weeks, because it has no capacity to suffer or feel satisfaction, has no interests and preferences, cannot be said to have embarked on a life journey, and lacks the essential characteristics of personhood. Singer's conclusion is that there is nothing to weigh against a woman's preference to have an abortion and no good reason for denying the moral permissibility of abortion. This position sparked outrage in various circles, including revoked invitations to speak, heckling from protesters before and during presentations, and cancelled private donations to universities where he has taught.

---

10   Peter Singer, "All Animals are Equal," in *Earth Ethics*, James P. Sterba, ed. (Upper Saddle River, N.J., Prentice Hall, 2000), p. 53. This article was originally published in *Philosophical Exchange* I (1974), pp. 103–116.
11   Ibid., p. 57
12   Ibid., p. 56–57

In regard to the treatment of animals, Singer's general conclusion is that the principles of utility and equal consideration enjoin us "to make radical changes in our diet, the farming methods we use, experimental procedures in many fields of science, our approach to wildlife and to hunting, trapping and the wearing of furs, and areas of entertainment like circuses, rodeos, and zoos."[13] "As a result," he says, "a vast amount of suffering would be avoided."

In regard to sexual activities between humans and animals, he wrote that "sex with animals does not always involve cruelty" and that mutually satisfying activities of a sexual nature may sometimes occur between humans and animals, in which circumstances they are morally permissible.[14] Regan took strong exception to this position, arguing that the same argument form could be used to justify having sex with children, and that Singer's conclusion is a consequence of his adopting a utilitarian approach to animal treatment rather than a strictly rights-based one.[15]

In making his case against meat eating and factory farming practices, Singer argues that horrendous pain and suffering are inflicted indiscriminately and unnecessarily on hundreds of millions of sentient animals and that these practices are unhealthy, economically unjustified, damaging to the environment, and would, if curtailed, contribute significantly to the reduction of Third World poverty. He calls himself a vegetarian and a "flexible vegan": "I don't go to the supermarket and buy non-vegan stuff for myself. But when I'm traveling or going to other people's places I will be quite happy to eat vegetarian rather than vegan."[16] He does not make a blanket condemnation of meat eating, however, arguing that it is permissible on utilitarian grounds to eat farm animals that are reared and killed painlessly and without suffering.

Never reticent about expressing his views publicly, Singer engaged in a debate with Judge Richard Posner of the US Court of Appeals for the Seventh Circuit on the issue of "animal liberation."[17] Posner said that his moral intuition tells him "that human beings prefer their own." Further: "If a dog threatens a human infant, even if it requires causing more pain to the dog to stop it than the dog would have caused to the infant, then we favour the child. It would be monstrous to spare the dog." Singer challenged this intuition by arguing that

---

13   Ibid., p. 60
14   Regan expressed this view in his *Heavy Petting* (2001), a reply to Midas Dekkers' *Dearest Pet: On Bestiality*.
15   Tom Regan, *Animal Rights, Human Wrongs* (Rowman & Littlefield, 2003), pp. 63–64, 89.
16   Quoted in Dave Gilson's "Chew the Right Thing" in *Mother Jones*, May 3, 2006.
17   Posner–Singer Debate, *Slate*, June 12, 2001.

discriminatory practices based on gender, race, ethnic background, and sexual orientation have been justified using appeals to intuition. Posner replied by saying that, in a legal context, facts-driven arguments prevail, not ethical arguments that run contrary to what most people believe. In regard to anti-discriminatory law, Posner continued, "facts mounted supporting the case that [there are] no morally significant differences between humans based on race, sex, or sexual orientation." Posner called his approach "soft utilitarianism." In his words, "The 'soft' utilitarianism position on animal rights is a moral intuition of many, probably most, Americans. We realize that animals feel pain and think that to inflict pain without a reason is bad." But, he adds, "Nothing of practical value is added by dressing up this intuition in the language of philosophy; much is lost when intuition is made a stage in logical argument. When kindness toward animals is levered into a duty of weighting the pains of animals and people equally, bizarre vistas of social engineering are opened up."

As discussed in the previous chapter, Brian Luke and many feminists contend that Singer's justice-based argument is not enough, relying instead on feelings-based intuition. But their intuitions lead in a different direction from that suggested by Posner, and they have no problem with "social engineering" that corrects what they see as grievous wrongs in the human treatment of animals.

3. Tom Regan's Applied Deontology

Tom Regan rejects a utilitarian approach to animal welfare because he believes that it fails to recognize the inherent value of animals that, like us, are experiencing subjects-of-a-life with desires, fears, memories, and a sense of self through time. Because these animals have a complex psychological life, feel pain, and suffer in much the same way we do, they are worthy of our moral respect and have a fundamental moral right not to be treated merely as means to human wants and needs.

For Regan, experiencing subjects-of-a-life have equal inherent value and equal rights not to be maltreated. It is rationally unacceptable to claim that humans have more value than animals simply because humans belong to the species *Homo sapiens*; this, Regan says, is "blatant speciesism." It is also rationally unacceptable, in Regan's view, to base a practical ethics on the controversial claim that humans have more value because they have an immortal soul. Although Regan says that he hopes that his psychic self continues to exist beyond physical death, he states that "rationally, it is better to resolve moral issues without making more controversial assumptions than are needed."[18] It is also rationally unacceptable, he contends, to claim that humans have greater value than animals because animals lack rational capacity, autonomy, or intellect. He argues that an appeal to rationality is no more acceptable than saying that a mature adult has greater moral value than a retarded child because the former but not the latter is able to reason and make autonomous judgments.

Regan opposes the utilitarian approach to thinking about rightful human relations with animals "because it has no room for their equal inherent value or worth." "What has value for the utilitarian is the satisfaction of an individual's interests, not the individual whose interests they are."[19] As previously noted, Regan categorically rejects Singer's utilitarian argument that sexual relations with animals are permissible when cruelty is not involved. The argument can be used to justify sexual relations with children, he argues, emphasizing that the fundamental wrong is a violation of the right of subjects-of-a-life not to be treated merely as a means.

Regan straightforwardly regards himself "as an advocate of animal rights—as part of the animal rights movement ... committed to a number of goals, including the total abolition of the use of animals in science, the total dissolution of commercial animal agriculture, [and] the total elimination of commercial and sport hunting and trapping." Regan's ethics are absolutist. He refuses to concede, as Singer does, that traditional animal agriculture is morally permissible if animals are raised and killed painlessly, or that animal testing in laboratories is permissible if it undertaken with the objective of finding a cure for cancer and the pain and suffering associated with testing are minimized. "You don't change unjust institutions by tidying them up," Regan insists. "What's wrong—what's fundamentally wrong—with the ways animals are treated isn't the details that vary from case to case. ... The fundamental wrong is the system that allows us to view animals as our resources, here for us—to be eaten, or surgically manipulated, or put in our crosshairs for sport or money."[20]

Regan's views are criticized for their uncompromising absolutism. They are also criticized by biocentrists for their failure to acknowledge that other life has inherent value and by ecocentrists who contend that Regan's prescriptions are sharply at odds with management practices informed by conservation biology and ecology. Ecocentrists contend that vertebracentric thinking in general

---

18   Tom Regan, *Animal Rights, Human Wrongs*, Op. cit., p. 71.

19   Tom Regan, "The Case for Animal Rights," in *Earth Ethics*, James P. Sterba, ed. (Upper Saddle River, N.J., Prentice Hall, 2000), Ibid., p. 69.

20   Tom Regan, *Animal Rights, Human Wrongs*, Op. cit., pp. 65–66.

breaks down when questions such as the following are posed: If humans have a duty to protect pets and domesticated animals from prey, do we also have a duty to protect animals in the wild from their prey? If overpopulation of a species is human-caused and likely to result in starvation of large numbers in the species-population, is it morally wrong to selectively cull members to reduce overpopulation?

4. David DeGrazia's Applied Animal Ethics

David DeGrazia develops an animal ethics in *Taking Animals Seriously*[21] and his shorter, less technical work, *Animal Rights*,[22] written for a more general readership. In the latter, he distinguishes three senses in which animals are said to have rights. In regard to the first meaning—the *moral status* sense—the claim is that animals have a right to be taken into moral consideration when they are harmed by human action. In an *equal consideration sense*, the claim is that equal weight should be given to comparable animal and human interests not to be harmed. In a third *utility-trumping sense*, the claim is that animals have certain vital interests that ought not to be violated, even when violation of those interests could be expected to produce significant human benefits.

Like Singer, DeGrazia argues that the capacity of sentient animals to experience pain and to suffer gives them human-independent moral status. He also defends the equal consideration principle, although he emphasizes that it is important to get clear on the respects in which human and animal interests in not being harmed are comparable. Singer eschews talk of animal rights in the third sense, but DeGrazia argues that certain animals (e.g. dolphins and Great Apes) have certain utility-trumping rights (e.g., the right not to be killed or kept in captivity). DeGrazia finds the equal consideration principle to be intuitively sound and needed to combat deep-seated human bias toward most animals. He argues that the burden of proof is on inegalitarians to justify the practice of giving unequal consideration to comparable interests. He considers a number of the arguments designed to justify unequal treatment (appeal to species, contract theory, appeal to moral agency, and appeal to social bonds), and finds each to be problematic and unconvincing. Although DeGrazia considers the

---

21   David DeGrazia, *Taking Animals Seriously: Mental Life and Moral Status*, (Cambridge, England: Cambridge University Press, 2001).
22   David DeGrazia, *Animal Rights: A Very Short Introduction* (Oxford: Oxford University Press, 2002).

equal consideration principle to be sound and needed, he makes limited use of this principle in *Taking Animals Seriously*.

a. The Mental Life of Animals and Comparability of Harms

In both of his books, DeGrazia discusses what recent studies reveal about the mental life of animals. Based on what we know phenomenologically about our own experience of *pain* as well as the observed behavior of other animals (e.g., avoidance of noxious stimuli, crying out, limited use of injured body parts to permit healing), findings in neurophysiology and neuroanatomy (how tissue-damaging stimuli are detected in nociception and transmitted as nerve impulses along axons to a brain, and how pain is modulated endogenously by the release of opiates and exogenously through anesthesia), and functional-evolutionary hypotheses (how the ability to experience pain has evolved as a survival mechanism), DeGrazia concludes there can be little doubt that all sentient animals feel pain in response to certain stimuli.

DeGrazia then weighs the behavioral, anatomical, neurobiological, and neurochemical evidence for attributing emotional states to other animals. He concludes that many animals experience negative emotional states, including *suffering* ("a highly unpleasant emotional state associated with more-than-minimal pain or distress"), *fear* (a type of distress defined as "a typically unpleasant emotional response to a perceived danger, usually in the immediate environment, a response that focuses attention to facilitate protective action"), and *anxiety* (another type of distress defined as "a typically unpleasant emotional response to a perceived threat to one's physical or psychological well-being, a response that generally inhibits action and involves heightened arousal and attention to the environment").[23] DeGrazia argues that other emotional states are common among animals as well, including *frustration* and *boredom*. In response to the argument that language is necessary for rich emotional experience, he points out that language is not required for *having* feelings (as opposed to verbally *expressing* those feelings), and that human babies obviously experience pain, pleasure, and fear even though they have not yet acquired a language enabling them to communicate their distress verbally. Without attempting to review in detail here DeGrazia's discussion

---

23   DeGrazia notes that other emotional states are common among animals, including *frustration* and *boredom*, but does not discuss these in any detail in *Animal Rights*. DeGrazia uses the general term "suffering" to refer to these and other discernible kinds of emotional distress.

of various emotions, this is what he concludes about anxiety: "While the available evidence, taken together, supports the conclusion [that vertebrates experience anxiety], it does not imply that human anxiety and animal anxiety are qualitatively similar beyond a common unpleasantness and heightened arousal and attention. Undoubtedly, the language-laden complexity of human thought produces anxious experiences very different from those of animals. The present claim is that animals representing a wide range of species are capable of having anxious states, as captured in our definition of 'anxiety.'"[24]

All sentient animals experience physical pain and at least threshold levels of anxiety, fear, frustration, and various other negative emotions. It can also be concluded, DeGrazia argues, that various "higher animals" have an abiding sense of self and exhibit cognitive capacities. The capacity of animals to suffer strongly suggests that animals have a sense of temporal self-awareness, of persisting as a self over time. "Fear would be impossible," he contends, "unless the subject has some awareness of persisting into the future." Further, "the growing field of ethology—which examines animal behavior in the context of evolutionary biology—tends to support the attribution of beliefs, desires, and intentional actions to many animals. The central claim is that the *best explanation* of their behavior, given everything we know about them, requires these attributions." Also, "there is considerable independent evidence that many vertebrate animals have memories as well as expectations for the future. For example, it has been rigorously demonstrated that many birds have extensive recall of where they have hidden food."[25]

While DeGrazia believes that the concept of personhood is too vague and contentious to be useful in animal ethics, he concludes that it is reasonable to attribute at least minimal degrees of intentional action, thinking, sociability, and self-awareness to mammals and certainly the higher primates ("even though such capacities may not meet the threshold for autonomy"), and that "these animals possess as much of these capacities as do many humans."

DeGrazia suggests that there are three basic ways in which human actions can harm animals: the harm of suffering, the harm of confinement, and the harm of death. He concludes that the harm of *suffering* is comparable across vertebrate animal species: "Since suffering is most fundamentally an experiential harm, it is reasonable to hold that if a human and an animal experience roughly equal amounts of suffering—however difficult, in particular cases, that

---

24   David DeGrazia, *Animal Rights*, Op. cit., pp. 47–48.
25   Ibid., p. 52.

may be to determine—they are comparably harmed."[26] In regard to the harm of *confinement*, DeGrazia's position is that such harm is comparable to the extent that it causes suffering, but not comparable with respect to widely varying species-typical functioning. Defining *death* as the foreclosure of opportunities for experiential well-being, DeGrazia sees death as harmful to all vertebrates, but not comparably harmful since human opportunities for experiential well-being are greater than other animals. He sums up his position as follows: "Our discussion has yielded several conclusions. First, a certain amount of suffering is a comparable harm, regardless of who the sufferer is. Second, when comparing humans with some animals—at least those 'below' mammals—death is not a comparable harm. In normal circumstances, death harms humans more. Third, confinement is a comparable harm across species in terms of causing a certain amount of suffering; it is not comparable, when comparing humans and at least some animals, in terms of interfering with valuable activities or possibilities for satisfaction."[27]

DeGrazia argues that the principle of equal consideration applies only to suffering, since this type of harm is comparable across species. In addressing the harms of death and confinement, DeGrazia appeals to the moral principle of nonmaleficence: that it is wrong to inflict unnecessary harm. This principle is needed, he argues, to keep in check the bias in what DeGrazia calls the "phylogenetic sliding-scale" approach to the moral status of animals. On this scale, "Humans are [placed] at the very top, with Great Apes and dolphins a bit lower, with hominoids other than *Homo sapiens* in between if extinct species are included. Elephants, gibbons, and monkeys would be somewhat lower on the scale, with canines and felines a bit lower, and rabbits and rodents lower still. … Mammals would generally be higher than birds, which are generally higher than reptiles and amphibians, which are generally higher than fish."[28] Further: "Beings at the very top have the highest moral status and deserve full consideration. Beings somewhat lower deserve very serious consideration but less than what the beings on top deserve. As one moves down this scale of moral status, the amount of consideration one owes to beings at a particular level decreases. At some point one reaches beings that deserve just a little consideration. Their interests have direct moral significance, but not much, so where their interests conflict with those of beings with much higher moral status, the former usually

---

26   Ibid., p. 54.
27   Ibid., p. 65.
28   Ibid., p. 35.

lose out. Right below the beings just described we may mentally draw a line. Any and all beings below this line have no moral status."

b. Fifteen Moral Norms

Rejecting the "sliding scale" model as crude and morally inadequate, DeGrazia works out a set of moral norms or principles in *Taking Animals Seriously*[29] to guide the human treatment of animals. In summary, these norms are:

1. Don't cause unnecessary harm to any sentient animal.
2. Make every reasonable effort not to provide financial support for institutions that cause or support unnecessary harm to sentient animals.[30]
3. Don't cause significant suffering to any sentient animal for the sake of your or others' enjoyment.
4. Apply equally any standards allowing the causing of suffering.
5. Don't kill sentient animals unnecessarily.
6. The presumption against killing humans, Great Apes, and dolphins is virtually absolute.
7. For a large class of sentient animals—at least fish, herpetofauna (amphibians and reptiles), and birds—the presumption against killing these animals is ordinarily weaker than that against killing humans, Great Apes, and dolphins.
8. Don't confine sentient animals unnecessarily (where "confinement" is understood as the imposition of external constraints on movement that significantly interfere with one's ability to live a good life).
9. There is a strong presumption against confining nondangerous sentient animals.
10. The presumption against confining innocent humans, Great Apes, and dolphins is virtually absolute.
11. To the extent we can separate out freedom interests in practice, for a large class of sentient animals—at least fish, herpetofauna, and birds—the presumption against confining them is ordinarily weaker than that against confining humans, Great Apes, and dolphins.

---

29   David DeGrazia, *Taking Animals Seriously*, pp. 35–36.
30   DeGrazia contends that each norm imposes a moral obligation not to support institutions that violate the moral requirement in question. The second norm makes this explicit, but it is implicit in each of the other norms.

12. The conditions of any justified confinement must be responsive to the animal's needs.

13. There is a presumption against disabling sentient animals (i.e. damaging their ability to function in ways that significantly interfere with their ability to live a good life) and, if they are non-dangerous, the presumption is virtually absolute.

14. Provide for the basic physical and psychological needs of your pet, and ensure that she has a comparably good life to what she would likely have if she were not a pet.[31]

15. If (hypothetically) there appears to be a genuine conflict between benefiting an animal and respecting her autonomy, unless the expected benefit is very great and the apparent infringement of autonomy very marginal, respect autonomy.[32]

DeGrazia contends that all but two of these normative guidelines are based on inferences drawn from the uncontroversial idea that we have a *prima facie* duty not to harm, in combination with insights about the ways in which sentient animals can be harmed. Only norms 4 and 13 depend, he believes, on the principle of equal consideration. DeGrazia summarizes his position in this way: "I have argued that equal consideration for animals is more reasonable than its denial, given the failure of opponents of equal consideration to meet their burden of proof. ... Anyhow, those who doubt that animals should be extended *equal* consideration should note that a commitment to giving animals *serious* consideration would be enough to support most of the conclusions."[33]

c. The Moral Norms Applied: Critique of Factory Farming and Zoos

The fifteen normative moral conclusions are applied by DeGrazia in his critique of factory farming practices and the capture and captivity of wild animals in zoos. In regard to the former, DeGrazia argues that factory farms cause massive harm for trivial purposes and are ethically indefensible. In particular, factory farms violate the following normative conclusions: (5) Don't kill sentient animals

---

31   DeGrazia notes that this obligation is a limited *positive* obligation to animals with which humans have a *special relationship* and that the basic needs requirement sets a floor of well-being for pets. In his view, the comparable life requirement is justified by the claim that animals should not unnecessarily be made worse off for becoming a pet.

32   David DeGrazia, *Taking Animals Seriously*, Op. cit., pp. 279–280.

33   Ibid., p. 281.

unnecessarily; (8) Don't confine sentient animals unnecessarily; and (13) "There is a presumption against disabling sentient animals and, if they are nondangerous, the presumption is virtually absolute." In addition to the killing of sentient animals *en masse*, factory faming also causes them significant suffering and restricts their liberty in ways incompatible with their living well. In many cases, they are also seriously disabled through injury.[34] DeGrazia allows that a case can be made that the factory farming of chickens is less morally problematic than that of cattle and hogs, but he insists that "no plausible argument can be made that the fate of factory farmed chickens is necessary, only that the way chickens are treated may be less bad."[35]

It is also morally wrong, DeGrazia contends, to buy and eat the products of factory farms. Per the second moral norm, one should make every reasonable effort not to provide financial support for institutions that cause or support unnecessary harm to sentient animals. He adds that there are other reasons for boycotting factory farms. "First, factory farming has had a terrible impact on the environment in terms of pollution and the consumption and inefficient use of soil, energy, and water. Second, factory farming has a pernicious effect on the global distribution of food for humans. ... Third, factory farming in the United States has greatly harmed family farmers and rural communities by putting some 3 million farms out of business. ... Finally, meat eating, especially at average American rates, is associated with several health problems, [including] heart disease, stroke, diabetes, atherosclerosis, and certain cancers."[36] He asks whether someone who largely abstains from meat but occasionally makes an exception (e.g., when visiting parents on a holiday) can be said to be making a reasonable effort. "Perhaps," he replies, "and it seems wise not to quibble about the finer points. The important idea is that people should recognize the wrongness of supporting factory farms and act accordingly."[37]

DeGrazia then considers the moral justifiability of eating fish, cephalopods (squid and octopi), shrimp, crabs, and lobsters. In regard to the former two, he comments that "Those who believe that these creatures are not harmed in death, and who doubt they suffer, might hold that the minor harm of any short-term unpleasantness they may feel is compensated for by the gains to humans: health, convenience, pleasure, and employment for fishermen. My [DeGrazia's] thesis is that death harms the sentient, and my inclination to give fish and cephalopods

---

34   Ibid., p. 284.
35   Ibid., p. 285.
36   Ibid., pp. 286–87.
37   Ibid., p. 286.

the benefit of any doubt regarding suffering, lead me to a different view. ... But certainly buying fish is much less morally problematic than buying factory-farmed or even family-farmed meat."[38] Given the unsettled question whether shrimp, crabs, and lobsters are sentient, DeGrazia is personally disinclined to condemn the eating of these animals.

DeGrazia's conclusions regarding the moral justifiability of zoos using the norms listed above are not summarized in detail here. His two most general conclusions are: that, mammals should not be captured for zoo exhibits and that, while not all captivity is confinement in the sense defined (restrictions on liberty that interfere significantly with an animal's ability to live a good life), zoo owners and directors should provide for the basic physical and psychological needs of the zoo animal and ensure that the animal has a comparably good life to what it would likely have in the wild.

B. Biocentric Perspectives

Biocentric theorists contend that all living beings, not just sentient animals, should be regarded as members of the moral community—that all living organisms are worthy recipients of moral respect in their own right. Two prominent biocentric ethicists within this tradition are discussed below: Paul W. Taylor and James P. Sterba.

1. Paul Taylor's Biocentric Egalitarianism

In his book, *Respect for Nature: A Theory of Environmental Ethics*,[39] Taylor developed a comprehensive biocentric ethics based on the principle of the equal inherent worth of all living beings. He articulates this principle in connection with a defense of what he calls the "biocentric outlook on nature." He then formulates four basic *prima facie* duties toward non-human life and five priority principles for resolving conflicts that may arise among these duties in particular situations.

---

38   Ibid., p. 289.
39   Paul W. Taylor, *Respect for Nature* (Princeton, N.J.: Princeton University Press, 1986).

a. The Biocentric Outlook

A person with a "biocentric outlook" gives his intellectual assent to four basic beliefs:

- that humans are an integral part of the natural order—a belief grounded in the recognition that the human species is a relative newcomer to an order of life established over hundreds of millions of years and that, while humans cannot do without other life, other life can do without humans;
- that all living beings exist in a system of interdependence in which the survival and well-being of each is determined not only by the physical conditions of its environment but also by its relations to other living things;
- that all organisms are teleological centers of activity in the sense that each is a unique individual exemplifying the functions and activities of its species and pursuing its own good in its own way; and
- that human beings are not inherently superior to other living beings.

Taylor contends that the biocentric outlook is a way of conceiving nature that informed people can readily adopt. In his view, the first two beliefs are accepted by most observers as founded on solid empirical facts. The third belief—that all organisms are teleological centers of activity—is no less scientifically obvious, he says: "To say [that an organism] is a teleological center of a life is to say that its internal functioning as well as its external activities ... have the constant tendency to maintain the organism's existence through time and to enable it successfully to perform those biological operations whereby it reproduces its kind and continually adapts to changing environmental events and conditions. It is the coherence and unity of these functions of an organism, all directed toward the realization of its good, that make it one teleological center of activity." Taylor defends the fourth belief—that humans are not inherently superior to living beings—by arguing, first, that the first two beliefs of the biocentric outlook, themselves widely accepted science-based facts, provide good reasons for accepting this egalitarian thesis; and, second, that the claim of human superiority on the basis of a selected characteristic that humans possess and non-humans lack already assumes that possession of the identified characteristic makes human superior. The claim that humans are superior by virtue of their unique ability to reason tacitly presupposes what is being claimed: that rationality is what makes humans superior.

If one accepts the four basic beliefs, Taylor maintains, one comes to "take on an attitude of respect toward nature": one readily acknowledges that an organism's teleological development oriented toward its own good is a sufficient reason for imputing inherent value to that organism and taking it into moral consideration when human action threatens to impede its development or end its life. Since there is no non-question-begging way of establishing that the good of any living being is superior to that of any other living being, one readily acknowledges, moreover, the principle that all living beings have *equal* inherent worth and are *equally* deserving of moral respect. A person who "takes up" the biocentric outlook is prepared to adopt this egalitarian principle.

b. Duties to Non-Human Life

Taylor then articulates four general duties owed to non-human individuals and five procedural principles for resolving conflicts that arise when actions beneficial to humans are harmful to non-human life. The four general *prima facie* duties are:

Duty of nonmaleficence: the duty not to harm any entity within a species-population or life community that has a good of its own.

Duty of noninterference: the duty to refrain from placing restrictions on the freedom of an entity having a good of its own and interfering with processes that occur naturally in species-populations and ecosystems.

Duty of fidelity: the duty not to break a trust with any wild animal capable of being deceived or misled (e.g., use of decoys or bait fishing), particularly when the trust has been established as a result of past human behavior (e.g., leaving food to later lure an animal into a baited trap).

Duty of restitutive justice: the duty to restore the balance of justice between a moral agent and a moral subject: between a human perpetrator of harm and a non-human victim of harm.

Although Taylor does not assign relative weights to these *prima facie* duties, he offers two general rules of thumb to guide their application: first, fidelity and restitutive justice generally override noninterference when a great good is brought about and no creature is permanently harmed by the interference; and second, restitutive justice generally outweighs fidelity when a great good is brought about and no serious harm is done to a creature whose trust in humans is betrayed.

c. Priority Principles

When unavoidable conflicts between human and non-human interests arise (e.g., clear-cutting a woodland to build a medical center, destroying a fresh water ecosystem to build a lakeside resort, replacing a cactus desert with a housing development), Taylor offers five procedural principles for resolving such conflicts. Each principle is consistent, he maintains, with the requirement that greater weight not be given to human interests. The five principles are:

> *The principle of self-defense*: It is not permissible to destroy plants and animals unless they unavoidably threaten human life and basic health.

> *The principle of proportionality*: It is not permissible to violate the basic interests of plants and animals (what is essentially required for survival and teleological development) in order to satisfy the non-basic interests of humans (what is not essential to human security, autonomy, and liberty).

> *The principle of minimum wrong*: It is permissible to pursue values highly prized for their contribution to cultural and personal well-being and excellence even though one or more of the duties to non-human life is thereby violated, provided that the harmful consequences of the pursuit of these values are fully known and no alternative way of pursuing these values involves fewer violations of duty.

> *The principle of distributive justice*: When conflicts between human and non-human living beings arise from the appropriation of a re-source beneficial to any one party (land, water, food, etc.), each party should be allocated an equal share of that resource.

The principle of restitutive justice: When harms consistent with the principles of proportionality and the principle of minimum wrong occur and the principle of distributive justice cannot be met in practice, appropriate restitution should be made, guided by the following two directives: (a) when restitution is undertaken to protect or promote the good of the particular animals and plants harmed, the resulting good should be commensurate with the amount of harm to be compensated for, and (b) when compensation to the harmed individuals is impossible or infeasible, compensation should be made to the species-population as a whole in the form of habitat protection and/or resource protection.

d. Criticisms of Taylor

Critics contend that Taylor's principle of minimum wrong contradicts the principle of equal inherent worth. In developing the latter, Taylor maintains that there is no basis for giving greater weight to human interests in moral deliberation when these interests conflict with those of other life, yet the principle of minimum wrong is said to do just this.[40] Some surmise that this inconsistency arises from Taylor's not wanting his normative ethics to require so much of humans that it would be summarily rejected as too extreme and impractical. Whether or not this was Taylor's motivation, the criticism is that the minimum wrong principle amounts to a departure from the strict egalitarianism of the biocentric outlook.[41]

Other writers contend that Taylor's biocentric principles are, indeed, too extreme and impractical and that Taylor's adoption of the principle of minimum wrong is not enough to make the overall ethics acceptable in the "real world." The principle of distributive justice—which requires that parties-at-interest be given equal shares of an essentially needed resource (in situations

---

40   It is not entirely clear whether Taylor believes that the connection between the proposition that all living beings have equal inherent worth and the proposition that that differential weighting is unjustified is logical (that the former logically entails the latter), or psychological (that accepting the former is tantamount to accepting the latter), or definitional (that the meaning of the former includes the meaning of the latter). Taylor probably regards the connection as psychological in view of his contention that one who adopts the biocentric outlook "takes on an "attitude of respect."
41   This criticism is further discussed in Chapter 6 in connection with four proposed life-centered ethical principles. It is argued there that a version of the principle of equal inherent worth is compatible with differential weighting in moral deliberation.

in which human appropriation of resources adversely affects the well-being of other life in significant ways)—is singled out in this regard. The objection is that widespread application of this principle would radically hamstring activities essential to human well-being, and that an ethics with this consequence cannot be taken seriously.

Another criticism made by ecocentrists is that Singer's biocentric *individualism* fails to recognize the central role and moral significance of collective wholes in nature: species and ecosystems. In regard to species, Taylor's position is that species are simply classificatory labels devised to distinguish populations sharing certain sets of characteristics from populations that do not share those characteristics. As discussed in the previous chapter, E.O. Wilson, Holmes Rolston, and others contend that species are nature's evolved "objective packages" and no less real than the individuals that instantiate them. For these writers, an ethics that fails to recognize the independent moral standing of species is seriously flawed.

Taylor is also criticized for not recognizing the independent moral status of ecosystems. While Taylor insists that humans ought not to destroy habitats and indiscriminately interfere with processes in ecosystems, for him such obligations are derivative from direct duties owed to individuals making up those ecosystems. Ecocentrists are quick to point out that what is good for wholes (ecosystems) may be not good for the individuals that inhabit them and that, from a resource management perspective, the good of wholes may take precedence over the good of constituent individual members. It may be imperative, for example, to eliminate individuals to control species overpopulation, or to eliminate the members of an invasive species to preserve a native ecosystem.

2. James Sterba's Biocentric Principles

James Sterba has attempted in several articles to reformulate a biocentric ethics that avoids the complexities of Taylor's theory and some of its criticisms. In the article "Reconciling Anthropocentric and Non-anthropocentric Ethics,"[42] he advances the following three principles:

---

42 James Sterba, "Reconciling Anthropocentric and Non-anthropocentric Ethics," in *Environmental Ethics: Readings in Theory and Application*, Louis P. Pojman, ed. (Thomson/Wadsworth, 2005), pp. 226–236.

Principle of Human Defense: Actions that defend oneself and other human beings against harmful aggression are permissible even when they necessitate killing or harming the aggressor.

Principle of Human Preservation: Actions that are necessary for meeting one's basic needs or the basic needs of other human beings are permissible even when they require aggressing against the basic needs of animals and plants.

Principle of Disproportionality: Actions that meet the nonbasic or luxury needs of humans are prohibited when they aggress against the basic needs of animals and plants.

He argues that all three principles are consistent with the claim that humans are not inherently superior to other life forms. He defends the reasonableness of the first two principles by pointing out that they have widely accepted counterparts in human ethics. He defends the third principle by arguing that a human ethics, even when predicated on the notion of superior human superior worth or merit,[43] does not legitimize a human right to domination. All the claim of human superiority justifies, Sterba maintains, is meeting basic human needs when doing so conflicts with needs in non-human nature; it does not justify aggressing against the basic needs of non-human entities when this conflicts with human non-basic or luxury needs. In rounding out his position, Sterba suggests that equality among species is best understood as the kind of equality espoused by libertarianism (equal liberties) and social liberalism (equal opportunity). He summarizes his position this way: "I have argued that whether we endorse an anthropocentric or a non-anthropocentric environmental ethics, we should favor a principle of human defense, a principle of human preservation, and a principle of disproportionality, as I have interpreted them. In the past, failure to recognize the importance of a principle of human defense and a principle of human preservation has led philosophers to overestimate the amount of sacrifice required of humans. By contrast, failure to recognize the importance of a principle of disproportionality has led philosophers to underestimate the amount of sacrifice required of humans. I claim that, taken

---

43 Sterba argues, as did Taylor, that there is no non-question-begging way of arguing that humans are superior to non-humans by virtue of some good-making characteristic that humans have or possess but non-humans lack.

together, the three principles strike the right balance between concerns of human welfare and the welfare of non-human nature."

In a follow-up article,[44] Sterba reformulates these principles to address the criticism that the earlier version has an implicit human bias and to add a fourth principle, the *Principle of Restitution,* requiring that appropriate restitution be made to victimized parties resulting from violation of any of the other principles. In another article,[45] he contends that species and ecosystems can meaningfully be said to have goods of their own. The claim that an entity has a good of its own if it can be harmed or benefited is, he says, a definitional explanation of what it means to have a good of one's own, and the claim that harm to a non-human entity is wrong unless there is a good reason for the harm is a fundamental premise of ethics in general. He then argues that, because there is no non-question-begging basis for a claim of human superiority (as Taylor argued), there is no basis for the claim that human interests always trump the interests of non-human life, reiterating his view that liberal justice theories that espouse basic rights to liberty, security, and opportunity provide adequate frameworks for adjudicating conflicting interests. His four biocentric principles are, he maintains, justifiable within a liberal justice framework.

Sterba perhaps overcomes some of the complexities and deficiencies of Taylor's biocentrism and perhaps manages to find common theoretical ground with anthropocentrists, but ecocentrists remain unconvinced that a biocentric perspective provides sound guidance for resource management policies and for balancing and adjudicating conflicts of interests involving non-human individuals, species, and biotic communities. An underlying difficulty is the lack of a precise definition of "basic needs." For humans, basic needs presumably include not only what is needed for survival but also for safety and security. If, for non-humans, basic needs include only survival needs (not safety and security needs), there is an implicit human bias in his principles: a violation of the principle of equal worth. If safety and security are included as basic non-human needs, much more is required of humans than Sterba says is morally required. Either way, there is a problem that Sterba does not resolve.

---

44 James Sterba, "A Biocentrist Strikes Back," in *Environmental Ethics*, vol. 20, pp. 361–207.
45 James Sterba, "From Biocentric Individualism to Biocentric Pluralism," in *Environmental Ethics* vol. 17, pp. 192–207.

C. PROTECTION OF ENDANGERED SPECIES

The concern expressed by scientists, ethicists, and concerned citizens over the rate of current extinctions was briefly reviewed in Chapter 1. As noted there, it is estimated by credible sources that 50% of all species existing in 1950 will have become extinct by the middle of this century, and that mammals, birds, amphibians, marine fish, and various plant and inspect species essential to healthy ecosystem functioning are among the species most endangered. Efforts in the US and other countries to protect members of endangered species are summarized below.

1. The Endangered Species Act

The Endangered Species Act (ESA) was enacted in 1973 "to protect critically imperiled species from extinction as a consequence of economic growth and development untempered by adequate concern and conservation." While the language of rights is not used, the Act effectively establishes protection for plants and animals listed as endangered and threatened species. The Act is administered by two federal agencies: the US Fish and Wildlife Service (FWS) of the Department of the Interior and the National Marine Fisheries Service (NMFS) of the National Oceanic and Atmospheric Administration. FWS is responsible protecting listed terrestrial animals and freshwater fish; NMFS is responsible for protecting listed marine fish and wildlife.

A species can be "listed" as endangered or threatened in two ways: through the Candidate Assessment Program of the two agencies or by petition by an individual or organization. A "candidate" can be a taxonomic species, a subspecies, or, in the case of vertebrates, a "distinct population segment." Once a petition for listing is received, a review is conducted by the responsible agency, which then issues a judgment as to whether the petition is "not warranted," "warranted," or "warranted but precluded," where "precluded" means (per a 1982 amendment) that a pending "higher priority" action may take precedence.

Section 4 of the 1973 Act requires FWS and NMFS to designate specific areas as "critical habitat zones" as part of the listing process. All areas on private and/or public lands that are essential to the conservation of the imperiled species must be included. A 1978 amendment to the original 1793 Act made critical habitat designation a mandatory requirement for all threatened and endangered species, with the requirement that each agency "shall designate critical habitat ... on the basis of the best scientific data available after taking into consideration the economic impact." The economic assessment require-ment had virtually stopped new listings and resulted in the withdrawal of almost 2,000 species for which petitions had been made. Another amendment in 1982 dropped the economic assessment requirement. Section 7(a)(2) of the ESA prohibits federal agencies from authorizing and funding projects that "destroy or adversely modify" critical habitats. This provision does not apply to non-federal land owners, but federal permits are required for large-scale private projects, and thus, they can become subject to critical habitat regula-tions. While the Act focuses primarily on the prevention of extinctions, the critical habitat provision is essential to recovery and potential delisting. More than half of critical habitat for species listed to date is on non-federal property.

Both FWS and NMFS are required to formulate an Endangered Species Recovery Plan outlining the goals, tasks, costs, and estimate of the time required for saving a listed species. No time limit was imposed for the completion of a plan. FWS has a policy that a plan must be completed within three years of listing, but average time has been approximately six years. Recovery plans are themselves ranked, with the highest priority given to species most likely to be benefited, particularly when the threat is from construction or other development. The 1988 amendment defined more precisely the information requirements of a recovery plan and added a public participation component.

If FWS or NMFS determines that a federal program or project might harm an endangered species and no "reasonable and prudent alternative" exists to prevent or minimize the harm, the Act includes a provision for exemption by the Endangered Species Committee. Only six exemption reviews have been conducted (as of 2009) and, of these, one was granted, one was partially granted, one was denied, and three were withdrawn. The granted exemption pertained to BLM timber sales and associated "incidental takes" of the endan-gered Northern Spotted Owl. The court denied the exemption, finding that three members of the Committee had been in illegal *ex parte contact* with then-President George W. Bush in violation of the Administrative Procedures Act.

The 1982 amendment authorized a permit process whereby an "incidental taking" (killing, injuring, or harming) of members of an endangered species can occur only if it is part of an approved Habitat Conservation Plan. A permit is given for a specified period of time and may be revoked at any time. The conference report issued in connection with the 1982 amendment specifically referenced the San Bruno Habitat Conservation Plan/Incidental Take Permit as a model for future plans, noting that the San Bruno plan was based on "an independent exhaustive biological study," that it protected approximately 87% of the habitat of listed butterflies, and that "the adequacy of similar conservation plans should be measured against the San Bruno plan." In the view of Robert Thornton, habitat conservation plans are "a major force for wildlife conservation and a major headache to the development community."[46]

Additional modifications to the ESA were made during the latter half of the 1990s as a result of initiatives taken by then-Secretary of the Interior Bruce Babbitt to shield the ESA from a Congress hostile to the law, including the "no surprises" rule and provisions for "safe harbor" and "candidate conservation" agreements. The "no surprises" provision is intended to protect private landowners if unforeseen circumstances make it impossible to achieve levels of protection or mitigation specified in an approved habitat conservation plan. This provision is problematic in the view of conservation groups because private owners are absolved of liability to set aside additional land or incur part of the costs associated with additionally needed protection measures. Under a "safe harbor" agreement, a private party may agree to alter his land in ways that enhance the survival of a listed species in exchange for assurances that FWS will permit future "takes" above a pre-determined level. A "candidate conservation agreement" (CCA) provides incentives to private landowners to restore, enhance, or maintain critical habitat for species known to be in decline but which have not yet been listed as threatened or endangered. Under such an agreement, the landowner will not be required to do more than what is agreed to in the CCA if the species in question are subsequently listed. Economists laud these incentives and think additional incentives are needed to improve the Act's effectiveness. Penalties for violations of provisions of the ESA can be fines as high as $50,000 and/or one year imprisonment and civil penalties up to $25,000 per violation. The most punishable offenses are trafficking and knowing "taking." Rewards can be paid for information leading to a conviction or revocation of a license or permit.

As of February 2012, a total of 593 animals and 794 plants are listed as endangered or threatened, 79 and 84% of which have active Recovery Plans, respectively. From 1967 to 2012, fifty-one species have been delisted, of which twenty-three have recovered, ten have gone extinct, ten have been taxonomically reclassified, six have been discovered to have larger populations than

---

46   Robert D. Thornton, "Searching for Consensus and Predictability: Habitat Conservation Planning under the Endangered Species Act of 1973" in *Environmental Law*, 1991.

previously estimated, one was associated with an error in a listing rule, and one was delisted as part of an amendment to the Act. Notable examples of delisted species are the Bald Eagle, the Whooping Crane, the Peregrine Falcon, the Gray Wolf, the Gray Whale, the Grizzly Bear, and the San Clemente Indian Paintbrush. Twenty-five species have been down-listed from endangered to threatened.[47]

Wilcove and Master estimate that the "known species threatened with extinction is ten times higher than the number protected under the Endangered Species Act."[48] In their estimate, 13% of vertebrates (excluding marine fish), 17% of vascular plants, and 6–18% of fungi in the US are imperiled.

2. International Initiatives

The International Union for the Conservation of Nature (IUCN) classifies organisms as Extinct, Extinct in the Wild, Critically Endangered (extremely high risk of extinction in the wild), Endangered (high risk of extinction in the wild), Vulnerable (high risk of endangerment in the wild), Near Threatened (likely to become endangered in the near term), and Least Concern (lowest risk). IUCN periodically releases a "Red List" of imperiled species. The 2006 release evaluated 40,168 species, finding 16,118 to be "endangered" (Critically Endangered, Endangered, or Vulnerable). Of these, 7,225 were animals, 8,390 were plants, and three were lichen and mushrooms. The 2007 release added 188 species to the "endangered" list. The 2008 release "confirmed an extinction crisis, with almost one in four [mammals] at risk of disappearing forever."

IUCN has established a broad network of conservation organizations, scientists, and research stations around the world for the purpose of identifying and categorizing the conservation status of animals, plants, and other organisms. Nearly 200 countries have signed an accord under the IUCN umbrella to create Biodiversity Action Plans to protect endangered species.

NatureServe is an IUCN Red List partner that focuses its efforts in the US, Canada, Latin America, and the Caribbean. It uses a 1–5 ranking scale (1 = Critically Imperiled, 2 = Imperiled, 3 = Vulnerable, 4 = Apparently Secure, and 5 = Secure) to assess the conservation of species on three geographic

---

47   Current statistics are available online at http://ecos.fws.gov/tess/pub/Boxscore.do.

48   D.S. Wilcove and L.L. Master, "How Many Endangered Species are there in the United States," in *Frontiers in Ecology and the Environment*, 3 (8), pp. 414–420.

scales: global (G), national (N), and state/province (S). The letter designations X and H are also used to classify species that are presumed to be extinct (X) and possibly extinct (H). NatureServe's data base and classification system is widely used by government agencies, non-governmental organizations, and researchers to monitor conservation status of known species in the region.

CHAPTER 4.
ENVIRONMENTAL ETHICS AND
RESOURCE MANAGEMENT

The discussion in Section A centers on the ecological ethical thinking of Aldo Leopold. Section A.1 reviews developments in the emerging science of ecology, and Section A.2 reviews how changing orientations in ecology influenced Leopold's thinking and how his writings have been variously interpreted by critics and defenders. Section B shifts to a review of how competing ethical perspectives have played out in famous debates related to the protection and management of wilderness areas. In connection with issues related to resource management more generally, positions concerning sustainable resource use (Section C), the moral status of future generations (Section D), and the appropriate role of markets (Section E) and government (Section F) are then taken up in turn. To put these issues and the positions taken in a broader social context, the chapter concludes with a discussion of the preservation/conservation movement (Section G) and the parallel but loosely related bioregional movement (Section H).

A. ALDO LEOPOLD'S LAND ETHIC

The outline of an ecocentric perspective in ethics is widely associated with Aldo Leopold's Land Ethic. Some of his views are not rigorously developed, and have consequently attracted extensive commentary, both negative and positive. Because Leopold was himself an ecologist and incorporated ecological concepts in the articulation of his Land Ethic, it is useful to begin with a brief overview of the development of the science of ecology during his lifetime.

1. Development of Ecology as a Science

Prior to Darwin's *Origin of Species*, the natural world was widely conceived by scientists as mechanistic and deterministic and, as such, essentially static. Although attention to changing dynamics in the natural order can be attributed in Western thinking to Heracleitus and other pre-Socratic philosophers, the study of ecosystem dynamics began to gain scientific credentials during the late nineteenth and early twentieth century out of the growing appreciation of adaptive relationships among organisms and the role played by changing physical conditions. A German biologist, Ernest Haeckel, coined the term "ecology" by combining two Greek words: *oikos* ("home" or "household") and *logos* ("study of").[1]

Frederick Clements, a pioneering ecologist in America during the early decades of the twentieth century, introduced the concept of succession to explain orderly biological changes in Midwestern prairies and grasslands. On his account, succession begins with the development of a barren site and progresses through several stages: arrival of colonizing plant species, establishment of initial vegetation, competition of established species for space, light, and nutrients, replacement of one plant community by another, and, finally, development of a climax community in which equilibrium or a steady state is reached. In the climax stage of development, the composition of species remains relatively stable and species-populations are well adapted to climate and other environmental conditions.

Clements viewed an ecosystem as a kind of superorganism. In his words: "As an organism, the formation arises, grows, matures, and dies ... The climax formation is an adult organism, the fully developed community, of which all initial and medial stages are but stages of development. Succession is the process of the reproduction of a formation." For Clements, the ecologist is akin to a physician: as anatomy and physiology are relied upon to diagnose maladies and restore health to the human body, so the ecologist consults and integrates multiple scientific disciplines to diagnose and prescribe treatments to ensure healthy and balanced biotic communities.

In the 1920s, Charles Elton conducted studies into "nature's economy" or "nature's household" by analyzing the function that various organisms play in the food chain of a particular ecological community. The commodity that is exchanged in this economy is food and its participants ("niche players") are food producers, food consumers, and food decomposers. Photosynthesizing plants

---

1   The German word for "ecology" is "oekologie."

and cyanobacteria are the producers (autotrophs); herbivores, carnivores, and omnivores are primary, secondary, and tertiary consumers (heterotrophs); and bacteria, fungi, and insects are the decomposers (detrivores) that restore nutrients to the environment and begin the trophic cycle anew. Clements observed that the loss of a species critically connected to other species in the food chain results in cascading effects that substantially alter trophic dynamics, oftentimes leading to massive die-offs and the potential extinction of other species.

Englishmen Arthur Tansley is credited for introducing the term "ecosystem" in 1935 and is recognized for the important role he played in the professionalism of ecology as a science. Arguing that the model of the organism is inadequate to explain the dynamics of biotic communities, he and others called attention to the great diversity within and among ecosystems and the need for explanatory models that take into account abiotic factors (e.g., moisture, temperature, light, pressure, wind, chemical cycles), disturbance events (e.g., fire, violent winds, invasive species), and the centrality of food exchanges and energy flows in these complex systems.

Following Elton's earlier work on trophic relationships, the emphasis shifted to energy flows or "circuits" within ecosystems. Attempts were made to model the energy and biomass conversions associated with the trophic exchanges involving autotrophs, heterotrophs, and detrivores. Solar energy is the energy source driving basic carbon, oxygen, nitrogen, water, and other chemical cycles in ecosystems—for example, the breaking of the chemical bonds of water molecules in photosynthesis, the transformation of carbohydrates and oxygen back into carbon dioxide and oxygen in respiration, and the conversion of atmospheric nitrogen into water-soluble nitrate ions and the latter into nitrogen-based proteins. These dynamic models incorporated feedback loops, de-emphasized the distinction between living (biotic) and nonliving (abiotic) components of ecosystems, and had the effect, if not the intent, of providing reductionist explanations of biological phenomena.

Observations of ecologists in the later decades of the twentieth century posed new challenges for the earlier view that ecosystems progress through stages of succession and eventuate in conditions of mature equilibrium. As Worster observed, ecologists were observing "lots of individual species, each doing their own thing" and "a landscape of patches … changing continually through time and space, responding to an unceasing barrage of perturbations, but not seeing progressions toward equilibrium, nor an "emergent collectivity nor any strategy to achieve one." Meanwhile, early developments in chaos theory were emphasizing that systems are sensitive to remote and seemingly insignificant exogenous influences and vulnerable to sudden change and collapse in unpredictable ways. These observations led Worster to characterize the ecology of the time as "ecology of chaos." Chaos theory has since evolved into chaos-complexity theory, with a focus on the capacity of complex systems to self-organize and achieve order and stability, temporarily at least, "at the edge of chaos."[2]

2. Contested Interpretations of Leopold

Aldo Leopold wrote near the mid-point of the twentieth century that "There is as yet no ethic dealing with man's relation to land and to the animals and plants which grow upon it." Leopold's "Land Ethic," the final section of his *Sand County Almanac* published in 1949, represents his attempt to sketch an outline of such an ethics. While his writings were, for the most part, initially ignored by the philosophic community, several early commentators wrote unflattering reviews. Australian philosopher H.J. McCloskey wrote that "there is a real problem in attributing a coherent meaning" to his ethic and English philosopher Robin Attfield called it "dangerous nonsense."

Leopold's most important interpreter, Baird Callicott, explains the conceptual foundations of the land ethic this way: "Its logic is that natural selection has endowed human beings with an affective moral response to perceived bonds of kinship and community membership and identity; that today the natural environment, the land, is represented as a community, the biotic community; and that, therefore, an environmental or land ethic is both possible and necessary, since human beings collectively have acquired the power to destroy the integrity, diversity, and stability of the environing and supporting economy of nature."[3] Callicott explains how Leopold was the heir of the Darwinian contention that ethics grow out of parental and filial affections common to mammals, that these bonds of affection have expanded to larger and larger groups as modes of social interaction have increased in size and complexity, and that, commensurate with the globalization of communications and trade, have expanded into a universal ethic encompassing all humans. Callicott also explains how Leopold, himself an ecologist, witnessed the development of ecology as a science and embraced the view that "land is a community."

---

2 Developments in chaos-complexity theory are discussed in Chapter 1, Section B.3.
3 Baird Callicott, "The Conceptual Foundations of the Land Ethic," in *Foundations of Environmental Philosophy*, Frederick A. Kaufman, ed. (New York: McGraw-Hill, 2003), p. 270.

The next step in the sequence of an expanding, sentiment-based ethic, is, as Leopold saw it, the land ethic. "The land ethic," Leopold wrote, "simply enlarges the boundary of the community to include soils, water, plants, and animals, or collective: the land.

Leopold wrote that "a land ethic changes the role of *Homo sapiens* from conqueror of the land-community to plain member and citizen of it." In his view, such an ethic "implies respect for fellow-members, and also respect for the community as such."[4] Here we have an ethic that has both an individualistic and a holistic cast. Individuals comprising a biotic community count morally, but so also does "the community as such." The good of both members (parts) and the larger biotic community (the whole) ought to be taken into moral consideration.

As an ecologist, Leopold was well aware that what may be good for a few individuals may not be good for a species population or an ecosystem, and what may be good for a species population or an ecosystem may not be good for some of its individual members. For example, while killing a wolf may be good for a farmer and his cattle, it would not be good for the wolf and not good for a species-population on the verge of extinction, and not good for an ecosystem in danger of losing its top predator. Because Leopold and other ecologists of his day called attention to situations in which human goods were at odds with the goods of larger biotic communities, with some writers drawing the conclusion that the good of the whole trumps the good of its individual members, Leopold's ethic was met with wary concern. Opposition was heightened by the use of holistic ideas by some Deep Ecologists to support controversial proposals. A striking example was the publication of a letter published by Earth First! citing the AIDS epidemic in Africa as a fortuitous means of reducing the human population. "If the AIDS epidemic didn't exist," Miss Ann Thropy wrote, "radical environmentalists would have to invent one."[5] Radical views such as this led William Aiken to write that Leopold's ethic implies that "massive human diebacks would be a good" and prompted Mark Sagoff to call Leopold's ethic "misanthropic" and Tom Regan to label it as "fascist."

For Leopold's interpreter, Baird Callicott, all of this is very unfortunate, noting that "Leopold never intended the land ethic to have either inhumane or antihumanitarian implications or consequences."[6] To set the record straight,

---

4   Aldo Leopold, *A Sand County Almanac*, Op. cit., p. 203.
5   Quoted from "Population and AIDS," in *Earth First!*
6   Baird Callicott, "The Conceptual Foundations of the Land Ethic," op. cit., p. 277.

Callicott pointed to Leopold's belief that humans are members of many communities, ranging from families to nations to larger biotic communities, each imposing its own set of moral requirements. "From the biosocial evolutionary analysis of ethics upon which Leopold builds the land ethic," Callicott wrote, "it [the land ethic] neither replaces nor overrides previous accretions. Prior moral sensibilities and obligations attendant upon and correlative to prior strata of social involvement remain operative and preemptive."[7] "Moreover," he continues, "the duties correlative to the inner social circles to which we belong [generally] eclipse those correlative to the rings farther from the heartwood when conflicts arise. ... Family obligations in general come before nationalistic duties and humanitarian obligations in general come before environmental duties."[8] In Callicott's view, then, "The land ethic is not draconian or fascist. It does not cancel human morality. The land ethic may, however, as with any new accretion, demand choices which affect, in turn, the demands of the more interior social-ethical circles."[9]

Writers have questioned whether Callicott is accurately expressing Leopold's position when he contends that family obligations generally come before nationalistic and humanitarian obligations, and that the latter generally come before environmental obligations. But whether or not he was expressing Leopold's view, a more fundamental criticism is that a decision rule is needed for determining whether the good of more intimate communities trump the good of more remote communities when conflicting obligations arise in particular circumstances. Paul Taylor proposed principles for resolving such issues, but his principles were designed to resolve conflicts involving human and non-human individuals (not species and ecosystems), and critics claim that his principles are internally inconsistent and impractical. The relevant point here is that Callicott does not provide definitive guidance for the resolution of conflicting obligations involving humans, animals, species, and/or ecosystems. If the good of members of "inner circles" generally overrides the good of "outer circles," as Callicott suggests, why is this case? Should individual or family or corporate goods outweigh national goods or overall human goods, or the goods of biotic communities? If, as Leopold suggests, the good of ecosystems

---

7   Ibid., p. 278.
8   Ibid., p. 278.
9   For more on this controversy and Callicott's attempted resolution, see Callicott's "Animal Liberation and Environmental Ethics: Back Together Again" and "Holistic Environmental Ethics and the Problem of Ecofascism," in *Environmental Philosophy: From Animal Rights to Radical Ecology*, Michael Zimmerman et al, eds. (Prentice Hall, 2001).

and species sometimes overrides the good of constituent members, how is this decided? Because judgments in such cases are moral judgments, ecological facts by themselves are not sufficient.

Leopold was not unaware that an ethical principle is needed and offered this: "A thing is right when it tends to preserve the integrity, stability, and beauty of biotic community ... [and] wrong when it tends otherwise."[10] Callicott interprets Leopold as asserting in this statement that integrity is an objective value: an inherent value that ought to be at the forefront of attempts to manage ecosystems in ethically acceptable ways. Bryan Norton argues that this is a misreading of Leopold. In his words: "While I agree with Callicott's identification of 'integrity' as the key concept in environmental ethics and management, we nevertheless differ strongly regarding how to interpret this conceptual centerpiece of the land ethic. Callicott believes that, by attributing integrity to the biotic community, *taken as a whole*, Leopold stepped across the line to non-anthropocentrism and declared his moral allegiance to the hypothesis that nature has inherent value."[11] Norton's interpretation is that Leopold was not abandoning an anthropocentric perspective, but rather was making "a *practical* remark on the *proper focus of conservation*," not making "a philosophical statement of what objects in nature are of ultimate value." He continues: "On this interpretation Leopold is not telling us *what to value* in nature, but rather telling us *what to protect* in our practical environmental management (given the diversity of values and scales involved)."[12]

In regard to Leopold's association of right action with those tending to preserve "integrity, stability, and beauty of biotic community," other critics have argued that *beauty* is an intrinsic value that exists in the eyes of human beholders, not a value (an inherent value) independently existing in ecosystems. Others contend that *integrity* is too vague a term and that *stability* needs to be scrapped because ecosystems seldom settle into stable homeostasis. As suggested previously, however, developments in complex systems theory provide a basis for reconstructing new meanings for these terms and preserving the non-anthropocentric contention that values exist independently in nature. Ecosystems maintain integrity and achieve relative stability as long as their

---

10   Aldo Leopold, *A Sand County Almanac*, Op. cit., p. 224–25.
11   Bryan Norton, "Integration or Reduction: Two Approaches to Environmental Values," in *The Environmental Ethics & Policy Book*, Donald VanDeVeer & Christine Pierce (Thomson Wadsworth, 2003), p. 246–47.
12   Ibid., p. 25. Norton's anthropocentrism is discussed in Section C of Chapter 4, along with a general critique of this orientation in environmental ethics.

capacity for self-organization is not overcome by exogenous factors or they do not finally succumb to entropic degradation. Without the kind of ordering latent in self-organization, ecosystems, like all complex organic systems, disintegrate and lapse into chaos. They are indeed subject to disturbance, but as self-organizing entities, they are capable of establishing and maintaining ordered integrity.

The holistic cast of Leopold's ethic underwent a change when the organismic model of ecosystems earlier championed by Clements came under attack by Tansley and others and was supplanted by a thermodynamic model emphasizing flows through energy systems. In Leopold's earlier writing, the role of the ecologist was likened (per Clements) to that of a doctor: as a physician examines and treats patients to restore their health, the ecologist similarly examines and treats ecosystems to restore their health. As the thermodynamic model gained a foothold in ecology, a "healthy" ecosystem took on a more abstract meaning in Leopold's thinking. As Callicott put it, "The maintenance of 'the complex structure of the land and its smooth functioning as an energy unit' becomes the *summum bonum* of the land ethic."[13] But this "summum bonum" does not translate into a moral decision principle or set of decision principles, but seems more a reduction of ethics to physics than anything else.

The holistic perspective that Leopold had in mind is revealed in this statement: "The last word in ignorance is the man who says of an animal or plant: 'What good is it?' If the land mechanism as a whole is good, then every part is good, whether we understand it or not. If the biota, in the course of eons, has built something we like but do not understand, then who but a fool would discard seemingly useless parts? To keep every cog and wheel is the first precaution of intelligent tinkering."[14] Species and individual members of species are good in relation to the role that they play in integrated, healthy ecosystems.

Leopold expressed concern throughout his writings about the accelerating rate of species extinction and the biological impoverishment that results from extinctions. He was also critical of the dislocation of endemic species through the invasion of non-native species, land uses causing soil erosion, the indiscriminate use of pesticides, and diversions and impoundments of water that disrupt and destroy ecosystems. In this connection, Callicott comments that numerous practical precepts augment Leopold's land ethic, including the following: "Thou shalt not extirpate or render species extinct; thou shalt

---

13   Baird Callicott, "The Conceptual Foundations of the Land Ethic," Op. cit., p. 276.
14   Ibid., p. 280.

exercise great caution in introducing exotic and domestic species into local ecosystems, in extracting energy from the soil and releasing it into the biota, and in damming or polluting water courses; and thou shalt be especially solicitous of predatory birds and mammals."

B. Preservation of Wilderness

As much as any recent figure, Leopold called attention to the importance of stewardship based in scientific understanding. Environmental stewardship has multiple dimensions and means different things, including the protection, conservation, preservation, restoration, and sustainable use of natural resources. As discussed below, these terms are given different meanings within the context of competing theories and approaches.

1. Wilderness Debates

An example of different and competing meanings assigned to the terms "conservation" and "preservation" is associated with the debate between Gifford Pinchot and John Muir during the first decade of the twentieth century concerning a proposal to dam the Hetch Hetchy River in a valley adjacent to Yosemite National Park in California. Pinchot was the head of the US Forest Service at the time and the leader of the conservation movement dedicated to wise and efficient use of resources for human benefit. In the case of Hetch Hetchy, he argued that damming the river was the most efficient means of providing much-needed water for millions of current and future residents of the San Francisco area. For John Muir, founder of the Sierra Club and the leader of the growing preservation movement, damming the Hetch Hetchy would be a terrible mistake. For Muir, natural resources were not mere commodities and their value transcended their instrumental value for humans. For decades, Muir had written passionately about the majesty and irreplaceability of wilderness areas, about the intrinsic values they embodied and their spiritual and aesthetic value for humans. Muir's personal relationship with President Theodore Roosevelt played a role in the establishment of Yosemite as the first national park. In regard to Hetch Hetchy, however, the utilitarian and anthropocentric views of Pinchot prevailed and the dam was built.[15]

---

15 Pinchot's utilitarianism is evident in this quotation from his *Training of a Forester* (p. 23–24): "The central idea of the Forester, in handling the forest, is to promote and perpetuate its greatest

A similar debate played out several decades later in connection with a bid by Walt Disney Enterprises to develop the Mineral King Valley in the Sierras as a ski resort complex, a plan that would involve building a highway and high voltage lines across a portion of Sequoia National Park. Soon after the US Forest Service approved the development, the Sierra Club filed suit in a federal court to stop portions of the development that they argued were inconsistent with wilderness preservation, arguing that the Forest Service gave disproportionate weight to economic factors over aesthetic factors and that no weight was given to the well-being of plants and animals and to the intrinsic value of a unique and irreplaceable ecosystem. This time the preservation argument carried the day and the development did not go forward.

Since the Pinchot-Muir debate, conservation has generally been associated with efficient resource use for human benefit, while preservation has been linked with initiatives to limit human use and appropriation of natural resources, with the objective of preserving natural values and enabling natural systems to function on their own. The tension between the two resource management orientations is highlighted in an exchange between Baird Callicott and Holmes Rolston at the end of the twentieth century. In his article, "The Wilderness Idea Revisited: The Sustainable Development Alternative,"[16] Callicott argued that the concept of wilderness preservation is flawed because it dichotomizes man and nature, because it overlooks or understates the impact that indigenous peoples have had on ecosystems around the world, and because it fails to recognize that ecosystems are dynamic and constantly change over time. To resolve the longstanding quarrel between conservationists and preservationists, Callicott recommends that conservation be reinterpreted in terms of the concept of sustainable development and that the concept of wilderness preservation be abandoned. He argues in this connection that sustainable development is consistent with Leopold's published and unpublished writings

---

use to men. His purpose is to make it serve the greatest good of the greatest number for the longest time. ... It was foreseen from the beginning by those who were responsible for inaugurating the Conservation movement that its natural development would in time work out into a planned and orderly scheme for national efficiency, based on the elimination of waste, and directed toward the best use of all we have for the greatest good of the greatest number for the longest time." As Joseph Des Jardins noted in his text, *Environmental Ethics*, Pinchot was progressive for his time, committed to combatting the laissez-faire monopolistic social Darwinism characteristic of much of nineteenth-century American economic life.

16   Baird Callicott, "The Wilderness Idea Revisited: The Sustainable Development Alternative," in *Reflecting on Nature Readings in Environmental Philosophy*, Lori Gruen & Dale Jamieson, eds. (Oxford, 1994), pp. 252–264.

and that it is unfortunate that Leopold has been associated with the preservationist tradition represented by the likes of John Muir. In a rebuttal article, "The Wilderness Idea Reaffirmed,"[17] Rolston addresses the several criticisms leveled by Callicott at preservationist thinking. First, recognition of obvious differences between human culture and wild nature does not amount to the radical kind of dichotomization alluded to by Callicott; humans are part of larger land communities and within these larger communities, nature and culture intersect and interact. Second, early humans obviously did modify the environments in which they lived, but not on the scale and with the degree of irreversibility that humans living in industrialized societies modify the environment today. And, third, it is absurd to claim that ecologists do not know that ecosystems change, or that students of natural history somehow object to changes that occur in geological time. Rolston finds merit in the concept of sustainable development, but not a conception that links sustainability exclusively to economic activity, or one that insists that nature has no value apart from human valuers, or one that supposes that humans can improve upon nature. Rolston also takes exception to Callicott's contention that Leopold opposed wilderness preservation, asking why Leopold would have written the following if, indeed, he was anti-preservationist: "I am asserting that those who love the wilderness should not be wholly deprived of it, that while the reduction of wilderness has been a good thing, its extermination would be a very bad one, and that the conservation of wilderness is the most urgent and difficult of all the tasks that confront us."

2. Wilderness Set-Asides

Today there are fifty-eight national parks in the US managed by the National Park Service under the Organic Act of 1916 "to conserve the scenery and the natural and historic objects and wildlife therein, and to provide for the enjoyment of the same in such manner and by such means as will leave them unimpaired for the enjoyment of future generations." The first national park, Yellowstone, was created by Congress and President Ulysses S. Grant in 1872, followed in 1980 by Sequoia and Yosemite. In addition, 756 Wildernesses have been set aside by Congressional acts covering nearly 110 million acres, an area larger than the state of California and constituting 4.82% of the country's

---

17 Holmes Rolston, "The Wilderness Idea Reaffirmed," in *Reflecting on Nature Readings in Environmental Philosophy*, Lori Gruen & Dale Jamieson, eds. (Oxford, 1994), pp. 265–278.

total land mass, much of which is in Alaska. These set-asides are variously managed by the Forest Service, the Bureau of Land Management, the Park Service (in the Department of the Interior), and the Fish and Wildlife Service (in the Department of Agriculture) under the umbrella of the Wilderness Act signed into law in 1964 (creating the National Wilderness Preservation System). The first administratively protected wilderness area in the US was the Gila National Forest in 1922, whose management strategy was developed principally by Aldo Leopold. The Eastern Wilderness Act of 1975 relaxed the definition of "wilderness" given in the Wilderness Act (as "an area where the earth and its community of life are untrammeled by man, where man himself is a visitor who does not remain"), thus permitting the inclusion of areas that could be returned to a "primeval" state through preservation. The smallest protected wilderness area is Florida's Pelican Island (five acres); the largest is Alaska's Wrangell-Saint Elias (over nine million acres).

According to Conservation International, 46% of the world's land mass is still in a wilderness state, although a report by the International Union for Conservation of Nature (IUCN) and the United Nations Environmental Programme (UNEP) found that only 10.9% of the world's land mass is currently Category 1 protected area, including the tundra, the taiga, Amazon rain forests, the Tibetan Plateau, the Australian outback, and the Sahara and Gobi deserts. The WILD Foundation, founded by Ian Player, has been at the forefront of the wilderness movement in numerous countries and a catalyst for international collaboration.

C. Sustainable Resource Use: The Economic Debate

Classical market economists in the "conservationist" tradition see the central economic question as that of how a growing economy can be sustained: how the production and distribution of goods and services can keep pace with growing demand on a continuing basis, given the constraints imposed by competition for and the relative scarcity of natural resources, capital, and labor. Several key assumptions are made: first, that the resources needed for unabated economic growth exist in abundance and are replenished and renewed by processes in the natural world; second, that the natural environment will be able to absorb the waste by-products of economic growth without diminishing regenerative capacity and resource availability; and, third, when sporadic natural resource scarcities occur, technology is capable of providing resource substitutes.

Other economists challenge this version of sustainability, sometimes by distinguishing between "weak sustainability" and "strong sustainability." "Weak sustainability" is said to rest on the assumption that man-made capital can substitute indefinitely for shortages of natural capital, while "strong sustainability" emphasizes that natural capital is a critical limiting factor of sustainable economic activity. A "weak sustainability" theorist contends, for example, that a lack of fish can be dealt with by building more fishing boats and implementing better fish harvesting methods. A "strong sustainability" theorist replies that more fishing boats and improved technology are useless if there are too few fish in the ocean, insisting instead that catches must be limited to ensure adequate fish populations for tomorrow's fishermen and consumers. According to Herman Daly, growth becomes "uneconomic" and eventually impossible when rates of consumption of renewable resources exceed renewal rates, rates of consumption of nonrenewable resources exceed the rate of development of resource substitutes, and/or rates of waste generation exceed the capacity of ecosystems to absorb and recycle those wastes. When this occurs, Daly maintains, more production results in more "bads" than "goods".[18]

William Rees agrees with Daly. In his view, "Our technological prowess feeds the common belief that humans and their economies have become increasingly independent of nature; in actuality, however, modern high income economies are becoming increasingly indebted to nature and are running massive unsustainable ecological deficits with the rest of the world ... Technology and trade have merely obscured this relational truth by displacing the negative consequences of growth to distant ecosystems and the future."[19] In Rees's view, the root problem is that economies are growing at faster rates than the ecosystems in which they are embedded, and that, exacerbating the problem, waste discharge and pollution back into the environment impairs ecosystem productivity.

---

18 For a fuller exposition of these views, see Herman Daly's "Sustainable Growth: An Impossibility Theorem," in *Environmental Ethics: Concepts, Policy, Theory*, Joseph DesJardins, ed. (Mountain View, CA: Mayfield Publishing Company, 1999), pp. 423–427.

19 William E. Rees, "Consuming the Earth: The Biophysics of Sustainability," in *Earth Ethics: Introductory Readings on Animal Rights and Environmental Ethics*, James P. Sterba, ed. (Upper Saddle River, NJ: Prentice Hall, 2000), pp. 382–386. See also Rees's "Sustainable Development: Economic Myths and Global Realities," in *Environmental Ethics: Readings in Theory and Application*, Louis P. and Paul Pojman, eds. (Thomson/Wadsworth, 2008), pp. 603–611.

Both Daly and Rees suggest that we think about ecosystems in the way we think about financial investment: when one invests money, it is with the expectation that one's capital (principal) will grow and will yield a continuing stream of income (interest). If we live off the interest generated by natural resources to meet future needs and at the same time diminish the capital that generates the interest, we undermine the possibility of a growing and continuing return on investment. As Rees put it, "Sustainable development is only possible if we are willing to live on the interest of our remaining ecological endowment without depleting this endowment."

Rees coined the term "ecological footprint" and estimates that Vancouver, BC has an ecological footprint twelve times greater than the territory it occupies; having overused or overdrawn local natural capital stocks, the population of this region is largely dependent on temporary surpluses elsewhere. The resulting ecological deficit must be met in three basic ways: trading through the worldwide exchange of goods and services, unsustainable exploitation of past resources (e.g., fossil fuels), and unsustainable borrowing from the future (e.g., overexploitation of forests and fisheries).

One of the most historically important definitions of sustainability is that given by the Brundtland Commission of the United Nations in 1987: "Sustainable development is development that meets the needs of the present without compromising the ability of future generations to meet their own needs."[20] Some writers see "sustainable development" as an oxymoron, or, if not, at least as biased toward economic development and the expansion of human wants, and these writers insist that the term "development" be replaced by the term "activity" and that attention be focused on demand reduction.

The 2005 World Summit referred to the "three pillars of sustainability"— social, economic, and environmental—and emphasized the need for the recognition of limits and the reconciliation of demands from these overlapping domains. In this context, much discussion has been directed at the formulation of strategies for "decoupling" economic growth and environmental degradation. The three pillars of sustainability (the "triple bottom line") have been the basis for numerous sustainability standards and certification systems in recent years, most notably in the food industry (e.g., the Rainforest Alliance, Fairtrade, UTZ Certified, and the Common Code for the Coffee Community).

---

20 The Brundtland reference to the "needs of future generations" does not encompass the needs of future generations of non-human species. As biocentric and ecocentric critics have pointed out, the definition is anthropocentric.

In 2011 the International Resource Panel hosted by UNEP warned that by 2050 the human race could be devouring 140 billion tons of minerals, ores, fossil fuels, and biomass per year—three times the current rate of consumption—unless nations can make serious attempts to "decouple" economic growth and environmental degradation through improved economic management, product design, and new technology. The onus, UNEP adds, is on developed countries that consume an average of sixteen tons of these four key resources per person per year compared, for example, to India's per person per year consumption rate of four tons.

D. THE MORAL STATUS OF FUTURE GENERATIONS

The Brundtland Commission definition of "sustainability" references the "needs of future generations." Questions about how we should think about these needs and about obligations owed to future generations have engendered lively debate in the philosophic community over the past forty years. An excellent summary of this literature is provided by Ernest Partridge.[21] He starts by posing some of the problematic dimensions of the question of the moral status of future generations: reproductive and other activity now determines who will and will not exist in the future; future persons cannot be known as individuals (as opposed to the abstract "unborn"), yet much moral theory is based upon respect for autonomous individuals; future persons will have no way of punishing or rewarding us; and one cannot tell with confidence what the resource requirements of future generations will be. He then outlines the philosophical positions that have been staked out: the libertarian, utilitarian, communitarian, rights, and contractarian positions.

The *libertarian* position is that privatization of resources represents the best prospect that resources will (out of self-interest) be wisely managed, and that private owners (not governments) are suitable surrogates of the interests of future generations. Libertarians such as Julian Simon contend that the ability of humans to find solutions to problems will enable future humans to cope with any problems that come their way. Partridge rejects this position, arguing that it is anti-ecological and that it sidesteps the ethical issues posed by the practice in economic analysis of discounting future costs and benefits.

---

21 Ernest Partridge, "Future Generations," in *A Companion to Environmental Ethics*, Dale Jamieson, ed. (Blackwell, 2001). Partridge's article is available at www.igc.org/gadfly.

The *utilitarian* position emphasizes that utility should be understood as what maximizes well-being over a time frame that encompasses future generations. Critics find this position inadequate for a number of reasons. First, if equal distributive shares are insisted upon, the enormously large number of expected future people leaves virtually nothing for current generations. Second, it is argued that there is no rational basis for taking into consideration the well-being of future individuals whose tastes, preferences, and needs we cannot know. And, third, it is claimed that utilitarianism flounders on the question of whether average or total utility should be maximized. Either response leads to what Derek Parfit referred to as "repugnant conclusions." If average utility is to be maximized, Adam and Eve should not have propagated; they lived in a "better" world than a later world of thousands or millions of individuals who, though quite happy on average, were slightly less so than the original people. If total utility is to be maximized, fertile couples living in an already crowded world are obligated to produce children whose lives will, on balance, be slightly happier.[22]

The *communitarian* position advanced by Avner de-Shalit is that we are morally bound to future generations by virtue our cultural links with them through the intergenerational transmission of cultural and institutional arrangements (e.g., the US Constitution) and moral similarity.[23] Critics have responded that institutional and moral frames of reference evolve and that it is questionable whether remote generations will be communally linked with current generations in the way de-Shalit postulates—even though, as de-Shalit emphasizes (as did Heidegger), human experience involves a temporal dimension that extends beyond the present and the span of a lifetime.

The *rights* position contends that human beings *qua* human beings are entitled to certain kinds of treatment. Critics have replied that this claim is not at all plausible if positive rights (rights to be benefited in certain ways) are referred to, but still not plausible if the claim involves negative rights (rights not to be harmed in certain ways) since we cannot know with any reasonable degree of certainty and specificity what will be harmful to future people, or harmful enough to place restrictions on what people may permissibly do now.

---

22 In regard to the utilitarian approach to future generations, Partridge refers the reader to *Obligations to Future Generations*, a collection of readings edited by R. Sikora and B. Barry (Philadelphia: Temple University Press, 1978). In regard to the average vs. total utility problem, he references M. Warren's "Do Potential People have Rights?" in the *Canadian Journal of Philosophy*.
23 For more on Avner de-Shalit's communitarian position, Partridge refers the reader to de-Shalit's *Why Posterity Matters* (London: Routledge, 1995).

Further, it is argued (e.g., by Richard deGeorge) that future generations cannot now be the present bearers or subjects of anything; they can have a right only to what is available when they come into existence.[24]

The *contractarian* approach has been most fully articulated by John Rawls in his book, *A Theory of Justice*. Fully aware that people not yet living are not able to enter into reciprocal agreements, Rawls frames the question as what people *would* agree to if they chose rationally under idealized conditions of choice. For Rawls, such choice would involve choosing educational, economic, and political arrangements that would benefit oneself and loved ones, provided that one chose arrangements under which the worst that could happen to oneself and loved ones could be expected to be better than what could be expected under any alternative set of arrangements, and that one chose as if one were choosing "behind a veil of ignorance."[25] If people in the "original position" chose in this way, Rawls contends that the following "rules of just savings" would be adopted: [1] "preserve the gains of culture and civilization ... [2] maintain intact those just institutions that have been established ... [and 3] put aside in each period of time a suitable amount of real capital accumulation ... [which] savings may take various forms from net investment in machinery and other means of production to investment in learning and education." Partridge observes that there is no direct mention of the conservation of resources in this list, although he suggests that conservation is arguably implicit in Rawls' just savings rules and notes that other theorists have included an obligation to conserve resources for future generations using a Rawlsian framework. He cites Edith Brown Weiss's effort to develop a contractarian approach that applies to all nationalities, not just to a particular socio-political context (as in Rawls).[26]

Regardless of the theoretical framework employed to argue for just provision for future generations, critics raise a motivational problem. If the "ought"

---

24   For a fuller exposition of DeGeorge's argument, Partridge references DeGeorge's "The Environment, Rights and Future Generations," in *Ethics and the Problems of the Twenty First Century*, K. Goodpaster & K. Sayre, eds. (Notre Dame: University of Notre Dame Press, 1979).

25   For Rawls, choosing "behind a veil of ignorance" involves choosing *as if* one does not know certain birth-related circumstances about oneself (e.g., whether one is male or female, white or black, intelligent or not so intelligent), and *as if* one does not know such things when the veil is lifted and one takes one's place in the society about to be ordered by the principles chosen. In regard to intergenerational equity, choosing behind a veil of ignorance also involves choosing *as if* one belongs to generation *x* or generation *y*.

26   For more on Edith Brown's views, Partridge refers the reader to her article in *Fairness to Future Generations: International Law, Common Patrimony, and Intergenerational Equity* (New York: Transnational Publication and the United Nations University), 1989.

implied in moral responsibility implies "can," a legitimate question is whether present generations are psychologically capable of caring for future persons in the way that they are capable of caring for people now living (of withstanding the "strains of commitment," as Rawls put it). Partridge cites the skepticism of Norman Care in this regard. Arguing that we can have no psychological and community bonds of love or concern for indefinite future persons or no sense of common humanity with persons of an abstract future, Care concludes that "certain familiar sorts of motivation are not available to support policies demanding serious sacrifice for the sake of future generations, and we may be discouraged by the further apparent fact that the cultivation of a form of motivation directly supportive of such policies might require something close to an overhaul of main elements in the makeup of our society which influence the moral psychology of citizens." Care's conclusion is challenged by writers who emphasize that moral concern is rooted in feelings of sympathy that extend inter-generationally, and by writers who explicitly and emphatically call for a "major overhaul."

Rawls addressed the question of moral motivation by stipulating that "original position" choosers should choose as if they were "heads of families." Partridge regards this as problematic because it seems to imply that childless individuals are incapable of caring for future generations and because it raises a "time discounting" problem in the sense that parental love for their children extends to grandchildren but diminishes to insignificance within a few generations. Partridge himself contends that "self-transcendent love" is not only possible but represents a healthy and normal process of maturation and socialization. He argues that self-transcending concern for persons, communities, locations, causes, artifacts, institutions, and ideals arises from the social origins of a concept of self, the objectification of values in valued objects, and the universal awareness of one's mortality—all leading to an inclination to believe that these entities will continue to flourish beyond the span of one's lifetime. He adds that alienation and narcissism are clinical abnormalities associated with a lack of normal socialization.[27]

While there is much that we cannot know about the well-being of future people—how could people of previous generations have known about the value to us of rare semi-conducting elements such as geranium, or that our need for petroleum to produce electricity would be greater than our need for

---

27 Partridge's views on the ability of present persons to be motivated to act morally toward future generations is developed in his "Why Care about the Future?" in *Responsibilities to Future Generations*, E. Partridge, ed. (Buffalo: Prometheus), 1981.

whale oil?—Partridge insists that there are fundamental facts that we *do* know: that they will be humans with well-known biotic requirements necessary to sustain their health; that they will be sentient and have a capacity to reason and choose among alternative futures; that, if they are to live and flourish, they must be sustained by functioning ecosystems; and that they will require stable social institutions and the knowledge and skills that will enable them to meet and overcome problems that may occur during their lifetimes."[28]

Given at least this level of understanding of future generations, Partridge concludes by offering a set of guidelines. The first is the common-sense principle of nonmaleficence: the principle that we ought not to inflict avoidable harm on future generations in the form of the kinds of environmental and biotic degradation that we know are harmful to us and have no reason not to be harmful to people in the future. Second, we ought not to jeopardize the opportunity of future generations to meet basic needs. We know that they will need energy and food and we ought not to deplete or otherwise render unavailable or unusable the natural resources that may be needed to meet future needs. This knowledge implies an obligation to leave some non-renewable resources by relying more on renewable resources and taking care not to diminish their capacity for renewal. Third, while we cannot predict with assurance the technological solutions to future resource scarcity, we owe to future generations a full range of options that will enable them to conduct research and development pertinent to the problems they will face. This entails a continuing investment in scientific and technical education and research. Fourth, if serious problems are anticipated (e.g., global warming), we should take actions to prevent or minimize those problems and, at a minimum, should exercise precaution (the principle of precaution) and forego activities known to cause future harms (the principle of just forbearance). Fifth, we should favor policies that work to the advantage of both present and future generations and which are least burdensome to the present generation. Sixth, since none of this will be accomplished unless people are inclined to do "the right thing," adequate investments should be made in environmental and moral education, including the teaching of critical thinking, natural history, human history, basic science, and respect for free institutions. Sixth, we ought to develop institutional arrangements that recognize the legal authority of "custodians" or

---

28   These ideas are developed more fully in Partridge's "Posterity and the Strains of Commitment," in *Creating a New History for Future Generations*, T. Kim and J. Dator, eds. (Kyoto: Institute for the Integrated Study of Future Generations, 1974).

"guardians" of non-human life and future generations to speak, advocate, and adjudicate on their behalf.[29]

E. RESOURCE MANAGEMENT: THE ROLE OF MARKETS

Gifford Pinchot believed that national forests, the minerals they contain, and the recreational and other uses they afford should be managed in a manner that promoted "the greatest good for the greatest number for the longest time." He was referring to the greatest good for humans, and thought this goal dictated using forest resources efficiently. In carrying out this mandate, Pinchot believed that forest managers should rely primarily on the judgment and expertise of professional foresters.

Resource economist Peter O'Toole challenged Pinchot's plea that forest management policies be formulated and executed by trained professionals, arguing instead that management issues should be settled by the workings of a competitive free market. Summarizing his five years of analyzing the activities of the US Forest Service, O'Toole wrote this: "I've visited national forests in every part of the country and have seen costly environmental destruction on a grand scale. Money-losing timber sales are reducing scarce recreation opportunities, driving wildlife species toward extinction, and polluting waters and fish habitat."[30] He continued: "My economic research has convinced me that Americans can have all the wilderness, timber, wildlife, fish, and other forest resources they want. Apparent shortages of any of these resources are due solely to the Forest Service's failure to sell them at market prices."[31]

For O'Toole, two major impediments stand in the way of "letting the market decide": first, the Forest Service is hamstrung by its responsibility to Congress and the competing and sometimes contradictory demands that come from this assemblage and the diverse interests it represents; and second, forest land

---

29 Christopher Stone suggests that such a guardian "might be authorized: (1) to appear before the legislatures and administrative agencies of states considering action with pronounced long-term implications; (2) to appear as a special intervener-counsel in a variety of bilateral and multi-lateral disputes; and (3) perhaps, most important, even to initiate legal and diplomatic action on the future's behalf in appropriate situations." See Stone's "Should We Establish a Guardian for Future Generations?" in a volume published by Oceana (1996). See also his "Should Trees have Moral Standing," in *The Environmental Ethics & Policy Book*, Donald VanDeVeer and Christine Pierce, eds. (Belmont, CA: Wadsworth/Thomson Learning, 2003).
30 Randall O'Toole, *Reforming the Forest Service* (Washington, DC: Island Press, 1988), p. 14.
31 Ibid., xi.

management is driven by its budget, much of which comes from revenues obtained from below-cost timber sales. Public land management does not function within the context of a free market economy and does not rely on markets to work out solutions that will provide the greatest good for the greatest number. If market forces were harnessed, timber sales would reflect their true market value and users of other forest resources would pay in the form of market-dictated user fees. O'Toole cites the writings of resource economists, in particular John Baden and Richard Stroup, who argue that it is a mistake to treat natural resources as "public goods" to be managed for the public welfare by experts within bureaucracies. The rational alternative is, they maintain, to privatize resources and rely on private owners to use their property in the ways that best serve their interests, as these interests are expressed in a free, open, and competitive marketplace.[32]

William Baxter also advocates a market-based approach to the solution of environmental problems: "To assert that there is a pollution problem or an environmental problem is to assert, at least implicitly, that one or more resources are not being used so as to maximize human satisfactions."[33] For Baxter, "there is no normative definition of clean air or pure water, hence no definition of polluted air or of pollution, except by reference to the needs of man."[34] The challenge is to find an "optimal level of pollution": "just those amounts that attend a sensibly organized society thoughtfully and knowledgeably pursuing the greatest possible satisfaction for its human members."[35] Baxter emphasizes the need to think in terms of trade-offs: the costs of reducing water or air pollution should be viewed as what would have to be given up to achieve this objective. The optimal level of pollution is that point at which the next increment of pollution results in a net loss in overall societal satisfaction. For Baxter, economic analysis of transactions in a free market economy is the only reliable gauge of the satisfaction of interests: "If individuals in a society are free to engage in whatever exchanges of resources are mutually satisfactory for themselves, then, at least in theory, every resource in society will be deployed in the way that yields the greatest possible human satisfaction."[36]

---

32   See Richard Stroup and John Baden, *Natural Resources: Bureaucratic Myths and Environmental Management* (San Francisco: Pacific Institute for Public Policy Research, 1983).

33   William F. Baxter, *People or Penguins: The Case for Optimal Pollution* (New York: Columbia University Press, 1974), p. 17.

34   Ibid., p. 8.

35   Ibid., p. 8.

36   Ibid., p. 27.

The kind of economic analysis that Baxter refers to primarily involves cost–benefit and cost-effectiveness analysis: one ought to adopt policies justified by cost–benefit analysis by the most effective and efficient means available. Sophisticated techniques have been developed for determining the point at which further expenditures to secure a benefit result in net societal loss (the Pareto optimum). In the arena of public policy, the goal is to maximize net public benefits: the utilitarian injunction to do what is expected to bring about the greatest good for the greatest number of people.

Market-oriented cost–benefit analysis is pervasive in public policy decision making. The Office of Management of Budget in the White House conducts cost–benefit analyses of federal agency budget proposals in preparing an Administration's budget proposal to Congress, and the Congressional Budget Office similarly scrutinizes legislative proposals. Critics outside government criticize policies such as logging bans to protect the Northern Spotted Owl on the grounds that they fail to demonstrate that benefits outweigh the costs. Cost–benefit analysis requires assigning monetary values to all relevant costs and benefits. While market transactions often directly dictate what monetary values should be assigned (e.g., the monetary value of a board foot of redwood timber or a ton of borax), this is not always the case. When market values cannot be derived for essentially non-monetary values (e.g., maintenance of biodiversity within a geographical region, protection of an endangered species, or the availability of opportunities for hiking and camping in a wilderness set-aside), economists rely on willingness to pay or some other contrived market proxy. In the context of utilitarian calculations, willingness to pay is regarded as an expression of people's wants and preferences when actual market values are not readily available.

The theoretical and practical objections to such an approach are numerous. Mark Sagoff argues that economic analysis rests on a serious confusion between wants or preferences, on the one hand, and beliefs and values on the other. When environmentalists argue that a national forest should be preserved for its aesthetic or symbolic meaning, they are stating a conviction about a public good, not merely expressing personal wants. Sagoff emphasizes that people are citizens as well as consumers; they have personal preferences as consumers, but they also have social and environmental concerns that are sometimes more important to them than their own personal wants. Sole reliance on economic analysis as a decision-making tool is, in Sagoff's view, not only a distortion of human nature but also a danger to a democratic way of life. As Sagoff puts it, "Our environmental goals—cleaner air and water, the preservation of the wilderness and wildlife, and the like—are not to be construed simply as personal wants or preferences; they are not interests to be 'priced' by markets or by cost–benefit analysis, but are views or beliefs that may find their way, as public values, into legislation. These goals stem from our character as a people, which is not something we choose, as we might choose a necktie or a cigarette, but something we recognize, something we are."[37] As citizens, people are rightfully disturbed by economic decisions that leave no room for discussion and debate. "This," Sagoff says, "is my single greatest criticism of cost–benefit analysis."[38]

The plethora of objections that moral philosophers have leveled at cost–benefit analysis is summarized by Ernest Partridge in this way: that by commensurating all values into cash, morality is factored out of policy considerations; that cost–benefit measures aggregate consumer preferences to the exclusion of community/citizen values; that economic analysis is descriptive, indicating what consumers value (economically), rather than prescriptive, expressing what they ought to value (normatively); and that, most significantly for posterity, by measuring value in terms of cash, the future is discounted.[39]

F. RESOURCE MANAGEMENT: THE ROLE OF GOVERNMENT

In a democratic society, government's indispensable role in the formulation and enforcement of resource management policy is that of providing a means of balancing the oftentimes competing and conflicting beliefs and preferences in society. Granted that resource management policies are, or ought to be, worked out in a democratic political process, the following discussion focuses on the role that government has, in fact, played and theorists argue it should play.

The government's role in enacting legislation, promulgating and implementing regulations, and enforcing these regulations has been at the center of actions undertaken to date in environmental protection. The list of legislation in the US is long, generally reflecting a command-and-control regulatory approach: the Environmental Protection Act, the Clean Air Act, the Clean Water

---

37   Mark Sagoff, *The Economy of the Earth* (New York: Cambridge University Press, 1990), pp. 28–29.
38   Mark Sagoff, "Economic Theory and Environmental Law," in *Michigan Law Review* 79 (1981), pp.1393–1419.
39   For a fuller articulation of these objections to cost–benefit analysis, see Partridge's "Future Generations," in *A Companion to Environmental Ethics*, Dale Jamieson, ed. (Blackwell, 2001).

Act, and the Endangered Species Act, among others. Examples of the preservationist "set-aside" approach (while still heavily command-and-control) is evident in legislation creating the National Park system and the Wilderness Areas system.

Few, if any, market-oriented environmental theorists advocate a completely unregulated economy, the kind of nineteenth century laissez-faire capitalism that Pinchot, Muir, and other environmentalists were united in opposing during the early years of the twentieth century. It is generally agreed that regulation of business activity is required to prevent force, fraud, and monopolization and to protect citizens from practices that pose serious threats to human health and safety. The argument has shifted from "no regulation" to minimal regulation coupled with measures designed to harness market forces to prevent serious harms and make business more environmentally friendly. Much of the discussion focuses on how the economy can be "decoupled" from environmental degradation.

The general macroeconomic argument made by Kenneth Arrow is that making companies pay is a surer and more efficient way of protecting the environment and human health than having taxpayers pay in order to support bureaucratic regulatory agencies. The basic reason is that of economic efficiency: private businesses operate in a competitive environment in which market forces dictate outcomes; government bureaucracies operate in a monopolistic environment in which market forces and competition are stifled.

Persuaded by advocates of free market economics, legislation has been passed granting expanded administrative authority to government agencies to implement such market-oriented measures as user fees, cap-and-trade systems for air emissions, and economic incentives to encourage investments in renewable energy and green entrepreneurship. Measures designed to shift the costs of environmental damage from taxpayers to parties responsible for causing the damage include the imposition of pollution and resource extraction taxes. Part of the rationale for making polluters and resource users pay is that such measures will have the effect of raising the prices for goods and services and that this, in turn, will have the effect of reducing consumer demand and associated negative environmental impacts.

Arguments and counter-arguments play out, of course, in a complex intergovernmental system and a rapidly expanding global context. Numerous factors influence government's role: powerful industrial and business lobbies that have a vested interest in sustaining a fossil fuels-driven economy and reducing the business costs of regulation; the national security issues associated with dependence on foreign oil; the influence of environmental organizations that gained strong momentum during the 1960s and 1970s and continue to influence outcomes through lobbying, litigation, education, and other forms of activism; technological innovation (e.g., satellite imagery, smart phones, the Internet) that make decision making in government and corporations more transparent; the rapid expansion of global trade; and efforts at the international level to deal with global environmental problems that affect all people more or less simultaneously (e.g., global warming and dissipation of upper atmosphere ozone).

G. The Preservation/Conservation Movement

The conservation movements in the US and internationally include many individuals and organizations, private and public, dedicated to the preservation of species, biodiversity, and wilderness areas and to making our ways of living more sustainable in the context of the environments in which they are situated. In addition to concerted efforts to preserve wilderness areas, many of these initiatives involve grass roots organizations that focus on local and regional issues, while others involve national and international organizations employing diverse strategies to lobby, educate, litigate, establish land trusts, encourage private/public partnerships, and otherwise encourage conservation and wise land use.

The term "green" is affixed to many of the positions taken and advocated for: green buildings, green economies, green lifestyles, green political parties, etc. The term "sustainability" has also come to be widely employed in numerous contexts ranging from the carrying capacity of the planet to the sustainability of economic sectors, ecosystems, countries, municipalities, neighborhoods, home gardens, individual lives, goods and services, occupations, and lifestyles. The term has received various definitions, standards, and metrics. Given this encouraging but at the same time perplexing use of the term, some writers have commented that "sustainability" is oftentimes used as a "feel-good buzzword," while others see it as representing a dialogue of values that defies consensual definition, as an unfocused but important concept like "liberty" and "justice," and as a "call to action."

Conservation biology has meanwhile evolved as a profession, with a national association (Society for Conservation Biology) which collaborates with numerous scientific groups and NGOs around the world. A key player internationally is the International Union for the Conservation of Nature (IUCN), established at an international congress convened in 1948 by UNESCO and attended by representatives of national governments, international bodies, and conservation organizations. IUCN articulated a "world conservation strategy" in 1980 based on the principle that protected areas and threatened species can most effectively be safeguarded if national and local interests consider it in their own interests to do so and if the development community, including international banks and UN development organizations, is part of the dialogue. The emerging concept of sustainable development provided a framework principle around which the disparate parties and their constituencies were able to coalesce. Six IUCN commissions have been established: Education and Communication, Environmental Law, Ecosystem Management, Species Survival, and Protected Areas. A separate IUCN initiative is the "Global Partnership on Forest Landscape Restoration."

As discussed in Chapter 3 in connection with endangered species protection, the IUCN has organized a global network of scientists and research stations to monitor biodiversity and to identify species and ecosystems most in need of protection. Lively debates arise among scientists and researchers within this network on the most effective ways of preserving critical genes, species, and ecosystems, all components of biodiversity. While virtually all conservation biologists are concerned about diminishing planetary biodiversity, not all agree that the sole focus should be on "biodiversity hotspots," i.e. habitats and ecosystems in which endangered species are concentrated and most threatened. The Nature Conservancy and others contend that priority should be given to "biodiversity coldspots," arguing that population-level biodiversity (biomass) is more critical than species-level diversity in sustaining nature's capacity to recycle nutrients and provide other essential ecological services, and that population-level diversity is thought to be disappearing about ten times faster than species-level diversity.

Various factors contribute to species extinctions and biodiversity loss, including habitat destruction, pollution, disease, resource overexploitation, and climate change. Of these, Nigel Stork singles out the latter as a key driver; in his view, rising temperature on a local and global level is making it harder for species to reproduce. But whatever weights might be assigned to causes, what distinguishes the Holocene (present era) wave of extinctions from those of the geological past is that diminishing biodiversity bears an unmistakable human imprint.

H. BIOREGIONALISM

Bioregionalism has gained prominence in recent decades. Like other move-ments, it is an admixture of theory and practice with a history involving many players and no consensus or definitive statement of what it involves and does not involve. Various labels are applied, including "eco-communalism," "region-based sustainable communities," and "place-based cultural transfor-mation." Doug Aberley gives this general characterization of the movement: "As people reinhabit their home place, a remarkable integration of philosophy and political activity evolves. Place is perceived as irrevocably connected to culture. Culture is seen as connected to past histories of human and ecosystem exploitation. Constraints to achieving the alternative of a socially just and ecologically sustainable future are identified, analyzed, and confronted." [40] Bioregionalism is, he says, "a synthesis of thought, applied technique, and persistent practice that is spreading like the patterns of a growing fractal." [41]

One of the earlier statements of the principles of bioregionalism was given by playwright and activist Peter Berg and cultural historian Raymond Dasmann. In their collaborative work, *Reinhabiting California*, bioregionalism involves "living-in-place" and "reinhabitation." Living-in-place is characterized by these authors as "keeping a balance with its region of support through links between human lives, other living beings, and the processes of the planet ... as revealed by the place itself," and reinhabitation as "understanding activities and evolving social behavior that will enrich the life of that place, restore its life-supporting systems, and establish an ecologically and socially sustainable pattern of existence within it."[42]

In activist terms, Jim Dodge characterized bioregionalism as "resistance" and "renewal": resistance combats "the continuing destruction of wild ecosystems" and "the ruthless homogeneity of national culture," and renewal is achieved "thorough knowledge of how natural systems work, delicate perceptions of specific sites, the development of appropriate techniques, and hard physical work of the kind that puts you to bed at night."[43] For Dodge, "Theories, ideas, notions ... have generative and reclaimative values, and certainly a loveliness,

---

40 Doug Aberley, "Interpreting Bioregionalism: A Story from Many Voices," available at http://jan.ucc.nau.edu/~dss4/aberley1.pdf, p. 38.
41 Ibid., p. 38.
42 Peter Berg and Raymond Dasmann, "Reinhabiting California," in *The Ecologist* 7 (10), pp. 339–40.
43 Jim Dodge, "Living by Life: Some Bioregional Theory and Practice," in *CoEvolution Quarterly* 32, pp. 6–12.

but without the palpable intelligence of practice they remain in the nether regions of nifty entertainment or degrade into flamboyant fads and diversions. ... If theory establishes the game, practice is the gamble."

In 1985, the Sierra Club published Kirkpatrick Sale's *Dwellers in the Land: The Bioregional Vision* in which he argues that machine-based civilization has abandoned the Greek mythological concept of Earth (Gaia) as a self-organizing entity and that, as a result, we face multiple social and ecological crises. Sale says that nature is viewed in bioregionalism as "nested scales of natural regions" and that the bioregional movement is a commitment to decentralized governance structures aimed at promoting autonomy, diversity, and the integration of urban, rural, and wild environments on a regional scale.[44]

Numerous initiatives are afoot in the US to put bioregional ideas into practice. The Planet Drum Foundation began publication in 1979 of its networking periodical *Raise the Stakes*. The Ozark Area Community Congress has been held every year since 1980 to provide a template for locally-oriented and place-based organizing. Similar bioregion-based groups have sprung up across the country (e.g., the Kansas Area Watershed Council, the Rioregional Journal of the Southern Appalachians, the Mississippi Delta Greens, the Wild Onion Alliance, and Pacific Cascadia), each with its own newsletters and "how to" publications. Similar initiatives are occurring throughout the world, including Sweden, New Zealand, Australia, Germany, and other European countries.

In broad outline, bioregionalism views the perceived inability of the nation-state and industrial capitalism to measure progress in terms other than monetary wealth, economic efficiency, and centralized political power as a root cause of much of the social and ecological crises confronting contemporary society. It sees the bioregion, discernible by biophysical and cultural similarities and co-dependencies, as the scale of decentralization best suited to support decentralized governance and to achieve a more just distribution of economic and social goods. It embraces democratic governance mechanisms that are open to participatory decision-making and that are held accountable to standards of sustainability and self-reliance.

These core themes are elaborated in various theoretical frameworks and activist platforms. Ecofeminist themes are sometimes incorporated or assimilated, as are vestiges of thinking from the earlier Deep Ecology movement and the views of social ecologists such as Murray Bookchin, who emphasizes that

---

44   Kirkpatrick Sale, *Dwellers in the Land: The Bioregional Vision* (San Francisco: Sierra Club Books). 1985.

environmental and ecological problems are rooted in conceptions of hierarchy that need to be rooted out. Philosophers such as Mark Sagoff, Joseph Des Jardins, Bryan Norton, and Ernest Partridge lend support to planning and management practices that are sensitive to democratic processes, local values, sustainability principles, and obligations owed to future generations.

Aberley ends his commentary on bioregionalism with this: "To those who hear only a part of the bioregional story, or who attempt to analyze bioregionalism only through the filters of academic of institutional specialties, it may seem to suffer a host of apparent weaknesses, contradictions, or unresolved conflicts. For those who take the time to listen to more of the voices that are speaking about bioregionalism, or better yet participate in the bioregional movement itself, chaos transforms into something that is properly perceived as a persistent and organic growth of purpose."[45] Needless to say, there are powerful forces that work against bioregionalism, but the movement has staying power and will not quietly go away.

---

45   Doug Aberley, "Interpreting Bioregionalism: A Story from Many Voices," Op. cit., p. 38.

CHAPTER 5.
LIFE-CENTERED
ETHICAL VIRTUES

S ection A below provides an overview of contemporary environmental virtue ethics. Section B amplifies one of the book's central theses: that conduct ethics (focusing on value-based principles for morally right decision making) and virtue ethics (focusing on human ideals, the moral virtues they imply, and the cultivation of virtues) are mutually reinforcing and needed components of a complete ethic. Section C further explores the virtues of respect, responsibility, humility, and gratitude, introduced in Chapter 1 as primary environmental virtues. Attention is given to the analysis of these four virtues by various virtue theorists and their relationship to other virtues emphasized in the virtue ethics literature. The concluding section, Section D, discusses the important roles that education, media news reporting, and religious practice are playing, or ought to play, in the cultivation of environmental virtue.

A. Environmental Virtue Ethics: An Overview

In her book, *Dirty Virtues*,[1] Louke van Wensveen provides an excellent primer on the field of "dirty" (environmental) virtue ethics. She observes that there is a seeming reticence on the part of many ecowriters today to identify with the virtue ethics tradition of the past. She says, "I have yet to come across a piece of ecologically sensitive philosophy, theology, or ethics that does not in some way

---

1   Louke van Wensveen, *Dirty Virtues: The Emergence of Ecological Virtue Ethics* (Amherst, N.Y: Prometheus Books, 2000).

incorporate virtue language. Ecological virtue language turns up in the writings of social ecologists as well as deep ecologists, bioregionalists as well as animal rights activists, creation theologians as well as environmental philosophers, mainstream theologians as well as radical ecofeminists." She outlines what she believes are reasons for this "virtue blindness." One is that ethics in general over the past two centuries has focused on rights, values, duties, principles, and consequentialist arguments, with relatively little attention given to virtue ethics. A second reason is that renewed interest in virtue ethics in the middle part of the twentieth century occurred about the same time that environmental ethics began to take shape as a new field of inquiry, with the two developing more or less independently. A third reason is that "the terms 'virtue' and 'vice' carry the stigma of sounding old-fashioned, preachy, and self-righteous."

What, then, accounts for attempts to analyze environmental and ecological problems using forthright virtue ethics concepts and terminology? In Wensveen's view, it is because many "ecologically-minded" people are very worried about the environmental and ecological devastation that they see around them, and because virtue ethics provides a vocabulary for expressing this concern and a commitment to address it. In her view, virtue discourse allows and encourages the integration of emotions, thoughts, and actions; it fits with the ideal of personal wholeness that many ecologically-minded people espouse; it depends on narratives, vision, and the power of examples; it fits with the preference of many ecologically-minded people for change through conviction rather than coercion; and it provides rich expression to many different facets of human experience.

Wensveen then makes a number of observations about the current of state of discourse in the field of environmental virtue ethics. Her first observation is that virtue ethics discourse is *integral*. Terminology connoting virtue (e.g., respect, adaptability, benevolence, care, creativity, cooperation, nurture, frugality, humility, gratitude, hope, moderation, discipline, restraint, openness, perseverance, wisdom) and vice (e.g., arrogance, carelessness, competitiveness, greed, contempt, cruelty, domination, indifference, insensitivity, pride, haste, wastefulness) are used to articulate integrated perspectives. Her second observation is that virtue environmental discourse is *diverse*, revealing differences in the worldviews, backgrounds, and characters of ecowriters. This diversity shows up in the configuration of virtues and vices used and the emphasis given to each. She notes in this regard that there is sometimes outright disagreement; one writer's version of "stewardly care" may be found to be presumptuous or to reflect a lack of sensitivity to another writer, or what may be a particularly worrisome vice to one author may seem like a small or misplaced concern to another. Her third observation is that the discourse is *dialectical*. The use of virtue terms can create tensions. While some tensions reflect the infancy of the discipline that need to be straightened out, others, she says, reflect a dialectical richness that ensures flexibility and prevents harmful extremes. Her fourth observation is that ecological discourse is *dynamic*. The language is emerging; its shape is not fixed, and it is connected with evolving realities and discoveries in science. Her final observation is that the discourse is, for the most part, *discourse without a social ethic*. While virtue discourse is intimately tied to visions of human and social ideals and conveys commitment to change, writers in this tradition rarely present developed social change theories. In her view, the discourse "needs to become more integrated with those sections of environmental literature where we do find the development of a social ethic."

In *Environmental Virtue Ethics*,[2] co-editor Ronald Sandler comments that the environmental virtue literature has centered around two basic questions: First, what are the attitudes and dispositions that constitute environmental virtue? Second, what is the proper role of an ethic of character in an environmental ethic? In regard to the first question, Sandler observes that writers have adopted one or a combination of four strategies for specifying environmental virtue: extensionism, considerations of benefit to agent, considerations of human excellence, and the study of role models. In regard to the *extensionist strategy*, Sandler explains that "Extensionists attempt to expand the range of certain interpersonal virtues to include non-human entities. ... For example, if compassion is the appropriate disposition to have toward the suffering of other human beings and there is no relevant difference between human suffering and the suffering of non-human animals, then one should be compassionate toward the suffering of non-human animals." The *human benefits strategy* takes stock of the many material, recreational, and aesthetic benefits that nature provides and argues that these benefits justify not only the disposition to preserve those goods and opportunities but also the character traits that enable one to enjoy and take advantage of them. The third strategy argues from *considerations of human excellence*. Excellence as a human being certainly involves character dispositions that promote community values and good relations among community members. Because humans are members of biotic as well as human communities, the argument is that human excellence encompasses dispositions to maintain

2   Ronald Sandler and Philip Cafaro, *Environmental Virtue Ethics*, Ronald Sandler & Philip Cafaro, eds. (New York: Rowman & Littlefield Publishers, 2005). The authors of this anthology include ten commissioned chapters and four previously published works in the field.

and promote well-being in both human and ecological communities. Sandler observes that the human benefits strategy accommodates religious conceptions of human excellence: "For example, if it is the divinely prescribed role of human beings that they be stewards of the land, the environmental virtues will be those characteristics or dispositions that make human beings reliable and effective stewards." The fourth strategy—*the study of role models*—examines the life, work, and character of exemplars of environmental excellence. "The lives of John Muir and Aldo Leopold, for example, are not just compelling narratives; they also instruct us on how to improve ourselves and our approach to the natural world." Good environmental role models are found in local communities and in many organizations working for the protection, preservation, conservation, and restoration of the natural environment.

Sandler then addresses the second main question posed in environmental ethics: What is the proper role of an ethic of character in an environmental ethic or, more generally, the appropriate role of virtue in ethical theory? Some theorists contend that virtues are simply dispositions to do the right thing. "On this account the environmental virtues are strictly instrumental and subordinate to right action. First one determines what the right ways to act or behave regarding the environment are, and then one determines which character dispositions tend to produce that behavior." In Sandler's view, however, "there is more to how one ought to be in the world than the rules, principles or guidelines of moral action," and more than this, "environmental virtue might provide the sensitivity or wisdom necessary for the application of action-guiding rules and principles to concrete situations." Indeed, he says, "Many moral philosophers have argued that it is implausible and unreasonable to believe that there is some finite set of rules or principles that can be applied by any human moral agent in any situation to determine what is the proper course of action in that situation." Some writers maintain, moreover, that an ethic of character is theoretically prior to an ethic of action: that a substantive account of the virtues and the virtuous person not only informs but is the authoritative source of what action one ought or ought not to perform.

It is instructive to recount in capsule form the views set forth by the authors included in the *Environmental Virtue Ethics* anthology:

> *Philip Cafaro* argues that reflections on the lives of writings of Henry David Thoreau, Aldo Leopold, and Rachel Carson reveal certain commonalities that must be embraced by any environmental ethic worth the name, including putting economic life in its proper place, cultivating

scientific knowledge, extending moral considerability beyond human beings, promoting wilderness protection, and believing in the goodness of life. Cafaro selects four vices—gluttony, arrogance, greed, and apathy—and argues that each is a vice by highlighting the ways in which it harms its possessor, other people, and nature.

Thomas Hill argues that there are examples of environmental behavior that are intuitively improper and this intuition is best understood in the context of an account of human excellence and the dispositions that we ought to express in our environmental interactions. In Hill's view, the question, "What is wrong with treating the environment in that way?" is best answered by addressing the question, "What is wrong with the kind of person who would do that?"

Holmes Rolston warns against casting environmental virtue in too fundamental a role in environmental ethics. For Rolston, natural entities do not derive their value from their relationship to human virtue and flourishing, but rather from the value they have in themselves. After all, Rolston writes, "it is hard to gain much excellence of character from appreciating an otherwise worthless thing." "Our deeper ethical achievement," Rolston believes, "needs to focus on values as intrinsic achievements in wild nature. These virtues within us need to attend to values without us."

Laura Westra, like Rolston, believes that natural value is not derived from the value of humans or human flourishing, even though the human focus is necessary and foundational. She stresses that the cultivation and exercise of moral agency depend on the capacity of natural ecosystems to provide their preconditions, and that virtuous dispositions are especially important in view of the centrality of basic rights discussions in environmental discourse generally and, more particularly, in discussions of international law and policy.

Bill Shaw examines Leopold's land ethic and suggests that, in this context, three "land virtues" are paramount: respect, prudence, and practical judgment. He notes, however, that any character trait that contributes to the land community and promotes its integrity, stability, and beauty is properly a land virtue.

David Schmidtz and *Matt Zwolinski* argue that virtue ethics provides a framework for addressing issues arising in connection with Parfit's "repugnant conclusions," the most notorious of which is: for any number of persons, all with lives well worth living, there is some much larger human population whose existence would be better, even though the lives of its members are only barely worth living. For these authors, an appropriate response does not consist in reformulating the principle of utility or any other principle of right action; the more promising approach is to invoke considerations of character and human excellence and to focus on the kind of person who would espouse marginalizing the lives of the "greater number" for the sake of the "greater good."

Geoffrey Fraz champions benevolence as an environmental virtue. He suggests that such virtues as compassion, friendship, kindness, and gratitude are meaningfully subsumed under the virtue of benevolence and that jealousy, selfishness, greed, and profligacy are vices counter to benevolence. He characterizes benevolence as a "genuine concern for the welfare of another" and suggests that such concern requires "an imaginative dwelling on the condition of the other" and an ability to understand the interests of another. The cultivation of such concern and such ability implies "an important role for the biological and ecological sciences, for nature writing, and for personal accounts of encounters with wild creatures." Fraz concludes his piece with the contention that "in cultivating the environmental virtue of benevolence we can discover who we really are and what it will take to live in a joyous way with the non-human world of which we are a part."

Charles Taliaferro discusses virtues and vices within Buddhism and the theistic traditions of Christianity, Judaism, and Islam. Regarding the former, he discusses mindfulness and compassion toward all living beings. Regarding the central tenets of theism—creation, divine ownership, and providence—he draws connections with such virtues as gratitude, respect, solidarity, and caring and their implications for good stewardship.

Louke van Wensveen considers the traditional cardinal virtues of wisdom, justice, temperance, and courage. Arguing that they need to be reinterpreted and applied in light of contemporary experience, she takes a middle course between clinging to old traditions and jettisoning them entirely. Her discussion focuses on how sensitivity and tenacity are constituents of humility, respect, gratitude, benevolence, attentiveness, and loyalty, and how these cardinals relate to the four traditional cardinals.

Peter Wenz argues that the traditional virtues promote both human and non-human flourishing, and that their associated vices diminish flourishing, and, for this reason, that both anthropocentric and non-anthropocentric ethical perspectives are needed. Each is stronger in combination with the other than alone. Arguing that the two orientations share a repugnance to runaway consumerism, he suggests that the "principle of anticipatory cooperation" is appropriate to individuals living in industrialized countries. This principle "calls for actions that deviate from the social norm in the direction of an ideal that virtuous people aspire to for themselves and others but which do not deviate so much that virtue impairs instead of fosters flourishing."

Ronald Sandler argues that there is a presumption, justified by the virtue of humility, against the use of genetically modified crops in agriculture. He qualifies this presumption by allowing that, in some cases (e.g., the modification of rice to produce the precursor to vitamin A), compassion for those suffering from malnutrition (e.g., vitamin A deficiency) may be an overriding consideration.

In *Ethics, Humans, and Other Animals*,[3] Rosalind Hurtshouse also takes up the subject of environmental virtue ethics. She views what she terms "green belief" as an alternative to principle-oriented utilitarianism and deontology. There are, she says, two distinguishable "green" approaches. "First, we might have an environmental virtue ethics that seeks to articulate and defend green belief in terms of old and familiar virtues and vices that are given a new interpretation when applied to the new field of our relations with nature." The second approach "goes beyond the first by introducing one or two new virtues, explicitly concerned with our relations with nature." In regard to the second approach, she notes that the introduction of a new virtue is a formidable task: "the introduction or

---

3   Rosalind Hurtshouse, *Ethics, Humans, and Other Animals* (Routledge, 2000). Hurtshouse has written extensively in the field of virtue ethics, including her *On Virtue Ethics* (Oxford University Press, 1999). The quotations below are taken from *Ethics, Humans, and Other Animals*.

discovery of an unfamiliar, 'new' virtue would, on the face of it, need to involve the invention or coining of a new term or concept, which named a complex unity of dispositions to act and feel for certain sorts of reasons, and to see and respond to things in certain sorts of ways, which we had discovered, or realized, was a way human beings, given human psychology, could be." And, she adds, "this complex unity would have to be the sort of thing we could conceive as being inculcated in children as part of their moral education—not totally against the grain, but expanding on and correcting some natural inclination(s) they have." This, she comments, would be a tall order and obviously one that could not be accomplished overnight. She does, however, suggest two candidate new virtues: *wonder* and *respect for nature*.

In regard to *wonder*, Hurtshouse says "The putative virtue of being disposed to feel the emotion of wonder the right way, towards the right objects, for the right reasons, to the right degree, and so on is, I think, explicitly concerned with our relations to nature."

In regard to *respect for nature*, Hurtshouse notes that Paul Taylor associated such respect with a set of beliefs that he (Taylor) termed the "biocentric outlook." Hurtshouse finds Taylor's account to be highly problematic. Her critique begins by emphasizing that "adopting" or "taking up" a set of beliefs is a far cry from "being rightly oriented to nature, through and through, in action, emotion, perception, sensibility, and understanding." "That is the sort of change," she says, "that cannot come about just as though, say, reading a philosophical book and deciding to change; it cannot simply be 'adopted' or 'taken up.'" Hurtshouse also objects to Taylor's sharp distinction between animate and inanimate nature. "But," she continues, "if we think of being 'rightly oriented to nature,' not as an attitude founded on an adult's rational recognition of such a one-sentence premise but as a character trait arising from a childhood training that gives us particular reasons for action (and omission) in particular contexts, and shapes our emotional response of wonder, the hard and fast line [Taylor] draws between the animate and the inanimate becomes insignificant." Hurtshouse also thinks that Taylor's normative principles offer only "the obvious prohibitions that even the palest green environmentalist is already living in accordance with." "So, if all we find are obvious prohibitions, but no guidance for further detailed examination, the questions are 'Why not?' 'What's still missing?'" In Hurtshouse's view, "virtue ethics has a straightforward … and extremely plausible answer." What's missing is what virtue ethics emphasizes: that virtues require careful cultivation, that they have an essential emotional component, "that 'being rightly oriented to nature' is but one virtue amongst many," and "whatever blocks virtuous activity also blocks *eudaimonia*."

Hurtshouse's conclusion is that *wonder* and *respect for nature* are, indeed, promising new environmental virtue candidates, and that "Our current task is, thereby, to do what we can to develop these virtues in ourselves and our children, and to adhere to the 'obvious prohibitions' in the hope that we may bequeath to them a world that is not irrevocably spoiled."

B. Virtues, Principles, and Attitudinal Orientation

Attitudinal orientation plays a central role in the morality of individuals and societies and is, it is contended here, an important part of the subject matter of ethics. Attitudinal orientation is formed by diverse elements of human experience, including instincts, impulses, sensations, feelings, beliefs, memories, and dispositions. One's feelings, beliefs, and dispositional inclinations are, of course, shaped by one's participation in family life and the educational, economic, political, and religious institutions of society, but they are shaped as well by one's genetic inheritance and what one encounters, directly and first-hand, in the world "out there," whether these encounters are immediately experienced as pleasing and interpreted as "good" (comforting, enriching, illuminating, etc.), or whether they are perceived as terrifying and interpreted as "bad" (menacing, impeding, etc.). As such, attitudinal orientation is aptly characterized as an interpretive and motivational framework, or as a kind of filter influencing how one "sees" things and is disposed to deal with them. This "seeing" is as much influenced by biological make-up as culture and as much instinctive as learned, as much pre-conceptual as conceptual, and as much normative as descriptive.

An attitude of respect toward nature was characterized in Chapter 1 as an attitudinal complex shaped by felt connections to the land and by feelings kindled by the direct experience of nature's beauty, wonders, and transcendent power; as an attitudinal orientation grounded intellectually by findings in evolutionary biology, ecology, and other sciences that progressively define what Holmes Rolston calls "nature for real"; as intellectual recognition that value inheres in self-organizing processes occurring not only in our brains and our participation in culture but throughout nature; as recognition that these processes and their products have incalculable instrumental, aesthetic, and educational value for human life; and as concern that massively damaging human activities are putting all life, human and non-human, in jeopardy. An attitude shaped by these diverse elements of experience inclines one to regard nature as a totality with respect, gratitude, humility, and a sense of responsibility. These inclinations, shaped by diverse dimensions of human experiencing, need to be cultivated as firmly entrenched behavioral dispositions and recognized as preeminent virtues; they need to be seen as desirable character traits that contribute to human excellence and well-being in a world that humans share with other forms of life, all having a well-being of their own. Virtuous dispositions provide a normative compass and lend stability to attitudinal orientation. Together, they contribute to a rightful orientation to nature.

But virtuous dispositions are not enough in ethics. In addition to virtuous dispositions informed by ideals of human excellence and cultivated by education and example-setting, one needs action-guiding principles informed by a value theory. One needs a map to go along with a compass to navigate the right way, and one needs to calibrate one's compass from time to time to ensure that its arrow points to "true north." The adage in ethics "Principles without dispositions are impotent, but dispositions without principles are blind" puts it succinctly. Without dispositions backing up principles, exhortations about how one ought to think and act are little more than just that: exhortations. Dispositions are needed to think and act in the prescribed ways. But principles are also needed to backstop for dispositions. In the endless situations in human life in which interests collide and dispositions may incline in different directions, priorities must be sorted out and decisions made. What should one do when one cannot be kind or help another without telling the truth, or when helping one harms another? Being disposed to be honest, be kind, be trustworthy, etc. are hallmarks of good character and necessary components of a morally good life, but such virtues cannot by themselves adjudicate conflicts of interest and tell what is actually right when *prima facie* obligations dictate different courses of action. A value theory is needed to define human ideals, to clarify what virtues are, indeed, virtues deserving of cultivation, and to inform the application of decision principles in conflict situations.

Sandler is surely right in his observation that environmental virtue ethics is not derivative from or subordinate to a principle-based ethics. But the view that ethics can dispense with decision principles is also an incomplete answer to the question of the proper role of an ethic of character in an environmental ethic. An environmental ethic is about more than the identification and cultivation of virtuous dispositions, no matter how thorough or how "Aristotelian" virtue definition and cultivation may be. It is sage advice to think of virtues as appropriate balances between excess and deficiency with respect to delineated areas of behavior. It is also reasonable to think, as Hurtshouse does, that thoughtful teaching and example setting enable learners to acquire practical wisdom: to be able to discern and take the "middle path" in decision contexts. In situations in which interests and obligations conflict and virtuous dispositions incline in different directions, however, the middle path is often difficult to discern.

Corporations have developed elaborate policies, rules, and procedures for decision making oriented toward what is judged to be necessary for profitability and return on investment, and it has been an after-thought in some corporations that consistent adherence to these policies, rules, and procedures requires attention to the deliberate creation of a "corporate culture" defined by mission, vision, and values statements, exemplified by role models, and backed up by education and training. The emphasis on fostering an appropriate corporate culture is recognized in many corporations today as necessary to reinforce profit-oriented policy, to avoid the consequences of unlawful corporate and employee behavior, and to be more responsive to interests of multiple stakeholders, not only shareholders. But corporate "virtue," however thoughtfully and effectively it might be cultivated, is not a replacement for action-guiding decision principles and for clearly defined procedures for implementing policies consistent with these principles. In public policy arenas, too, mission statements, policies and procedures, and codes of conduct cannot be dispensed with, even though it is essential that public officials embrace democratic ideals, exemplify professional and personal virtue, and receive the kind of education and training that foster democratic, professional, and personal virtues.

Chapter 6 focuses on the formulation of what are regarded as adequate life-centered ethical principles and on methodologies for applying them. Without attempting a summary statement of these principles here, it is acknowledged that they would indeed be "impotent" absent an attitude of respect for nature backing them up: an attitude whose normative content includes the virtuous dispositions of respect, responsibility, humility, and gratitude. Each of these virtues is further discussed below.

C. Four Life-Centered Virtues Revisited

1. Respect

Various authors included in the Sandler and Cafaro anthology singled out respect as a centrally important environmental virtue. Several of these authors observed the close connection between respect and caring and the cluster of virtues with which caring is associated, notably compassion, kindness, and sensitivity. Caring was also contrasted with the vices arrogance, callousness, and apathy. Hurtshouse singled out respect for nature as a candidate new virtue, sharply contrasting her characterization of how this virtue needs to be conceptualized and worked out with the characterization given by Paul Taylor: as an attitude that one "takes up" or "adopts" when one subscribes to a certain set of beliefs. Agreeing that respect is closely linked to caring, and agreeing with Hurtshouse that respecting nature is far more than an intellectual exercise, the following discussion further examines the nature of human caring.

To respect something one must, first and foremost, *care* for or about it: one must have a caring attitude of respect toward it. In physical terms, human caring can be described as a complex phenomenon occurring (if it occurs) in a highly complex self-organizing brain in a body interacting with its environment. In psychological terms, caring can be characterized as positive feeling shaping and shaped by "attitudinal orientation": an integrated complex that includes genetic predisposition (*biophilia*), present experience, memories of past experiences, habits, and acquired beliefs. While one's feeling of care for something is conditioned by many factors, belief obviously plays a major role. If one is taught and believes that something has no inherent or intrinsic value, one will care little, if at all, for the object of interest, and one will certainly not regard it as something *worthy* of respect.

Human caring has a normative dimension, appropriately described as *felt respect*. If one perceives that the object of one's care is threatened or somehow jeopardized, the care becomes a *concerned care*. This felt respect or concern carries with it the pre-conceptual feeling that respectful treatment is called for and a feeling that disrespectful treatment is "wrong." This feeling of "being obliged" is not yet conceptual recognition that one has an obligation to treat the cared-for object in a certain way. If one judges at a conceptual level that one has an obligation to treat the cared-for object in a certain way, one's pre-conceptual inclination to be respectful is a motivating force; the convergence of feeling and cognitive judgment provides motivation for compliance. If, on the other hand, one judges that one does not have any such obligation, one's sense of feeling obliged is muted. Caring generates motivational impetus in a way that mere intellectual assent cannot. It is for this reason that Taylor's account of "respect for nature" is seriously deficient and open to the kind of criticism that Hurtshouse makes of it.

It was noted above that Geoffrey Fraz sees caring as closely associated with benevolence and its kindred emotions compassion and kindness, and that he characterized benevolence as "genuine concern for the welfare of another" and the cultivation of benevolence as "an imaginative dwelling on the condition of the other." Ecofeminists say much the same. Iris Murdock uses the term "attentive love" to describe what is involved in an imaginative dwelling in the condition of the other. One imagines not only how one would feel if one were in the other's position, but how the other feels. When one exercises such imaginative concern, "The direction of attention is outward, away from the self, which reduces all to a false unity, toward the great surprising variety of the world, and the ability to so direct attention is love."

Holmes Rolston emphasizes that not only humans care. Animals and plants care as well, although their caring is not as complex as human care. When we care for or about an animal, Rolston says, "There is somebody there behind the fur or feathers. Our gaze is returned by an animal that has a concerned outlook. Here is value right before our eyes, right behind those eyes," a caring that affects our caring.

Anthropocentic theorists contend that the value of nature consists entirely in its value for human beings; nature is seen as an instrumentality for human well-being and as a domain devoid of non-human values, valuing, and valuers. "Enlightened" anthropocentrism puts a plausible spin on this position by emphasizing that it is important to recognize the manifold respects in which nature contributes to human well-being and to include the well-being of future generations in deliberations about how human–nature relationships should be managed. An enlightened anthropocentrist emphasizes that non-renewable resources should not be "used up" recklessly, that rates of renewable resource consumption should not exceed the rates at which they are renewed, that the wastes of production and consumption should be recycled and reused for further production and consumption, and that non-reusable wastes should not be indiscriminately dumped onto the land and into the water and atmosphere, causing health problems and further diminishing nature's regenerative capacity. An enlightened anthropocentrism recognizes, moreover, that nature enriches our psyches and provides venues and opportunities for aesthetic experience, enjoyable recreational activities, the advancement of knowledge, and the achievement of human happiness and excellence. If an enlightened anthropocentrism entails all of this, what more is needed? Nothing, the anthropocentric virtue ethicist answers, except the kind of education and example setting that firmly disposes people to think about nature in an enlightened way, the wisdom to make environmentally sound decisions, and the strength of character to carry them out.

But a satisfactory environmental ethic requires a deeper sense of respect toward nature than anthropocentrism can provide. What is missing is a deep-seated caring: the kind of caring called for by ecofeminists and a caring grounded in the recognition that products and processes in nature possess and exhibit their own value. If, as Rolston emphasizes, we understand the story of life and tell this many-faceted story as participants, inheritors, and embodiments of processes and capacities that makes life (all life) possible, we will give up the myopia that caring and valuing are human capacities exclusively; we will recognize values in nature, not only the value of nature for humanity. Value resides in nature itself. It resides in the capacity of organisms to survive, adapt, thrive, reproduce, and achieve biological potential in oftentimes perilous environments. It resides in the capacity of genomes to encode and convey information controlling structural and functional development over the lifetimes of living members: a capacity that makes self-actualization and species continuation possible. It resides in the capacity of ecosystems to generate conditions out of which new kinds emerge and in their capacity to enable a great diversity of existing kinds to co-exist, co-adapt, and co-evolve in relations of mutual benefit. These values readily translate into extrinsic or instrumental goods for humans, but they are also goods for the biotic entities possessing and exhibiting them. Surely entities possessing and exhibiting these capacities are worthy of respect in their own right, as is nature as a self-organizing integrated whole.

Deep respect for nature comes as well from the recognition that we are the inheritors of grand achievements in the long history of life on Earth; that we are, literally, highly complex embodiments of capacities and processes that have been handed over to us. As Rolston tells life's story, intelligence and caring are not phenomena associated exclusively with human life and culture. Humans possess information-processing intelligence because simpler life achieved and have refined information-processing intelligence over the evolutionary millennia. Humans care in the complex ways they do because ancient ancestors also cared about their lives, albeit it in less complex ways. Many of the parts of a functioning human body are not "human," notably the mitochondria in the nucleus of human cells generating energy for metabolism per instructions encoded in their own DNA, not that of the host human cells. These and other non-human organisms within our bodies are part of what make us human, no less than our participation in culture makes us what we are. Culture has been superimposed on a biological inheritance millions of years in the making.

2. Responsibility

It has been emphasized that respect requires caring, and that caring engenders a pre-conceptual feeling that one ought to be respectful (show respect) toward that which we care about. Caring has an essential normative component: it carries with it the sense that one ought to be respectful (to take care). Taking re-sponsibility is an ethical "owning up" to this normative inclination and involves the intellectual recognition that one is obligated to do so. Such "owning up" is reinforced by argument and by moral and legal sanctions, but it originates in caring and is grounded in respect. Behavior can be compelled, but respect cannot.

If one believes that a non-human entity is not worthy of respect in its own right, one's sense of responsibility for the harm that one inflicts is bound to be weak, particularly when respect for non-human entities is not a widely held sentiment and social sanctions are weak, or when law and legal penalties do not deter the harm. Developed institutional infrastructure is in place for deterring grievous harm inflicted by humans on other humans and for taking corrective action when prohibited harms occur. In comparison, institutional arrangements for preventing human-inflicted harm to non-human life are notable by their relative absence. The important practical implication of this reality is that dispo-sitional personal responsibility—the cultivation of responsibility as a virtue—is the only viable alternative (in the absence of effective moral and legal sanc-tions) to continuing large-scale environmental and ecological devastation. But this must begin with the cultivation of respect for non-human life, and respect begins with caring. If there is a paramount environmental virtue, it is respect. The telling of life's story is an important part of what is needed. So also is the sense of belongingness that comes from identification with biophysical place, and so also is direct exposure to wildness and the respect that experiences in nature can instill.

The basic problem with an anthropocentric ethics is the claim that only humans count morally and are worthy of moral respect in their own right. If the premise is that only humans have moral standing—that harm to non-human biotic entities does not matter morally unless it matters to humans—one's sense of responsibility toward non-human life is truncated. If, on the other hand, it is acknowledged that other biotic entities in nature have goods of their own which they pursue, and if it is acknowledged that they are worthy of respect because they are value-able in this way—which value-ableness is of value to them—one's sense of responsibility to them and to nature as a whole takes on a very different cast.

3. Humility

Hurtshouse suggests that the cultivation of sensibilities and opportunities to experience wonder is fertile ground for environmental virtue ethics. It is agreed that it is fertile ground, but it is suggested that the case is strengthened if wonder is associated with beauty, awe, and other aesthetic sensibilities that work together in instilling a measure of humility (along with respect) in our attitudinal orientation toward nature. Several of the authors in the Sandher and Cafaro volume reference humility as an important environmental virtue, and Cafaro singles out arrogance as an opposing vice standing in the way.

Humility as an element of an appropriate attitudinal orientation toward nature has been emphasized by many writers in many contexts—certainly by Thoreau, Muir, and Rolston, by scientists contemplating the wonders of the cosmos and nature's intricate workings, by religious teachers reflecting on right religious orientation, by adventurers and explorers in the mountains and on the seas, and by many less illustrious people growing gardens, caring for crops and animals, and attempting to live in harmony with the places they inhabit and call home. Quotations of passages from writers in these various quarters were included in the Chapter 1 discussion of the virtue of humility. As suggested there, humility in its most elemental form comes from the realization that nature's powers and achievements transcend human powers and achievements, and that its history transcends human history. One does not exaggerate one's power or significance when one is immersed in wild nature, when one encounters wonders that one cannot decipher, or when one stands before forces one cannot control. Like respect and other environmental virtues, humility is instilled when one is directly exposed to nature: by the indelible impressions that unmediated experiences in nature can imprint. Such experience may be characterized as a delightful beholding of beauty, a strangely pleasing experience of the sublime, an induced sense of wonder, a feeling of awe, an unsettling sense of foreboding and fear, or perhaps sheer terror. A common phenomenon associated with all of these experiences is that humility is induced and arrogance throttled.

Numerous writers have commented on the folly of the belief that humans have gained the upper hand in life's evolution and are in control of their own destiny and that of other life. Scientists remind us that vast forces such as climate change, continental drift, massive volcanic eruptions, and meteor collisions are "game changers" for all life, that dinosaurs and other dominant species have had their moments in the sun but are now long gone, that the more we think we know the more we realize that there is more to be known, and that it is dangerously arrogant to think that nature can be redesigned and engineered to suit human purposes. We need to live safely and comfortably in our environments and have developed advanced technologies that help secure these ends, but mastery of wild nature is not in the cards.

A person with humility is a person who rightly assesses one's own powers and potentiality (influence, significance, performance, contributions) in relation to ideals and the powers and potentialities one finds around one. Humility comes from "sizing oneself up" when honest comparisons of this sort are made, and is shown when one presents and represents oneself to others with appropriate modesty. Humility is not self-aggrandizement, nor is it self-depreciation or insincere humbling; it is rather a demeanor grounded in the realization that there are powers and achievements in comparison with which one comes up short. Humility toward nature is rooted in the realization that mastery of the natural order is not only a morally flawed aspiration but an illusion propped up by arrogance.

4. Gratitude

Everybody knows and acknowledges in the abstract that nature's resources are *needed* for human survival, comfort, convenience, and enjoyment. Nature is where food is grown and harvested, where water, energy sources, and raw materials for the manufacture and provision of goods and services are extracted, where we like to go for recreation, relaxation, and an escape from the routines of daily life, and where processes responsible for the generation, maintenance, and renewal of the resources upon which we depend occur. For the most part, however, people living in urban environments take nature for granted. Homes, cars, gas, food, beverages, phones, computers, and other household and personal items are purchased from stores, and public and private service providers make electricity, water, phone service, radio and television programs, and

Internet access available. In today's world, there are a vast array of intermediaries between food on the table or light emanating from a light bulb. City dwellers are remotely aware that life's necessities come from nature, but they do not care until breakdowns in delivery systems occur, immediate needs are frustrated, health and safety problems crop up, or natural places that they enjoy and want to enjoy in the future disappear or deteriorate.

People living in cities seldom express gratitude for the land and its bounty. They may be grateful for the food on their table and may express appreciation to a divine provider and perhaps to farmers who grow crops and raise livestock, but the land, its fertility, and plants and animals are rarely included in perfunctory expressions of thanksgiving. They are grateful when power is restored and may express appreciation to parties responsible for its quick restoration, but appreciative reference to nature as the source of energy seldom comes to mind. There are exceptions to this scenario, of course. Urban gardeners appreciate the land and its soils, plants, and pollinators and recognize that their gardening success is owed as much to the vital capacities of plants as the nurture they provide. Also, some people appreciate the flora and fauna of well-maintained urban parks and nature preserves, where appreciation is shown for the naturalness of these places as well as to city officials for planning foresight and the appropriation of funds. People who go outside cities to recreate in the mountains and its lakes and rivers, seek out ocean shorelines for their charm and venues for enjoyable activity, or are otherwise attracted to relatively wild places are grateful that these places are there, even if, as visitors, they may take these places for granted.

The remoteness of nature in the daily lives of urban dwellers is part of the explanation of the general absence of feelings and expressions of appreciation. Another is the all-too-human tendency to simply take things for granted. As Aldous Huxley observed "Most human beings have an almost infinite capacity for taking things for granted." But still another part—a critical part—is that natural things are conceived by many people as not the kinds of things toward which gratitude is appropriately directed. If, as the anthropocentrist contends, nature is conceived as having value only insofar as and to the extent that it has value for humans and is devoid of value in its own right, there is nothing to which gratitude is appropriately directed. One does not show appreciation for something one thinks has no well-being, purpose, intelligence, striving, achievement, or value of its own; one may have a dim realization that good and necessary things come from nature, but there is little, if any, inclination to be grateful for the non-human source and to see it as a gift.

Gratitude as a virtue has a position of prominence in religion and has always been a central dispositional orientation in aboriginal cultures. Along with respect, responsibility, and humility, it is contended here that gratitude as an environmental virtue merits greater attention. The rationale for emphasis on respect applies to gratitude. Self-actualizing organisms in self-organizing ecosystems produce immense benefits for human beings: the food we consume, the raw materials used in construction and fabrication, the decomposition and recycling of organic matter as nutrients and soil, the purification of air and water, etc. These contributions to human life are the products of genetic expression at the cellular level, neural coordination at the level of organisms having brains, and system-generated mutually advantageous co-adaptation at the community level. We are grateful for manifestations of these processes in human life and have no less reason to be grateful for their manifestations in all living beings and the communities they co-inhabit. One ought to be grateful not only for the obvious benefits that ecosystems provide to humans but also for their promise of ongoing creative potential and rich diversity. There are ample reasons for gratitude and there are "things" in the natural order to which gratitude meaningfully attaches. If it is meaningful to be grateful for what an organization does, or for the providence of divinity, it is meaningful to be grateful for life-enhancing capacities and processes in nature *writ large* as well as for the tangible benefits that nature in all of its particularity provides.

D. The Cultivation of Life-Centered Virtues

1. Education

The virtues of respect, responsibility, humility, and gratitude are mutually reinforcing; each is stronger in combination with the others. They constitute the normative foundation of a "right" attitude toward nature. If so, formation of these virtues in an educational context depends on opportunities for learners to experientially connect with biophysical place and acquire a sense of belongingness; to develop an appreciative, science-informed understanding of "life's story" as a basis for understanding ourselves as biological as well as cultural beings and realizing how profoundly humans share commonalities and interconnections with other life, past and present; to get out into wild nature to discover its ever-changing presentations on a micro- and macro-scale; to experience first-hand its wonders, beauty, and sublimity; and to instill greater awareness of how personal choices and lifestyles affect environmental health. An attitude of respect, responsibility, humility, and gratitude toward nature will not take hold in the minds of students unless educators themselves take environmental education seriously and see virtue formation as an important component of what is needed to produce "environmentally educated" students. In this context, it is helpful to begin with a snapshot of the environmental education movement.

The good news is that school systems, primary to post-secondary, are paying attention to environmental education. A notable example of an early initiative to promote environmental studies in school curricula was the "Handbook for Nature" authored by Anna Botsford Comstock of Cornell University in 1911 and her enlistment of support from community leaders, teachers, and scientists to reorient the way science was taught in schools across the country. Following the Great Depression and Dust Bowl of the 1920s, new emphasis was given to conservation education. Modern attention to environmental education emerged out of the larger environmental movement of the 1960s and 1970s and growing societal concern about the health effects of pesticides and other toxic products, radiation fallout, and air and water pollution. A definition of "environmental education" first appeared in *Educational Digest* in 1970 by William Stapp, who later became UNESCO's first Director of Environmental Education. That same year, the first Earth Day (characterized as "a national teach-in about environmental problems") was held and President Nixon signed the National Environmental Education Act, whose stated purpose was to incorporate environmental education in K–12 school curricula. A year later the National Association for Environmental Education was established (later renamed the North American Association for Environmental Education). Passage of the Environmental Act of 1990 established the Office of Environmental Education in the Environmental Protection Agency. Internationally, environmental education gained recognition at the UN Conference on the Human Environment held in 1972 in Stockholm and the resulting Stockholm Declaration. Both the United Nations Education, Scientific, and Cultural Organization (UNESCO) and the United Nations Environment Program (UNEP) have sponsored meetings and workshops in connection with which charters have been signed (e.g. the 1975 Belgrade Charter) and declarations issued (e.g., the 1977 Tbilisi Declaration) outlining goals and guidelines for environmental education.

Environmental education in the US has continued to gain momentum. In K–12 schools, there are science field trips, conservation projects, teaching of "green principles" in "green facilities," and attempts to integrate science curricula with outdoor education and experiential education, sometimes called "science enrichment." Professionally developed videos are used (e.g., the Life on the Planet series and documentaries shown on TV channels such as Nature and National Geographic) and tested lesson plans are made available through state and national associations. In middle schools and high school, there are similar developments, together with more emphasis on basic environmental science and school-sponsored student environmental clubs. In undergraduate and graduate education, there are departments (environmental studies, environmental science, conservation science, ecology, etc.) offering a broad curriculum covering basic science, policy studies, interfaces with economics and other disciplines, resource management courses, etc. Professional associations have emerged, the Journal of Environmental Education has been established, and extensive environmental research is conducted with federal funding.

All of this is encouraging, especially initiatives in the earlier years of education designed to integrate factual and experiential learning through field trips, outdoor learning, conservation projects, and other activities which directly involve students with the subject matter, particularly when emphasis is given to witnessing nature's ways first-hand and learning from nature. If one of the goals of environmental education in the schools is to foster virtuous environmental character traits, young learners must be given the opportunity to have the kinds of experiences that foster these dispositions. If attitudinal re-orientation is necessary, they must be exposed to ideas and experiences that make this a psychological possibility. Teachers as role models are an indispensable part of what is needed. If a teacher attitudinally conveys a lack of personal respect, responsibility, humility, and appreciation with respect to an environmental "lesson" to be gotten across to students, the learning opportunity is sabotaged. Teachers are not the only role models, of course, but in formal educational settings they are the ones that matter most.

As part of students' overall education, it is essential that they are told and participate in the telling of "life's story," in the meaning of this term constructed by Homes Rolston, Thomas Berry, and others. This requires robust science education, including natural history, evolutionary biology, molecular genetics, ecology, and human ecology. It is also important that students acquire critical thinking skills, quickened aesthetic sensibilities, the desire to continue to learn over a lifetime, and respect for intellectual integrity. An important part of intellectual integrity is not resorting to fallacious arguments when they are known to be fallacious and not deliberately misconstruing known facts. A person of intellectual integrity not only refuses to obfuscate and misrepresent, but calls out and challenges those who do. Fallacious arguments and deliberate misrepresentations of fact in attempts to justify ideologically-driven policy positions are serious impediments to solutions to our most serious environmental problems.

The cultivation of moral and intellectual virtue occurs in many contexts, of course. Young people learn not only from teachers in educational systems, but they learn as much or more from parents, religious teachings, and the media.

2. The Media

Based on a survey conducted in 2010 by the Pew Center Project for Excellence in Journalism, "Traditional news organizations are still very important to their consumers, but technology has scrambled every aspect of the relationship between news producers and the people who consume news. That change starts with the fact that those consumers now have the tools to be active participants in news creation, dissemination, and even the 'editing process.'"[4] The survey reveals that 56% of Americans follow the news "all or most of the time, 25% "some of the time," 12% "now and then," and 7% "hardly ever" or "never," findings that match up with previous surveys conducted by the Pew Research Center. Affluent, well-educated, and older Americans are more likely to follow the news "all or more of time," while young adults are least likely to be avid news consumers. In regard to news sources, on a typical day, 78% of Americans get news from a local TV station, 73% from a national television network or cable TV station, 61% from an online news source, 54% from car or home radio, 50% from a print version of a local newspaper, and 17% from a print version of a national newspaper. Six in ten Americans (59%) get news from a combination of online and offline sources, and the Internet is now the third most popular news platform. The survey also revealed that Americans would like more coverage in the following areas: science news and discoveries (44%), religion and spirituality (41%), health and medicine (39%), state government (39%), and local community and neighborhood (38%).

According to the 2011 News Coverage Index published by the Pew Center, news coverage of environmental issues fell from 2% in 2010 to 1% in 2011, about the same coverage given to celebrities and half that given to sports and lifestyle. A recent national poll taken by the Opinion Research Corporation found that 85% of Americans feel the quality of environmental coverage needs

---

4   An analysis of the survey results is available at http://www.journalism.org/analysis_report/news_environment_america.

to be improved. Not only is there scant coverage of environmental issues, there is much room for improvement in how the news is reported. Critics observe that environmental reporters themselves need to be better informed of environmental science and better trained, that editorial preference for topics involving human-interest, prominence, timeliness, celebrity, and proximity screens out environmental coverage or pushes it to the back pages, often with little science content, that the narrative tone of "disaster" can lead to "action paralysis" and create the impression that there are no solutions, and that the journalistic practice of "balanced coverage" is not always appropriate. Boyce Rensberger, director of MIT's Knight Center for Journalism, believes that "balanced coverage of science does not mean giving equal weight to both sides of an argument. It means apportioning weight according to the balance of evidence."[5] Rensberger is an advocate for the subgenre of journalism that puts "fact checking" and the search for evidence at the center of responsible reporting. In a survey of 636 articles from four mainline US newspapers on the topic of global warming published between 1988 and 2002, it was found that most articles gave as much coverage to climate change doubters as the scientific consensus view.[6] Given the overwhelming consensus among scientists on the reality of global warming and its causal link to human activity, many observers find the media's propensity to portray the topic as a scientific controversy and to give disproportionate weight to ideologically-driven "doubters" to be a gross extortion.

Peter Sandman summarizes his research in the field of environmental communications with these observations: "1. The amount of coverage accorded an environmental risk topic is unrelated to the seriousness of the risk in health terms. Instead, it relies on traditional journalistic criteria like timeliness and human interest. 2. Within individual stories, most of the coverage is not about risk. It is about blame, fear, anger, and other nontechnical issues—about 'outage,' not 'hazard.' 3. When technical information about risk is provided in news stories, it has little if any impact on the audience. 4. Alarming content about risk is more common than reassuring content—except, perhaps, in crisis situations, when the impulse to prevent panic seems to moderate the coverage. 5. Exactly what information is alarming or reassuring is very much a matter of opinion. The media audience tends to be alarmed even by the information the experts would consider reassuring. 6. Reporters lean most heavily on official sources. They use

5   B. Rensberger, "Reporting Science Means Looking for Cautionary Signals," in *Nieman Reports Special Issue on Science Journalism* (2002, p. 12).
6   M. T. Boykoff and J. M. Boykoff, "Balance as Bias: Global Warming and the US Prestige Press," in *Global Environmental Change* (2004), pp. 125–136.

more predictably opinionated sources—industry and experts on the 'safe' side and activists and citizens on the 'risky' side—when they need them. 7. Although the competition for journalistic attention is tougher for sources seeking to reassure than for those seeking to alarm, coverage depends even more on a different distinction: skillful sources versus inept ones."[7] Sandman notes that four general biases prevail in both coverage and the responses of news consumers: alarm over reassurance, extremes over the middle, opinions over data, and outrage over hazard.

Various efforts are being taken to improve environmental news coverage. One such initiative is the Project for Improved Environmental Coverage.[8] Its "vision" is founded on three beliefs: public environmental literacy depends in significant measure on media coverage; the public wants more environmental news; and the media have an important role to play in bridging the political and ideological divisions standing in the way of the resolution of problems affecting health, quality of life, and the economy. Its message to journalists has four main points: integrate the environmental angle into other stories and make the connection explicit; make environmental stories appealing to a larger cross section of society; focus more on solutions; and increase the visibility of environmental stories. There are, of course, notable examples of news sources that provide environmental news with these perspective in mind—for example, *Grist Magazine*, *The Environment Magazine*, the Environmental News Network, Environmental Health News, People & the Planet, the Earth Policy Institute, environmental news sections of some major newspapers, online environmental news aggregators, and government agencies relatively immune from political influence.

It is certainly newsworthy that the land, the water we drink, and our bodies contain high concentrations of a large number of toxins, that ecosystems are being destroyed on a large scale, that we are living in an age of human-caused mass extinctions, that global warming is occurring, that grasslands, soils, forests, and pollinators are declining, that aquifers are being depleted, and that fisheries are collapsing from pollution and overharvesting. These and other occurrences of environmental and ecological decline and their causes are certainly

---

7   Peter M. Sandman, "Mass Media and Environmental Risk" at http://law.unh.edu/riskVol5/summer/sandman.htm

8   The advisory group includes journalism professionals from the Society of Environmental Journalists, *TIME Magazine*, Knight Center for Environmental Journalism at the University of Michigan, *Huffington Post*, *Grist Magazine*, *San Francisco Chronicle*, Michigan Radio, and *Solutions Journal*. The Project's website is available at http://environmentalcoverage.org/vision/.

as newsworthy as sports scores and the latest developments in the lives of celebrities. Environmental news is *worthy* because environmental productivity and health is critically important. Given the findings of national polls indicating that Americans want more environmental coverage, there would appear to be a good business reason for increased coverage, but preference as an indicator of sales potential is not the determinant of news*worthiness*.

Media selectivity on what to include and exclude as news and how covered items are portrayed (the narrative) plays an important role in shaping beliefs and attitudes in society. Acknowledged or not, journalists are educators. If so, journalists should be concerned with producing educated minds in the constituencies they reach and serve. Granted that journalists are expected to report, not advocate, this does not mean that they should abandon the responsibility of raising public consciousness on issues of obvious importance to people's lives, future human generations, and other life. If the "balance of evidence" suggests that policies and projects are massively harmful to non-human life and pose serious threats to human well-being, it goes without saying that news coverage is merited, even if actual and potential harm to human life is the organizing theme. Moreover, in reporting on the many newsworthy issues, journalists themselves need to get the facts straight and keep each other and news sources intellectually honest, exposing factually incorrect and fallaciously argued accounts for what they are.

It is hoped that journalists regard non-human life and life systems as considerable in their own right and are concerned when developments in human affairs portend serious harm for non-human life, and, further, that a respectful attitude toward nature informs their approach to their professional role as journalists. This is the hope because journalistic news reporting plays a central role in shaping how society as a whole is oriented toward nature, and because personal attitudinal orientation influences what journalists write about and how narratives are crafted. At the least, it is hoped that media coverage and presentation does not undermine a broader societal shift toward a more enlightened attitudinal orientation toward nature. Albert Schweitzer emphasized that professionals (philosophers among them) have the responsibility of shaping a *Weltanschauung* capable of sustaining life and civilization. This is perhaps regarded as "old fashioned" talk today—but is a central thesis of this book.

3. Religion

Recent attention within religious and spiritual traditions to environmental problems and to a rethinking of the relationship of humans to the natural order is producing new theological interpretations, concerned responses of religious leaders, active engagement adding up to movement proportions, and a spate of interest in academia with new degree programs, conferences, journals, and publications. The impetus can be characterized as "religious environmentalism," where interpretive frameworks and motivation come from established religions and religious practice, and "spiritual ecology," where individuals are inspired by the transcendence of nature itself and see respect for nature as a form of religious expression.

Milestones in the growth of religious environmentalism in the US include the following:

1970

> Release of a policy resolution by the National Association of Evangelicals calling the destruction of nature a sin.

1987

> Founding of the North American Conference on Christianity and Ecology.

> Participation of congregations in the first Earth Day (initiated by UNEP and observed annually).

1990

> Release of an "Open Letter to the American Religious Community" signed by thirty-two scientists and 271 spiritual leaders from eighty-three countries.

1993

> Founding of the Evangelical Environmental Network;
> Founding of the Coalition on the Environment and Jewish Life;
> Founding of the National Religious Partnership for the Environment.

2000

> Founding of Interfaith Power and Light, a national organization promoting energy efficiency and conservation with a membership today comprising more 11,000 congregations in thirty states.

2002

> Launch by the Evangelical Environmental Network of its "What Would Jesus Drive?" campaign.

2005

Initiation of the Sierra Club's partnerships with religious groups, resulting in the publication several years later of *Faith in Action* and *Holy Ground.*

2007

Release of "Climate Change: An Evangelical Call to Action" signed by eighty-six evangelical leaders;

Launch of the Catholic Coalition on Climate Change;

Founding of DC Muslims for the Environment.

2008

Publication of "An Urgent Call to Action" signed by twenty-eight evangelicals and scientists;

Release of the feature-length film documentary "Renewing Hope";

Publication of the Harper Collins Green Bible.

2009

Launch of the Catholic Climate Covenant.

2010

Launch of the Annual Day of Prayer for Creation Care, sponsored by the Evangelical Environmental Network, the National Association of Evangelicals, the National Hispanic Christian Leadership Conference, the Billy Graham Center, Esperanza USA, and others.

Major conferences have been held at academic institutions exploring religious environmental and ecological themes, including the ten-conference series between 1996 and 1998 organized by Harvard's Center for the Study of World Religions and another ten-conference series organized by Yale's Forum on Religion and Ecology. Each program maintains an active website and publishing office.

On the international scene, the Global Forum of Spiritual and Parliamentary Leaders held meetings between 1988 and 1993 in Oxford, Moscow, Rio, and Kyoto to address the importance of religious participation in efforts to address environmental concerns; the Parliament of World Religions held meetings between 1993 and 2009 in Chicago, Capetown, and Barcelona on "the ethics of cooperation of religions on human and environmental issues"; and the International Union for the Conservation of Nature organized a panel on "Spirituality and Conservation" at its World Conservation Congress in 2009.

Roger Gottlieb comments that the religious environmental movement shows itself in new forms of theology that reinterpret scripture and think about God "from the standpoint of earth community." "There have been," he says, "extremely powerful statements by institutional leaders ... and thousands of examples of self-consciously religious people participating in environment activism for *religious* reasons. We have seen interpretations of the Koran that forbid dynamite fishing in Tanzania and of the Torah that question whether or not SUVs are kosher. The World Council of Churches has challenged the 'prevailing economic paradigm' ... and Buddhist monks have organized against Asian deforestation. The Pope has called on us to think of nature as the 'sister of humanity,' and American Lutherans have demanded that the Home Depot stop selling lumber from old growth forests."[9] In commenting on what he sees as common features of the religious response, Gottlieb points out a willingness to engage in shared political work both with other religions and with secular groups and a frequent appeal to universal concerns defined in terms of "life," "the earth," or "creation." He also sees a shared vision of "ecojustice": the realization that justice in our relations with nature affect and are affected by the quest for justice in human society.

Respect, responsibility, humility, and gratitude—environmental virtues emphasized here—are included in the vocabulary of all religious environmentalists and are articulated in frameworks that foster their cultivation and motivate compliant behavior. A person of faith in Appalachia may not be moved by a news article commenting on the adverse ecological impacts of mountaintop removal to expose coal seams but is moved to action when his or her pastor calls it a sin. In all religions, narratives, symbols, and rituals provide orientation for living. When the narrative focuses on the relation of humans to the natural world and traditional symbols are given new or expanded meaning, they become sources of ethical transformation.

It would be misleading to conclude from this overview that sharp disagreements do not exist between and within the many religious orientations on how humans should be understood in relation to broader nature and what stances should be taken on policy issues. Some Christians believe that the world was created some ten thousand years ago, that non-human nature is utterly lacking in spiritual significance, and that, indeed, humans have been given dominion over the rest of creation. Their focus is on individual salvation and the literal truth of revealed scripture. They recoil in indignation at suggestions made by

---

9   This commentary by Gottlieb on religious environmentalism is taken from the Social Science Research Council's *The Immanent Frame,* found at http://blogs.ssrc.org/tif/2008/11/17/the-case-of-relgious-environmentalism/. For Gottliebe's fully developed perspective, see his *A Greener Faith: Religious Environmentalism and our Planet's Future* (Oxford University Press, 2006).

ecotheologians such as Dominican priest Matthew Fox or Protestant theologian Sallie McFague that nature might be viewed as God's body (incarnation), and that centuries of human injury and abuse (crucifixion) urgently call for recovery and renewal (resurrection). They see such suggestions, even if they are offered as metaphors, as direct attacks on the core truths of Christianity and as outright heresy. They also reject the notion that other world religions or the nature-religions of indigenous people offer insights into the human condition and how humanity can get into right relationships with the broader natural order and progress toward a more sustainable future. Expressions of common religious environmental concern have been cited, but examples of anti-religious environmentalism can be noted as well. One example is the twenty-five evangelicals, including James Dobson, who publicly denounced Richard Cizik, then Vice President for Government Affairs of the National Association of Evangelicals, for his support of "creation care" and stance on global warming. But the encouraging sign is that many across the religious spectrum are coming together in cooperative efforts to address serious environmental problems, and effective grass-roots initiatives are occurring across the globe.

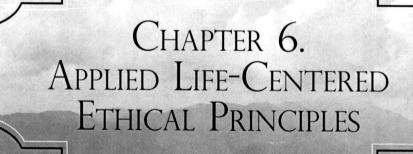

CHAPTER 6.
APPLIED LIFE-CENTERED
ETHICAL PRINCIPLES

A. INTRODUCTION AND OVERVIEW

A complete life-centered ethic includes an integrated conduct ethic and virtue ethic. The previous chapter developed the outline of a virtue ethic. This chapter presents four life-centered ethical principles and a methodology for applying them in situations in which proposed policies and projects portend serious and extensive harm for both human and non-human life. Principles are said to be impotent without virtuous dispositions backing them up: dispositions enabling people to think and act in the way that decision principles dictate. But principles are of little practical value if, in situations involving multiple parties and multiple interests, they cannot be applied with the expectation that they are not being misapplied. A complete applied ethics requires mutually reinforcing principles and virtues and adequate methodological guidance for the application of principles in decision making.

Four life-centered ethical principles are articulated below. The first principle, the *Principle of Moral Consideration*, states that the question of the moral permissibility of significant harm to a morally considerable entity ought to be raised. The second principle, the *Principle of Moral Permissibility*, states that an action is morally impermissible if taking that action can be expected to result in more harm than the alternative of not taking it, and permissible if taking it can be expected to result in less harm than not taking it, provided that no actual right is violated. The third principle, the *Principle of Restitution*, states that an agent of a morally impermissible action is morally required to make morally permissible restitution. The fourth principle, the *Principle of Care*, states that one ought (out of care, not duty) to do what is morally permissible to prevent, mitigate, and ameliorate human-inflicted harm to a morally considerable entity. The meaning and moral implications of each of these principles are discussed in detail. A person who has an attitude of respect for nature will acknowledge the moral imperatives of the four principles and will be dispositionally inclined to follow them.

Application of the four life-centered principles requires the translation of the predicted negative and positive impacts of proposed policies and projects on biotic entities into harm terminology. To clarify how negative impacts are harmful, six harm types are defined: physical damage, resource deprivation, functional impairment, physical pain, emotional distress, and/or life termination. To characterize how positive impacts are harmful, reference is made to the complements of these six harm types: physical integrity, resource availability, functional capability, physical pleasure, emotional well-being, and/or life continuation. Further, negative impacts of a proposed policy or project (P) are characterized as not-P avoided harms and positive impacts are characterized as not-P lost opportunity harms. With respect to the expected impacts of a proposed policy or project, then, a not-P avoided harm refers to conditions that would (if P were implemented) cause physical damage, resource deprivation, functional impairment, physical pain, emotional distress, and life termination, and a not-P lost opportunity harm refers to conditions that would (if P were implemented) enable, enhance, or otherwise contribute to physical integrity, resource availability, functional capability, physical pleasure, emotional well-being, and life continuation.

Also required is a practically useful and theoretically adequate way of gauging the magnitude of harm associated with predicted impacts. In this regard, five harm parameters are identified and defined: extent, onset, duration, proliferation, controllability, and remediability. For each predicted impact, scalars are used to estimate its probability of occurrence and the degree of harm associated with each relevant harm parameter. The magnitude of harm associated with a predicted impact is represented as its scaled probability multiplied by the sum of the scalars assigned to gauge the degree of harm associated with each harm parameter.

Use of the model involves the following: the designation of aggregate entity types to be included in the assessment (e.g. humans, vertebrate animals, non-vertebrate organisms, plants, other organisms, endangered species, at-risk ecosystems); predictions of P's positive and negative impacts of identified populations of each of these aggregate entity types; characterization of the predicted impacts as instances of not-P lost opportunity harm (foregone P "benefits") or not-P avoided harm (avoided P "costs"); estimates (using scalars) of the probability of occurrence of each predicted impact; and estimates (using scalars) of the degree of harm associated with each relevant harm parameter. Given these *inputs*, the model computes harm magnitude (per predicted impact) and several harm indices, including, at the policy/project level, a project benefit/cost ratio. If the ratio is not greater that 1.0, P is judged to be morally impermissible. If the ratio is greater than 1.0, P is judged to be morally permissible, provided that an actual right is not violated. The benefit/cost calculations and the meaning and practical significance of the no-rights-violation requirement is discussed at length subsequently.

Since the reliability of the computed indices depends on the reliability of the model's input values, a suggested approach for obtaining and validating model inputs is then outlined: an approach that elicits and refines expert opinion in multiple rounds of inquiry utilizing structured questionnaires and selected feedback from previous round results. The model permits permissibility determinations of proposed policies and projects, where the choice alternatives are acting or not acting on the proposal in question (P or not-P). The model can also be used to analyze "what if" modifications by making appropriate modifications of original (baseline) input values. It can also be used to evaluate alternative courses of action, where the choice is that of P or Q or R. It also permits value weighting. In this connection, detailed consideration is given to a weighting approach that is consistent with the Principle of Moral Consideration and avoids morally unacceptable inter-species bias.

The chapter concludes with a discussion of model uses and how the proposed principles and methods for applying them reconcile some of the theoretical and practical differences between and among the anthropocentric, animal, biocentric, and ecocentric perspectives examined in previous chapters.

B. Four Life-Centered Ethical Principles

1. The Principle of Moral Consideration

When policies and projects are expected to cause significant harm to one or more entities with moral standing, the Principle of Moral Consideration states that one morally ought to raise the question of the moral permissibility of that harm, taking all potentially harmed morally considerable entities into consideration.

The case for the moral considerability of non-human individuals, their kinds, and ecosystems was made in Chapter 2. As discussed there, the minimum level of respect owed to a morally considerable entity is acknowledgment that the question of the moral permissibility of harm to that entity is a *relevant* moral question. The Principle of Moral Consideration states that this question *ought* to be raised when the harm in question is significant. This obligation is incumbent not only on agents of actions expected to result in significant harm to one or more morally considerable entities, but also on bystanders and third party observers. Its applicability to moral agents is grounded in the *principle of nonmaleficence* found in virtually all moral and legal codes: the principle that it is one's prima facie duty not to cause direct avoidable harm. Its applicability to concerned third parties is grounded in the Principle of Care, which requires (as a matter of care, not duty) that one ought to do what one permissibly and reasonably can to prevent, mitigate, or ameliorate human-inflicted harm. A methodology is developed below for assessing harm significance, but definitional and analytical precision is not necessary for a threshold judgment that harm to non-human morally considerable entities is "significant enough" to legitimize the *question* of moral permissibility. As emphasized in previous chapters, a person whose attitudinal orientation toward nature is one of concerned care will be motivationally disposed to raise this question.

The Principle of Moral Consideration requires that all potentially harmed entities be taken into account and that the question of the moral permissibility of the harm involved be raised. This principle is, by itself, silent on the question of how moral permissibility ought to be determined, and silent on what weights should be given to the harms and/or entities involved.

2. The Principle of Moral Permissibility

The Principle of Permissibility has two formulations: first, an action is morally *impermissible* if taking that action is reasonably expected to result in greater harm than not taking it; and, second, an action is morally *permissible* if acting on it is reasonably expected to result in less harm than the alternative of not acting on it, provided that no actual right is violated. The Principle of Moral Permissibility, as stated, applies to situations in which the permissibility of an action is evaluated prospectively. As discussed in Section 3 below, the Principle of

Restitution makes use of the Principle of Moral Permissibility both prospectively and retrospectively.

The Principle of Moral Permissibility directs one to ask the most basic of all substantive moral questions before acting: Ought one to act in a contemplated way or ought one not to act in that way. The question arises in many organizational contexts: Ought a policy be adopted, ought a law be enacted, ought an investment be made, ought a budget be approved, ought a proposed development be implemented, *or* ought these actions not be taken? The question is pervasive in personal life as well: Ought I recycle, drive less as a single occupant to work, buy organic locally grown food, *or* ought I not to do these things. On a personal level, Shakespeare put it dramatically and most fundamentally: "To be or not to be. That is the question."

The Principle of Permissibility directs one to ask whether the total harm associated with taking an action could reasonably be expected to be greater or less than the total harm of not taking it. "Reasonably expected" in this context means that a good faith effort is made to take all potentially harmful impacts on all potentially harmed entities into account and to base permissibility determinations on best available information and methods for making such determinations. The model developed subsequently, together with suggestions for applying it, are regarded as a "best available" approach when proposed policies and projects are complex, resource intensive, and/or portend far-reaching consequences for humans and non-humans alike.

a. Permissibility, the Principle of Utility, and Cost–Benefit Analysis

To clarify what a moral permissibility determination involves and does not involve, it is useful to compare it with applications of the principle of utility and monetary cost–benefit analysis. The principle of utility associates the moral rightness of an action with the goodness and badness of its consequences, where all affected parties are taken into consideration and the like interests of the parties are given like consideration. An action is judged to be morally permissible if the good associated with its consequences is expected to outweigh the bad, and "best" if, compared to alternative courses of action, its consequences can be expected to produce the greatest balance of good over bad. In hedonistic utilitarianism, "good" is identified with happiness, where the latter is associated with pleasure (joy, contentment, satisfaction, and the like) and "bad" is associated with physical pain and emotional suffering. In preference utilitarianism, "good" and "bad" are associated with the satisfaction/frustration of preferences. In cost-benefit utilitarianism, "good" and "bad" are associated with monetary gain/loss. In public policy deliberations (e.g., adopt a new regulation, approve an agency budget proposal, or open public lands to oil and gas development), the principle of utility is typically linked to cost–benefit analysis, where all relevant benefits (goods) and costs (bads) are taken into account and assigned monetary values. The rest is simple arithmetic: total benefits are divided by total costs to come up with a ratio. If the ratio is positive, a course of action is judged to be justifiable. If alternative courses of action are evaluated in this manner, the best course of action is the one yielding the highest positive ratio.

Not all cost–benefit analyses are conducted in a utilitarian framework, of course. In deliberations about what is best for a particular organization (e.g., a business, a university, or a nation), only the monetary costs and benefits to that organization are typically taken into consideration. Critics of the practice call for "extended" analyses that take into account the costs and benefits attributable ("passed on") to others. When this is done, "external" costs are "internalized," including the monetary costs attributable to death, injury, illness, and pollution. In effect, the internalization of external costs becomes a cost–benefit utilitarian analysis, with one important difference. In business decision making, costs to the business or shareholder are regarded as having greater weight than costs imposed on other stakeholders; fiduciary responsibility to shareholders overrides any responsibility that may be owed to other stakeholders.

Economists identify the benefits and costs of a contemplated action with the lost opportunity costs and the avoided costs of not taking that action, respectively. This conceptualization enables economists to evaluate decision alternatives in cost terminology alone. To enable an assessment using the vocabulary of harm, a moral permissibility determination can be structured along similar lines: the positive impacts (benefits) of a proposed policy or project (P) P benefits (positive impacts) are associated with nont-P lost opportunity harm (the harm of foregoing benefits if P is not implemented), and P costs (negative impacts) are associated with non-P avoided harm (the harm that would be incurred if P is implemented). Using this conceptualization, six basic types of harm are defined subsequently to characterize how predicted impacts are harmful, i.e., to characterize the nature of the harm. For negative impacts (non-P avoided harms), the six defined harm types are: physical damage, resource deprivation, functional impairment, physical pain, emotional distress, and life termination. For positive impacts (not-P lost opportunity harms), the complements of the six types are: structural integrity, resource availability, functional capability, physical pleasure, emotional well-being, and life continuation. A negative impact is characterized, thus, as one that causes, directly or indirectly, physical damage, resource deprivation, functional impairment, physical pain, emotional distress, and/or life termination, and a positive impact is one that is expected to enable, enhance, or otherwise contribute to physical protection, resource availability, functional capability, physical pleasure, emotional well-being, and life continuation. A test of moral permissibility structured in this way encompasses a greater range of harms than those included in the permissibility tests advocated by practitioners of traditional hedonistic, preference, or cost-benefit utilitarianism. Harms to all morally considerable entities are taken into account, and harms are not limited to physical pain, emotional distress, frustrated preferences, or monetary costs.

b. Avoiding Methodological Bias

Cost–benefit analysis is criticized for its representation of essentially non-monetary values in monetary terms: a reduction that trivializes important disvalues (e.g., injury, death, suffering) and undervalues important positive values (e.g., aesthetic appreciation, achievement, biodiversity). It is also criticized for its anthropocentric and monetary bias. The onus is on a methodology that expresses monetary values in the idiom of harm to make the case that human interests are not misrepresented and treated in a biased manner. To avoid inadvertent bias against humans in permissibility assessments of a development intended to benefit human parties, the opportunity costs of not developing must be taken into account, including not only lost opportunities for developers and investors to gain financially but also lost opportunities of others to benefit from the jobs, recreational facilities, or whatever other benefits that development is expected to bring. But the no-development option potentially involves the "benefit" of avoiding the costs of development, including not only the capital and operating costs to the developer but also the costs incurred by other parties. The opportunity costs associated with not developing must not be overlooked in an assessment to avoid anti-development bias, but neither should potentially offsetting avoided costs be overlooked to avoid pro-development bias.

It is also essential that permissibility determination not involve bias against non-human biotic entities. Such bias is avoided most fundamentally by taking non-human entities into consideration. To guard against bias *toward* non-human entities, it is important not to overlook any benefits that development may portend for them.

It is contended that the proposed life-centered ethical principles are free from bias against any and all morally considerable entities. Actions undertaken to redress, prevent, abate, or ameliorate non-human harm, no less than development projects intended to promote human benefits or prevent human harm, must be morally permissible.

It is also important to note that the question of bias also arises in connection with the value weighting of predicted impacts using the proposed assessment model. An approach to weighting is suggested in Section D that avoids what is argued to be morally unacceptable inter-species bias.

c. Moral Permissibility and Rights

Because situations arise in which doing something may involve especially egregious harm that plainly ought not to occur, even though doing that thing may be expected to involve less total harm than not doing it, the no-rights-violation requirement is essential. While there is growing recognition that humans are entitled to certain basic rights, rights recognition for vertebrate animals and endangered species is highly selective, and, for non-vertebrate animals, plants, and many biotic communities, virtually non-existent. This is problematic in situations where a proposed action might meet the permissibility test but involve specific harms to specific non-human entities that are morally objectionable

It is the position here that all entities with moral standing have two general prima facie moral rights: the right not to be seriously harmed and the right to restitution if such harm occurs. If only humans have moral standing, only humans have these rights. If certain non-human entities have moral standing as well, then they, too, have them. Lest this claim seem too outlandish, several qualifying and explanatory comments are needed. *First*, the general right of a morally considerable entity not to be seriously harmed is acknowledged to have little practical import. Meaningful protection depends on the delineation of specific kinds of harm to specific kinds of morally considerable entities and on the recognition and enforcement of such rights in moral and legal codes.

Second, the right not to be seriously harmed is a *negative* right, not a positive right. Negative rights impose duties on others not to act in certain ways, whereas positive rights require certain others to do what is necessary to provide a benefit claimed as an entitlement. Duties not to harm and to make permissible restitution have negative rights-correlatives, but non-dutiful obligations to prevent, ameliorate, or come to the aid of non-human biotic entities do not.

Third, the right not to be harmed is not viewed here as a "fact" in natural or divine law waiting to be discovered, intuited, revealed, or deciphered by reason. It is, rather, a moral concept whose theoretical and practical usefulness in moral and legal systems is open to challenge and debate. When Jeremy Bentham called talk of rights "nonsense on stilts," he was referring to the claim that rights somehow exist in a divine or natural order, awaiting revelation or discovery. Bentham advocated legal protections justified by the principle of utility and saw such protections as limiting what may be done in particular choice situations to promote the "greatest good for the greatest number."

Fourth, the harm in question must be serious, or serious enough, to warrant rights status, i.e. to warrant the claim that protections are needed to prevent the harm and, in the case of legal rights, to justify coercion and the use of force to enforce compliance. The term "serious" or "serious enough" obviously requires explanation, and this requires a methodology for gauging harm magnitude. A methodology is presented below for assessing harm magnitude and making judgments about when harm is "serious enough" to merit rights protection.

Fifth, the right of a morally considerable entity not to be seriously harmed is a *prima facie* right, i.e., an actual right in a given situation only if other rights are not judged in that situation to take precedence over it. When *prima facie* rights conflict in a particular situation, the position here is that the conflict should be resolved by appeal to the Principle of Permissibility, where the prevailing right would be that right whose violation would involve less total harm.

Sixth, the recognition of action-constraining *prima facie* rights is important in an ethics whose set of principles does not include a principle of distributive justice, i.e. a principle that speaks to how the costs and benefits of actions ought to be *distributed* among the parties that stand to be affected negatively or positively. The set of ethical principles proposed here does not include a principle of distributive justice, but in the context of a life-centered ethic this is not viewed as a flaw. It is contended that a principle of fair distribution is not useful in an ethics that takes all morally considerable entities into consideration, potentially millions of species-populations that can be harmed in manifold and diverse ways. Rather, the focus should be on rights protections whose intent is to avoid the most serious and egregious harms, not an approach that attempts to delineate what constitutes fairness in the distribution of harms among potentially very large human and non-human populations. Paul Taylor's biocentric ethics includes a principle of distributive justice, saying, in effect, that shares of a scarce resource (brought about by human action) should be allocated equally among human and non-human species-populations that depend for their survival and well-being on that resource. This principle has been roundly criticized in the literature and is regarded here as unworkable in a life-centered ethic.

The concept of rights plays a central role in contemporary moral discourse and in the progress made over the past century in combating racial, gender, ethnic, and other forms of discrimination against humans. This progress has been fueled and sustained by a growing consensus that all human beings have inherent worth and are deserving of moral respect. Some writers view the question of rights for non-human entities as a "red herring." But, given the central role that rights claims have played and continue to play in moral reform and moral discourse generally, the position here is that arguments making the case for expanded rights protection to non-human biotic entities—arguments grounded in the recognition that non-human biotic entities are morally considerable in their own right—are warranted and needed. Again, the reference is to negative rights not to be harmed in certain ways; positive rights claims for non-human biotic entities would indeed be a "red herring."

Christopher Stone makes a plea for an expanded recognition of non-human legal rights. Whereas only landowning white adult males enjoyed legal rights two centuries ago in the US, Stone notes that legal standing now extends to non-landowners, women, blacks, Native Americans, and such things as corporations, trusts, cities, and nations. He contends that the time has come to extend legal rights protection to non-human entities and for courts to appoint guardian-attorneys to represent their interests in national and international courts of law. For this to occur, Stone says, the entity must be such that "first, legal actions can be instituted *at its behest*"; ... "second, in determining the granting of legal relief, a court must take *injury to it* into account; and, third, that relief must run to the *benefit of it.*"[1]

3. The Principle of Restitution

The Principle of Restitution states that one morally ought to make morally permissible restitution for the harms caused by morally impermissible actions.

If an action is judged to be impermissible because a rights violation is involved, the duty to make permissible restitution seems immune to challenge because it, too, is grounded in a fundamental precept embraced by all developed

---

1   Christopher Stone, "Should Trees Have Standing? Toward Legal Rights for Natural Objects," in *Environmental Ethics: Readings in Theory and Application*, Louis P. Pojman, ed. (Wadsworth, 2000), p. 264.

codes of conduct: the idea that, when someone is wronged by the wrongdoing of another, the wrongdoer has a duty to make restitution to the party wronged and, correlatively, the party wronged has a right to restitution. Two qualifications are generally made: the wrongdoing is not trivial and the restitution made is proportional to the wrongdoing. Provisions exist in developed systems of law for administering remedies for violations of a wide array of recognized human rights, but the situation is starkly different in regard to non-human protections. Few non-human rights are recognized and scant institutional means are available to enforce compliance and provide avenues of recourse when violations occur.

Appropriate restitution for non-human harm obviously depends on the type of entity harmed, the nature and seriousness of the harm, and a host of other factors. In general, restitution involving non-human lives and life systems might take several forms:

Restoration: Attempting to restore lands or ecosystems to conditions similar to those that existed before they were disturbed or modified, or to restore processes and conditions the disruption, destruction, or impairment of which have deprived life and life systems of what is needed for growth, development, or natural functioning.

Repair: Attempting to repair what has been broken, replace damaged parts, restore structural integrity, or provide functionally equivalent substitutes.

Emergency aid: Administering emergency aid to prevent death, extinction, or ecosystem destruction, including medical aid when imminent terminal harm is human-inflicted.

In-kind compensation: Making equivalent compensation to entities when restitution cannot be made to the entities directly harmed. For example: if an animal is impermissibly injured or killed, taking steps to prevent comparable injury or death to other members of its kind; if a species is on the brink of extinction as a result of human activity and cannot be saved, saving another endangered species; if a fishery has been so overharvested that it cannot be restored, restoring another depleted fishery; if an ecosystem or wilderness area has been so disrupted that it cannot be restored to conditions approximating its previous condition, restoring another restorable ecosystem or wilderness area.

Given the general lack of institutionalized means for determining and administering appropriate restitution for human-inflicted harms on non-human life, the most reliable guidelines are found in management practices grounded in the interdisciplinary sciences of conservation biology and ecology as well as "lessons learned" from successful and unsuccessful attempts at restoration, repair, emergency aid, and in-kind restitution. In looking to these practices for guidance, the moral requirement per the Principle of Restitution is that a selected means of restitution not lead to more harm than the harm caused by the human activity for which restitution is due, or that making restitution in that way is likely to cause greater harm than doing nothing at all. If a contemplated approach does not meet this test, the responsible agent is not relieved of the moral duty to make restitution; rather, the responsible agent has the duty to look further and to implement other means that satisfy the moral permissibility test. The duty to make restitution is the duty to make morally permissible restitution, not the duty to select an approach designed to minimize harm.

4. The Principle of Care

The Principle of Care states that one morally ought to prevent human-induced harm to entities with moral standing and in general to improve the conditions of non-human life, provided that such initiatives are justified by the Principle of Permissibility.

Application of the Principle of Permissibility in this context mirrors its application in connection with the Principle of Restitution: permissible personal and organizational initiatives to prevent, abate, remedy, or ameliorate human-caused harm are not permissible if taking those initiatives could be expected to result in more harm than not taking them, or if such initiatives lead to harms greater than the harms that they are intended to prevent, abate, remedy, or ameliorate. Examples of unjustified "help" are protecting wild animals from their natural prey, feeding wild animals, or otherwise creating human dependencies that jeopardize their chances of surviving in the wild. Here, again, wildlife and land management practices formulated in conservation biology and ecology provide guidelines for applying the Principle of Permissibility.

For a person whose attitudinal orientation is one of respect for nature, an ethics that does not recognize positive obligations to protect and promote non-human well-being is an incomplete ethic; respect for nature calls for more than doing what is morally permissible or minimally morally required. Paul Taylor's and James Sterba's biocentric principles do not entail positive moral obligations, but Albert Schweitzer's principle of reverence for life does. In Schweitzer's words: "The fundamental principle of morality is that good consists in maintaining, promoting, and enhancing life, and that evil consists in destroying, injuring, and limiting life."

Critical masses of individuals and organizations motivated out of respect to prevent and ameliorate human-inflicted harm—and motivated as well to ensure that good intentions do not create unintended greater harm—are needed for numerous reasons: to provide a voice for life that otherwise would have no voice in decision- and policy-making forums; to serve as "watchdogs" calling attention to grievous harms and holding responsible parties accountable; to personally do more than what is minimally morally required and to backstop for people who shirk responsibility or deny any moral responsibility for non-human life at all; and to provide momentum for additional areas of warranted legal protection. Broad-based expressions of moral concern for animal cruelty and abuse (the animal welfare movement) have led to legal protections in the US and other countries, and concern for human health and safety has led to landmark environmental legislation. Despite these achievements, there has been little momentum for protection of life forms other than primates, domesticated animals, pets, captive animals in laboratories and zoos, critically endangered species, and selected wilderness tracts valued for the scenic and recreational opportunities they provide. People motivated to promote non-human well-being are needed to provide momentum for additionally needed protection.

C. APPLYING THE PRINCIPLES: A MODELING APPROACH

Personal moral decisions are typically unsystematic and usually do not invoke explicitly stated principles and methodologies for arriving at right courses of action. Nevertheless, it is important to consider (informally) questions such as the following: Would acting as I am contemplating acting lead to more harm than doing nothing at all or taking some other course of action? What are the important ways in which other people and the environment might be harmed? How likely is the harm and, if it occurred, how soon might it occur, how long might it last, how likely might it lead to other harms, and how feasibly might it be stopped, reduced, or remedied? Personal decisions and lifestyles are informed and defensible to the extent that such questions are considered, systematically or not.

While personal choice is often informal and unstructured, elaborate cost–benefit and optimization models are employed to inform decisions made in corporate and public policy contexts, particularly when policy proposals and development projects have far-reaching and potentially serious consequences. Such methodologies are designed to assess human and, more narrowly, monetary, impacts. Exclusive use of such methodologies is problematic for reasons discussed throughout this work. To supplement narrowly anthropocentric and monetarily-oriented approaches to decision making, or to address problems associated with the exclusive use of such methodologies, a model for assessing multiple harmful impacts on multiple morally considerable entities is needed.

1. Types of Harm

A satisfactory explanation of the nature of a harmful impact on a particular biotic entity requires a description of a changed condition (brought about by human action) and an explanation of how the change is thought to be harmful. An increase of airborne asbestos fibers is an "impact," but the characterization is not complete. A more complete characterization requires saying how a predicted increase of airborne asbestos fibers is harmful. This might involve saying that this condition diminishes respiration and is potentially carcinogenic, but this prompts explanation of how these conditions (described in technical terms) are harmful. Asking how something is harmful is consistent with what people ordinarily think and care about. When they learn they have cancer, they think about how the cancer and its treatment will affect their lives: what deprivations, losses of functional capability, and levels of physical pain and/or emotional distress are likely, and, above all, how long they are likely to live with and without treatment. While the asbestos example is framed in terms of harm to humans, the general point is that impacts on any morally considerable entity require clarification of how predictions of altered conditions (resulting from human action) are harmful. In environmental impact assessments, negative impacts are typically described in technical terms, often without clear reference to the nature of the harm involved.

For the purpose of developing a methodology for assessing harms inflicted by humans on a wide range of morally considerable entities, six basic types of harm are distinguished:

Physical damage: conditions that destroy structural wholes or parts (breaking, crushing, tearing), that burn and freeze (temperature extremes), or that poison (toxic and corrosive substances).

Resource deprivation: conditions that deprive biotic entities of critically needed resources (nutrients, food, water, shelter).

Functional impairment: conditions that disrupt growth or development, interfere with internal regulatory processes, or impede freedom or movement and expression.

Physical pain: conditions that cause an intense sensation of discomfort (felt pain).

Emotional distress: conditions that cause unpleasant mental states (suffering, anxiety, frustration, loneliness, boredom).

Life termination: conditions that cause the cessation of functional capability and vitality and result in immediate or near-term individual deaths, species extinctions, or the radical transformation or collapse of ecosystems; conditions that terminate self-organizing capacity.

Characterization of the nature of the harm associated with predicted negative impacts is generally straightforward. A negative impact is one that can be associated with physical damage, resource deprivation, functional impairment, physical pain, emotional distress, and/or life termination. Such descriptors clarify how a negative impact is harmful (the nature of the harm involved). To clarify how predicted positive impacts are harmful, reference is made to the complements of each of these basic harm types: physical integrity, resource availability, functional capability, physical pleasure, emotional well-being, and life continuation. Working definitions of these desirable conditions are:

Physical integrity: conditions that protect against physical damage (structural failure, temperature extremes, poisoning).

Resource availability: conditions that enable access to critically needed resources and enable basic needs fulfillment.

Functional capability: conditions that contribute to growth and development, promote health, protect against disruptions of internal regulatory processes, or enable freedom of movement and expression.

Physical pleasure: conditions that occasion immediate felt satisfactoriness.

Emotional well-being: conditions that contribute to happiness, contentment, or a sense of safety, security, belongingness, acceptance, and self esteem.

Life continuation: conditions that promote the continuation of life, kinds of life, and communities of life.

There are, of course, many particular ways in which humans can be harmed. Examples include toxic poisoning (physical injury), unavailability or lack of access to potable water (resource deprivation), paralysis (functional impairment), sensation of extreme heat or cold (physical pain), sadness caused by the loss of a loved one (emotional distress), and life-ending trauma (death). Non-human entities can also be harmed in many (not all) of these ways. The clear-cutting of rainforests to harvest hardwoods, removal of mountaintops to expose coal seams, and the filling in or draining of wetlands to build homes or commercial centers are examples of large-scale projects that result in physical injury, resource deprivation, functional impairment, and mass death to many species-populations as well as physical pain and emotional distress to some of these species-populations.

A few introductory comments are needed to indicate how the above-stated categories of harm are used in the proposed assessment methodology and to clarify what is presumed and not presumed. *First*, it is presumed that the six general harm types encompass all of the major ways in which a biotic entity might be harmed (are "jointly exhaustive") and that they refer to distinct kinds of harm (are "mutually exclusive").

Second, it is not presumed that all harmable entities can be harmed in all of these ways. Invertebrates, plants, microbial organisms, species, and ecosystems do not experience physical pain. Vertebrates feel physical pain in ways comparable to humans but invertebrates do not. Mammals are capable of suffering and experience emotional states such as fear, boredom, and loneliness, but are incapable of emotions involving complex cognitive components (e.g., regret or shame). Also, the intensity of certain kinds of emotional distress is greater in humans because of the cognitive components involved.

Third, it is not presumed that policies and projects can harm an entity in only one of these ways. On the contrary, multiple harms are often involved, sometimes involving complex causal relationships. For example, functional impairment may be caused by physical damage and/or resource deprivation, and itself may be a cause of physical pain and/or emotional distress. When a predicted condition is expected to involve several types of harm, each should be identified. In the model, each is subsumed under the relevant harm type.

Fourth, a predicted consequence of human activity may be harmful to populations within one or more aggregate entity types. A diverted water course might negatively impact numerous species-populations of plants and animals and have the potential to disrupt entire ecosystems. If a predicted condition is expected to be harmful to multiple species-populations within a general entity type (e.g., vertebrates), each predicted impact identifies the species-population impacted and is listed separately. If the same predicted condition is expected to be harmful to species-populations of one or more other aggregate entity types (e.g., Non-vertebrate Animals and/or Plants), each predicted impact identifies the species-populations impacted and are listed separately under the relevant aggregate entity type or types.

Fifth, it is not presumed that predicted conditions harmful to species-populations in any one of six ways are the same. For example, a predicted condition may be resource depriving for different species-populations in quite different ways. What makes harmful conditions comparable across species-populations is not their "sameness," but the scalability of the *magnitude* of those harms along the various dimensions discussed subsequently: their extent, onset, duration, proliferation, controllability, and remediability.

Sixth, the generality of the six harm types is advantageous in most harm assessments of proposed policies and project. The general harm categories can, of course, be disaggregated. For example, Resource Deprivation might be broken down by resource type (e.g., diminished access to water, nutrients, or shelter), and in some assessments initial disaggregation may be useful. The appropriateness of further disaggregation depends on various factors, including what the information needs of policy makers are and how potentially large amounts of information can most effectively be managed.

Seventh, it needs to be understood that the methodology requires the translation of both negative and positive impacts into harm terminology. With respect to the negative impacts of a proposed policy or project on a biotic entity, the translation is straightforward: a predicted condition is characterized as an instance of one or more of the six defined harm types: physical damage, resource deprivation, functional impairment, inflicted pain, inflicted emotional distress, and life termination. Positive impacts are characterized with reference to the complements of these harm types: as a condition that promotes, enables, or enhances physical integrity, resource availability, functional capability, physical pleasure, emotional well-being, and/or life continuation. A negative impact is treated as a harm that would be avoided if P is not implemented, and a positive impact as a lost-opportunity harm (a foregone benefit) if P is not implemented.

It is useful to identify the harm category Resource Deprivation with conditions that hinder *basic need fulfillment*. Various writers have developed comprehensive accounts of human needs. Abraham Maslow, for example, views human needs as emerging (generally sequentially) as part of a developmental process of self-actualization. The most basic needs are physiological and refer to what is required for survival (e.g. the need for food, water, protection from heat and cold, etc.). If basic physiological needs are regularly and dependably met, safety and security needs come into prominence (e.g., the need to feel safe in the presence of others and one's surroundings, or the need to feel that one will not be the victim of future adversities and misfortunes). If needs at this level are consistently met, still other needs press for fulfillment, including belongingness needs (e.g., the need to be accepted by one's parents, friends, and peers) and esteem needs (the need to be valued by associates within the groups and organizations to which one belongs). Higher-order needs are more idiosyncratic and refer to activities and relationships that enable persons to pursue their particular interests and talents and to live productive and personally satisfying lives.

While the needs of other organisms are not as complex and multi-layered, basic physiological needs (e.g., food, water, shelter) are common to all plants and animals, and some higher-order human needs have counterparts in the lives of primates and other vertebrates. Discerning the basic needs of animals and plants is often straightforward and in some instances involves less uncertainty than the identification of human needs. As Christopher Stone famously remarked, "I am sure I can judge with more certainty and meaningfulness whether and when my lawn needs water, than the Attorney General can judge whether and when the United States needs to take an appeal from an adverse judgment by a lower court. ... The guardian-attorney for a smog-endangered stand of pines could venture with more confidence that his client needs the smog stopped, than the directors of a corporation can assert that 'the corporation' needs dividends declared." It is not meaningless to speak of the need of an ecosystem for minimal levels of stream flow or the need of wilderness areas to be let alone so natural processes of self-organization can operate as they have for many millions of years, so human-inflicted wounds can heal.

It is also useful to associate the harm category Functional Impairment with conditions that impair *health* (healthy functioning). The problem with airborne asbestos fibers is that they cause impaired lung function and are potentially linked to cancer, jeopardizing the healthy functioning of organs. The introduction of an invasive species in native ecosystems is not unlike cancer in an organism; it may multiply rapidly and impoverish the health of the ecosystem and its endemic species. Similarly, the problem of disrupted water flows is that healthy ecosystem functioning is put in jeopardy. There is concern in some quarters that genetic manipulation impairs the ability of genomes themselves to adapt to changing environmental conditions, thus jeopardizing their capacity to control internal growth and development in individuals of a genomic kind and to perpetuate new generations. Typologies for characterizing functional maladies in humans (human health science) and animals (veterinary health science) are well developed and progress is being made in ecology and conservation biology for comparable diagnosis of maladies in ecosystems and in molecular biology for the diagnosis of maladies in genomes.

In regard to the entity type At-Risk Ecosystems, the focus should be on key indicators of ecosystem health, cumulative effects, or "key drivers." Examples are loss of a top predator, number of inhabitants per specified area, miles of road per specified area, and percentage of remaining original vegetation. In regard to Endangered Species, the focus should similarly be on conditions judged to be particularly relevant to potential rapid decline within an endangered species population. As relevant, all species listed as endangered under the Endangered Species Act or those flagged by the International Union for the Conservation of Nature should be included in an assessment. In general, assessments of ecosystem and species risk should focus on key indicators and avoid a simple and indiscriminate re-listing of the potentially numerous predicted impacts on constituent members.

Life Termination is defined above as total loss of opportunity associated with the permanent end of vitality and essential functionality. In regard to organisms, individual death entails a total loss of opportunity to self-actualize: to grow, develop, and flourish. In regard to species, the harm of extinction represents the permanent loss of opportunity of kinds of life to perpetuate though intergenerational transmission of self-executing, growth-directing genetic information. In ecosystems, radical alteration of conditions required for self-organization spells the end of opportunity for constituent members of diverse species to co-adapt in relations of mutual benefit and to co-evolve in increasing diversity and complexity.

The harm assessment methodology developed here is intended to include all morally considerable entity types and all significant ways in which each entity type can be harmed by human activity. In applying the methodology, consideration is initially given to the identification of particular ways biotic entities could be expected to be harmed by a policy or development proposal. The next step is the development of estimates of the magnitude of the predicted harms. This brings us to a discussion of parameters of harm and how they can be measured.

2. Parameters of Harm

For a predicted harm impact (a particular way in which human action may be expected to lead to conditions harmful to individuals within an identified species-population), the following questions can and should be asked:

Extent: How widespread is the harm within the identified population? Are small or large numbers affected?

Onset: How soon is the harm expected to occur? Is it expected to occur right away, or is its onset expected to be many months or many years in the future?

Duration: How long is the harm expected to last? If not stopped, is it expected to continue for a short, relatively long, or very long time?
Proliferation: Is the harm in question expected to lead to one or more other types of harm within the identified population? Is it expected to initiate or contribute to a spreading syndrome of harm?

Controllability: Can the harm be stopped or arrested once it occurs? Can it be mitigated (reduced or lessened)? Does technology exist for stopping or mitigating the harm?

Remediability: Can the harm be remedied? Is restitution to the harmed entity (restoration, repair, aid, in-kind compensation) technically and financially feasible?

The six harm types are used to characterize the nature of the harm associated with predicted conditions: to clarify *how* they are expected to be harmed. The six harm parameters are used to specify *how harmful* the harm is expected to be. Harm of any type (physical damage, resource deprivation, functional impairment, physical pain, emotional distress, or life-termination) that is widespread, imminent, long-lasting, the cause of other harms, and not controllable or remediable is worse than harm that affects a few, is not imminent, is short-lived, does not lead to other harms, and can be controlled and remedied.

Again, however, clarifications and qualifications are needed. *First*, it is presumed that the identified parameters are "jointly exhaustive" in the sense that they encompass all of the important factors contributing to judgments about harm magnitude: about *how harmful* an identified harm may be. They are also presumed to be "mutually exclusive" in the sense that the questions associated with each are distinctly different questions.

Second, while the questions associated with each of these parameters are distinctly different questions, an informed answer to one question (e.g., whether the harm is expected to be long-lasting) may presuppose an answer to another question (e.g., whether the harm in question can be stopped).

Third, the parameters apply generally both to not-P avoided harms (Physical Injury, Resource Deprivation, etc.) and not-P loss of opportunity harms (Physical Integrity, Resource Availability, etc.), albeit with exceptions. For example, Duration is not meaningfully applied to Life Termination (a not-P avoided harm) since death and extinction are immediate once-and-for-all events. Also, Remediability is meaningfully applicable to Physical Pain and Emotional Distress (not-P avoided harms), but not to Physical Pleasure and Emotional Well-Being (not-P loss of opportunity harms).

Fourth, one or more of the parameters might be broken down into more specific categories. As with the question of harm type disaggregation, the question of whether or not a parameter is usefully disaggregated depends on circumstances associated with the policy or development proposal evaluated, the information needs of decision makers or other interested parties, and the logistics of dealing with the complexities involved. Controllability could be divided into Arrestability and Abatability, or Remediability could be broken down into Restorability, Aidability, and In-Kind Compensability, but such disaggregation would be useful only if special policy questions are pertinent. In most cases, such disaggregation is presumed not to be useful.

Fifth, it is possible to combine certain parameters. For example, Onset could be combined with Duration, or Controllability could be combined with

Remediability. While this may be a way of simplifying a harm assessment, a rigorous assessment would still involve asking the distinctly different questions that each involves. Since actions taken to stop or mitigate harm are distinguishable from actions taken to remedy harm (to provide relief, restore, or repair) and the latter is linked to the duty to make morally permissible restitution, the parameters Controllability and Remediability are generally best kept separate.

3. Harm Magnitude

Not all of the parameters lend themselves to counting or exact measurement using clocks, yardsticks, and other measurement tools. However, each (all) of the parameters can be consistently scaled to indicate whether the degree of harm associated with a predicted harm impact is "very high," "very low," or somewhere in between. Using a 3-point scale, the following illustrates how scalars can be defined using an ordinal scaling approach:

Extent: 1 = the harm is not widespread within the identified population; small numbers are affected; 2 = the harm is moderately widespread; 3 = the harm is very widespread; large numbers are affected.

Onset: 1 = onset of the harm is expected to occur in the distant future; 2 = onset of the harm is expected to occur in the mid-term; 3 = onset of the harm is expected to occur immediately.

Duration: 1 = the harm is expected (after its onset) to last a short time; 2 = the harm is expected to last a moderately long time; 3 = the harm is expected to last a very long time.

Proliferability: 1 = the harm is not expected to cause other types of harm within the identified population; 2 = the harm is expected to cause limited additional harm; 3 = the harm is expected to play a causal role in an expanding chain or syndrome of harms.

Controllability: 1 = stopping and abating the harm is technically and financially feasible; 2 = the harm can be stopped or mitigated but significant technical and/or financial constraints stand in the way; 3 = the harm cannot be stopped or mitigated.

Remediability: 1 = remedy is technically and financially feasible; 2 = remedy is possible but significant technical and/or financial constraints stand in the way; 3 = remedy is not technically or financially feasible.

While a three-point scale for estimating degrees of harm is presumably adequate for most feasibility assessments, a scale with greater resolution may be warranted. In assessing degrees of happiness, felt pain, and other subjective states, psychologists and physicians often use a 10-point scale. In the context of harm assessments involving multiple biotic entities types, however, a 3-point scale is probably appropriate in most cases. Whatever scale is used, it is essential that it is used consistently for all harm and entity types. Precise parameter definitions can reduce vagueness, particularly if this is done in the context of a well-defined project description that includes a construction, operations, and a mitigation plan. A detailed project description and definitional precision can reduce but not completely eliminate the vagueness associated with ordinal scaling. But more important is the credibility of the scalars assigned. As discussed in some detail in Section D below, the use of panels of experts to predict impacts and estimate their magnitude and probabilities in an iterative process of inquiry involving structured round-to-round feedback is regarded as a "best available" approach to obtaining credible model inputs, at least in most cases.

In regard to the scalar definitions for the parameter Onset, it is assumed that harm with an early onset is more harmful than harm expected to occur in the future. The assumption that future harm is less harmful than present harm involves time discounting, but not the kind of discounting that is objected to in discussions of obligations owed to future generations.[2] Other factors being equal, it is worse for a harm to occur in the near-term than in the long-term (to have an earlier onset) simply because it would have a longer duration. An early-onset harm is also *worse* than a late-onset harm in the sense that the former, if uncontrollable and irremediable at present, may be controllable and remediable in the future. In saying that early-onset harm is worse than late-onset harm, the reference is to time of occurrence, not to the harm in question or to entities harmed. It is not saying that it is worse for a currently living individual

---

2   Economists contend that a dollar invested at time t_1 is worth more than a dollar at some future time t_n because its value has the potential of increasing in the interim through investment (the compounding of interest). Given this rationale, future benefits and costs are discounted. Applied to future generations, discounting has the effect of reducing future benefits and costs to miniscule amounts.

to be harmed in a certain way (e.g., deprived of an essential resource) than for a future individual to be harmed in that way.

4. Categorization of Entity Types

It has been noted that the use of aggregated harm and parameter types is advantageous in most harm assessments. It is also advantageous to utilize general *entity types* (e.g. Humans, Vertebrate Animals, Invertebrate Animals, Plants, Other Organisms, Endangered Species, and At-risk Ecosystems). As with harm and parameter types, general entity types can be broken down into sub-categories, and in some instances this may be useful. Again, decisions on appropriate levels of aggregation should take into consideration the information needs of policy makers and the logistics of managing large amounts of information, but, most importantly, they should include all potentially affected morally considerable biotic entities and should facilitate impact prediction. In general, the use of general entity types is recommended.

5. Two Dimensions of Harm Seriousness: Magnitude and Value Significance

Harm *seriousness* has two dimensions: the magnitude of the harm involved and how that harm is judged in value terms. In regard to the quantitative dimension of harm, the seriousness of an identified harm is defined by the scalar values assigned to the parameters that collectively define its magnitude. If an action is expected to occur immediately, cause other harms, be widespread, and be difficult or impossible to control and remedy, the harm in question is appropriately characterized as *serious*. To avoid confusion, it is important to note that "seriousness" is not viewed as a dimension of harm on par with the parameters Extent, Onset, Duration, Proliferation, Controllability, and Remediability. Scalars assigned to these parameters collectively define the degree of seriousness.

If a policy or project (P) is expected to result in numerous near-term and long-lasting harms that will likely create additional harms because controls and remedies appear infeasible, its implementation is judged to be *worse* than the alternative of not implementing it (not-P). "Worse" is used here in a non-value sense; it is a statement that P is expected to bring about *more* harm than not-P, as measured along one or several of the *quantitative* dimensions of harm. A judgment of this sort is an empirical judgment, albeit a complex one.

To say that something is worse in a *value sense* is to say something more than its scaled parameters ratchet up its magnitude to such an extent that not taking the action is worse than taking it. It is to say, in addition, that something of significant value is at stake—that some harms have greater intrinsic disvalue than other harms, or that some harms diminish well-being (human and/or non-human) in a more significant way than other harms.[3] The clear-cutting of large tracts of virgin redwoods in an old growth forest in northern California is troubling to many people because more than jobs, tax revenues, and forest products are involved. Also at stake is the loss not only of an irreplaceable ecosystem valued for its beauty and wonders by humans but also the loss of non-human value: the inherent value of the ecosystem itself and the well-being of its many non-human inhabitants. These are value judgments. A primary purpose of weighting is to factor value considerations such as these into a per-missibility assessment. The value dimension of harm seriousness is addressed in Section E below in connection with a discussion of how predicted impact might be value weighted in a harm assessment and in a manner that does not involve morally unacceptable inter-species bias.

Rights have been associated with duties not to inflict *serious* harm. If harm dimensionality is viewed in terms of harm magnitude as well as judgments concerning the value significance of the harm, the debate about ascribing rights to non-human entities can be conducted in a more coherent and pro-ductive fashion. Candidate rights are those attributable to morally consider-able entities that are vulnerable to multiple kinds of human-inflicted harm, particularly when the magnitude of the harm is great and repugnant to many people in light of its perceived value significance.

---

3   The idea that some harms are "intrinsically worse" than other harms is not dissimilar to John Stuart Mill's contention that some pleasures are "intrinsically better" than other pleasures. As value hedonists, Jeremy Bentham and Mill agreed that the experience of pleasure is an intrinsic value and the criterion of other intrinsic values (activities that directly contribute to pleasure). Contrary to Bentham, however, Mill argued that intellectual pleasure has greater value than sensual pleasure, and that intellectual pleasure and activities contributing to such pleasure are more important constituents of happiness than sensual pleasure. Bentham was a "quantitative hedonist," Mill a "qualitative hedonist."

6. Probability, Risk, and the Precautionary Principle

a. Probability and Risk

It is important to ask questions related to the extent, onset, duration, causal implications, controllability, and remediability of predicted impacts. It is also important to ask how *probable* it is that predicted outcomes will actually occur. To accommodate this question in the assessment methodology, the probability of a predicted impact (its probability of occurrence) can be scaled on a 3-point scale as follows: 1 = probability less than 30%, 2 = probability in the 30–70% range, and 3 = probability greater than 70%. A 5-point scale could be employed if more exacting probability estimates were thought to be appropriate in light of data availability. While it is essential that a consistent scale be used to assign parameter scalar ratings, the scale used to make probability estimates need not be the same as that used for scalar estimates.

High risk is typically associated in economic analysis with actions expected with a high degree of probability to pose significant costs. To express such risk, cost estimates are typically multiplied by probability estimates. In the harm assessment model developed here, the risk of a predicted impact (a harmful condition) is estimated by multiplying its estimated probability by the sum of the parameter values that collectively define its magnitude. The proposed model provides a tool for assessing the risk of a particular predicted impact, entity-level risk, and policy or project-level risk.

b. The Precautionary Principle

For policies and projects believed to pose high risk for the public and the environment, there is growing concern that *precaution* needs to be taken. For example:

- The 1992 Earth Summit concluded with this declaration (the "Rio Declaration"): "In order to protect the environment, the precautionary approach shall be widely applied by States according to their capabilities. Where there are threats of irreversible damage, lack of full scientific certainty shall not be used as a reason for postponing cost-effective measures to prevent environmental degradation."

- At the conclusion of a conference convened by the Science and Environmental Network in 1998, a similar statement (the "Wingspread Statement") was issued: "When an activity raises threats of harm to human health or the environment, precautionary measures should be taken even if some cause and effect relationships are not established scientifically."
- The European Union issued the following Communication on the Precautionary Principle in 2000: "The precautionary principle applies where scientific evidence is insufficient, inconclusive or uncertain and preliminary scientific evaluation indicates that there are reasonable grounds for concern that the potentially dangerous effects on the environment, human, animal or plant health may be inconsistent with the high level of protection chosen by the EU."

When policies and projects can reasonably be expected to cause serious harm to the public or the environment, international declarations such as those above have urged decision makers to postpone action until such time that there is conclusive evidence that proceeding is acceptably safe, and not to use risk uncertainty as justification for "going ahead." They also have the effect of shifting the burden of proof: rather than opponents being expected to prove that a proposed policy or project is unacceptably unsafe, advocates are expected to prove that it is acceptably safe. Such precaution has been characterized as "caution practiced in the context of uncertainty," a "no regrets approach," "informed prudence," and "due care."

In the debates that have ensued since the Rio Declaration, a distinction has been drawn between "weak precaution" and "strong precaution." Advocates of the former insist that there is a legitimate role for cost–benefit analysis that incorporates the opportunity costs of precaution, that economic and other factors may trump the case for delay, and that the burden of proof appropriately falls on opponents of an action to prove that taking the action is unacceptably unsafe. Advocates of the "strong" version claim that substantial risk in the face of uncertainty justifies delayed action, that responsible parties should take due care to establish that risk is within acceptable bounds, and that, in the absence of such care, responsible parties should be held liable for the harms that result ("polluter pays").

The precautionary principle, particularly in its strong form, has met a barrage of criticisms. Some object to calling it a "principle," preferring the term "approach." Others object to the vagueness of the terms "substantial risk" or "serious harm," and call instead for definitions of thresholds. Others charge that insufficient attention is given to probabilities and to the opportunity costs of not taking action.

It is suggested that the harm assessment methodology advanced here provides a useful framework for assessing the risk of proposed policies and projects for both human and non-human life and the physical environments that sustain them. The proposed methodology compares acting with not acting, explicitly takes both the opportunity costs and the avoided costs of not acting into account, and enables "serious" harm to be defined with some degree of precision. Whether it is called a principle or an approach, precaution is a moral imperative consistent with the Principle of Moral Permissibility.

7. Structuring the Model: An Illustration

The proposed model provides a structure for evaluating the moral permissibility of policies and projects that are resource intensive and have far-reaching positive and negative consequences for non-human life and life systems. The model computes a number of policy-relevant indices, permits value weighting, and facilitates "what if" analysis (by modifying input values). Computed harm indices of a proposed policy or project (P) can be compared, moreover, with those associated with alternative policy or project approaches (P or Q or R).

The model's matrix structure illustrated in Table 1 incorporates the following components:

> *Aggregate entity types.* In the illustration, Vertebrate Animals is assumed to be one of the aggregate entity types incorporated in an assessment.

> *Aggregate harm types*: Physical Damage/Physical Integrity, Resource Deprivation/Resource Availability, Functional Impairment/Functional Capability, Physical Pain/Physical Pleasure, Emotional Distress/Emotional Well-Being, and Life Termination/Life Continuation, where the first term in each complementary pair refers to conditions expected to impact biotic entities negatively and the second term refers to conditions that impact biotic entities positively.

> *Harm parameters*: Extent, Onset, Duration, Proliferation, Controllability, and Remediability (as defined).

Predicted impacts. Note that the predicted impacts of a policy or project (P) are subsumed under a relevant aggregate entity type (Vertebrate Animals in the illustration) and a relevant harm type. Note also that the predicted harms are listed as instances of not-P lost opportunity harm (foregone P "benefits") or not-P avoided harm (avoided P "costs").

Probability estimates of predicted impacts, where 1 = probability of occurrence less than 30%, 2 = probability of occurrence in the 30–70% range, and 3 = probability of occurrence over 70%.

Parameter degree-of harm estimates. A scalar (ranging between 1 and 3) is entered in each cell at which a harm parameter and a predicted impact intersect.

Harm Magnitude: Computed by multiplying the probability scalar assigned to a predicted impact by the sum of the scalars assigned to each corresponding parameter.

Entity-Level Total Lost Opportunity Harm: Computed by summing the Harm Magnitude totals for each predicted impact listed as a not-P lost opportunity harm (under an aggregate entity type).

Entity-Level Total Avoided Harm: Computed by summing the Harm Magnitude totals for each predicted impact listed as a not-P avoided harm (under an aggregate entity type).

Project-Level Total Lost Opportunity Harm: Computed by summing the Entity Total Lost Opportunity Harm totals (all aggregate entity types).

Project-Level Total Avoided Harm: Computed by summing the Entity Total Avoided Harm totals (all aggregate entity types).

Project B/C Ratio: Computed by dividing Project-Level Total Avoided Harm by Project-Level Total Lost Opportunity Harm. If the quotient is less than 1.0, not-P is judged to be morally impermissible and P morally permissible. If the quotient is greater than 1.0, not-P is judged to be morally permissible and P morally impermissible. As clarified in Table 2 below ("Model Terminology and Logic"), acting on P is morally

Table 1. Model Illustration

POLICY/PROJECT (P): Open Section 1002 of the Alaskan Native Wildlife Refuge to oil and gas development

AGGREGATE ENTITY TYPE: Vertebrate Animals (see **Note 1**)

Predicted Impacts (see **Note 2**)	Model Inputs								Computed Harm Indices (See **Note 3**)	
	Proba-bility (scaled 1-3)	Harm Parameters (scaled 1-3)						Harm Magnitude (each impact)	Total Lost Opportunity Harm	Total Avoided Harm
		Extent	Onset	Duration	Prolif-eration	Control-lability	Remedi-ability			

NOT-P LOST OPPORTUNITY HARM (loss of opportunity to realize potential P "benefits")

Prevented **Physical Damage**
Prediction 1
Prediction 2
Prediction 3
(etc.)

Prevented **Resource Deprivation**
(predictions as above)   (matrix format as above to scale probability and prameter estimates)

Prevented **Functional Impairment**
(predictions as above)   (matrix format as above to scale probability and prameter estimates)

Prevented **Physical Pain**
(predictions as above)   (matrix format as above to sale probability and prameter estimates)

Prevented **Emotional Distress**
(predictions as above)   (matrix format as above to sale probability and prameter estimates)

Prevented **Terminal Harm**
(predictions as above)   (matrix format as above to sale probability and prameter estimates)

NOT-P AVOIDED HARM (opportunity to avoid P "costs")

Avoided **Physical Damage**
Prediction 1
Prediction 2
Prediction 3
(etc.)

(other not-P avoided harm predictions as above)

Note 1: A matrix is completed for each aggregate entity type included in an assessment (e.g. Humans, Vertebrate Animals, Invertebrate Animals, Plants, Other Organisms, Endangered Species, and At-Risk Ecosystems). N/A is pre-entered in certain harm type/parameter intersections (cells) to indicate that a parameter is not applicable to a harm type or a harm type is not applicable to an aggregate entity type.

Note 2: Each predicted impact of a proposed policy or project (P) is stated as a condition expected to affect positively or negatively a specified species-population of an aggregate entity type, is listed as a not-P lost opportunity harm (a loss of opportunity to realize a P "benefit") or a not-P avoided harm (an opportunity to avoid a P "cost") to facilitate the use of harm terminology in an assessment that takes multiple entity types into consideration, and is listed under a harm type to characterize the nature of the harm involved.

Note 3: The several indices are computed as follows:

Harm Magnitude is computed by multiplying the probability estimate (scalar) of each predicted impact by the sum of the scalars assigned to each corresponding harm parameter.

Total Lost Opportunity Harm is computed by summing the computed Harm Magnitude of each predicted impact listed as a not-P lost opportunity harm.

Total Avoided Harm is computed by summing the computed Harm Magnitude of each predicted impact listed as a not-P avoided harm.

Note: The Policy/Project (P)-level indices used to determine moral permissibility are not shown in the illustration since they are computed by summing the Total Lost Opportunity Harm and the impermissible if not acting on P is morally permissible, and acting on P is morally permissible if not acting on P is morally impermissible (assuming no actual rights violations).

Table 2. Model Terminology and Logic

Traditional cost-benefit language:

1. If the benefits of P are greater than the costs of P (b/c ratio >1.0), P is permissible.
2. The benefits of P are greater than the costs of P (b/c ratio > 1.0).
3. Therefore, P is permissible.

Avoided and opportunity cost terminology:

1. If not-P opportunity costs are greater than not-P avoided costs, not-P is not permissible.
2. Not-P opportunity costs are greater than not-P avoided costs.
3. Therefore, not-P is not permissible.
4. Therefore, P is permissible.

Equivalently:

1. If not-P avoided costs are not greater than not-P opportunity costs, not-P is not permissible.
2. Not-P avoided costs are not greater than not-P opportunity costs.
3. Therefore not-P is not permissible.
4. Therefore, P is permissible.

Harm terminology:

1. If not-P harms of lost opportunity to promote (enable, enhance) physical integrity, resource availability, functional capability, physical pleasure, emotional well-being, and/or life continuation are greater than the not-P avoided harms of physical damage, resource deprivation, functional impairment, physical pain, emotional distress, and/or life termination, not-P is not permissible.
2. Not-P harms of lost opportunity are greater than not-P avoided harms.
3. Therefore, not-P is not permissible.
4. Therefore P is morally permissible.

Equivalently:

1. If the not-P avoided harms of physical damage, resource deprivation, functional impairment, physical pain, emotional distress, and/or life termination are not greater than not-P harms of lost opportunity to promote (enable, enhance) physical integrity, resource availability, functional capability, physical pleasure, emotional well-being, and/or life continuation, not-P is not permissible.
2. Not-P avoided harms are not greater than not-P lost opportunity harms.
3. Therefore, not-P is not permissible.
4. Therefore, P is permissible.

Notes:

The proposition that P is morally permissible is logically equivalent to the proposition that not-P is not morally permissible.

Moral permissibility assumes that an actual right is not violated.

D. DEVELOPING AND VALIDATING MODEL INPUTS: A SUGGESTED APPROACH

To be credible and of practical value, careful attention needs to be given to the development and validation of model inputs. Impact prediction and the estimation of probabilities and harm magnitude should reflect the judgment of experts or otherwise be obtained from credible sources and should be documented and made available for interested parties for review.

An assessment will require a qualified *assessment manager* with broad knowledge across multiple scientific disciplines and good organizational skills. Key responsibilities of the *assessment manager* include:

- Structuring the assessment by making judgments about the appropriate level of aggregation of entity types, harm types, and harm parameters based on the policy or development proposal to be assessed, the information needs of decision makers, and usefulness for impact prediction.
- Developing a detailed description of the policy or project proposal in question, including its stated justificatory rationale, an implementation and operations plan, a mitigation plan for dealing with contingencies and accidents, timelines associated with these plans, etc.
- Enlisting the participation of panels of experts to predict impacts, estimate probabilities, and scale impact magnitude in an iterative multi-round process of inquiry involving previous-round summaries and next-round feedback.
- Developing forms, questionnaires, and other materials for eliciting and organizing panelist responses.
- Ensuring that final-round predictions and estimates (model inputs) are documented and made available to interested parties for review, challenge, and refinement.

The assessment manager would establish at least one expert panel for each aggregate entity type incorporated in the assessment. Each panel should consist of at least three persons with expertise and ready access to available information in the field. More than one panel could be established for each aggregate entity type, but this may not be feasible or necessary, particularly if the assessment manager provides check-list questions corresponding to areas of concern around which two or more panels might be formed. For example, rather than setting up several panels to address economic impacts, security impacts, cultural impacts, etc. under the aggregate category Humans, the assessment manager might pose targeted questions to a single panel to ensure that important impact areas are not overlooked. If appropriate, panel size could also be expanded (from three to five members, say).

Once the assessment manager has prepared a detailed description of the proposed policy or project to be assessed and lined up the panels, the task of eliciting panelist judgments in an iterative multi-round process of inquiry could be organized as follows:

Round 1. The objectives of Round 1 are to begin to identify predicted positive and negative impacts, and, for each prediction, to identify the impacted species population, to associate the impact with one of more harm types, and to indicate whether the harm is direct or indirect, i.e., an immediate first-order harm or a causally related follow-on harm. A questionnaire would be used for this purpose.[4]

Since the language of positive and negative impacts is commonly used and intuitively understood, the predictions made by the panelists should be stated in these terms, where it is clearly understood that positive impacts (benefits) and negative impacts (costs) are treated in the model as not-P lost opportunity harms and not-P avoided harms, respectively. The assessment manager will play an important role in appropriately characterizing positive impacts as instances of not-P lost opportunity harm and negative impacts as instances of not-P avoided harm, where the former refers to benefits that would be foregone if P is not implemented and the latter refers to harms that would be incurred if P is implemented.

An assessment should aim to identify all significant harms in what may be a causally related and temporally sequenced chain of harms. The strategy of distinguishing between direct and indirect harms at the outset facilitates thinking in causal and temporal terms and helps avoid the problem of overlooked harms. If a predicted harmful condition is expected to lead to a follow-on harmful condition, the latter is listed separately and associated with the type of harm involved. For example, if one of the direct impacts were physical injury to members of a vertebrate species-population and this impact were expected to be causally related to the subsequent inability of injured entities of that species-population to procreate or adapt to changes in their environment, the immediate and follow-on harm would be noted separately and associated

---

4 For an example, see the form in the Appendix titled "Initial Impact Prediction."

with the type of harm involved. In this example, the relevant harm types are Physical Injury (the immediate harm) and Functional Impairment (the follow-on harm).

After receiving panelist responses, the assessment manager would then compile the results in a format similar to that shown in Table 1. In effect, this will involve an initial construction of the leftmost column of the model's matrix format. This compilation would be completed for each panel/aggregate entity type.

Round 2. The objectives of Round 2 are to identify additional impacts, to elicit comments on how predictions have been categorized by harm type, as direct or indirect, and as instances of not-P lost opportunity or avoided harm, and to elicit initial probability and parameter degree-of-harm estimates for impacts predicted in Round 1. Some or all of the predictions made by the other panels in Round 1 would be included as pertinent feedback information. A matrix format as illustrated in Table 1 would be used to enter Round 2 probability and parameter estimates.[5] The panelists should be requested to identify additional impacts that were not identified in the first round, but may be suggested by the feedback information. They would also be asked to edit the language used to state predicted impacts, with the objective of eliminating confusion and enabling succinct yet concise impact descriptions that identify the species-populations impacted.

A potential problem can arise when some predicted impacts are very general while others are very specific. The problem here is that the sheer number of highly specific predictions can play a disproportionate role vis-à-vis generalized predictions in the calculation of computed indices. It would be problematic, for example, to predict that a policy or project would result in starvation for large numbers of vertebrate animals, while comparable harm (starvation) to a comparable number of invertebrate animals is enumerated in detailed particularity (e.g., loss of x, y, z ... as food sources for a, b, c ... species-populations of invertebrates). Assuming roughly equal numbers of impacted populations within the two aggregate entity types, the numerous predictions of invertebrate starvation can be generalized to roughly the level of generality of predicted vertebrate starvation. The role of the assessment manager is critical in helping to ensure consistent levels of generality among impact predictions.

---

5 For an example, see the matrix in the Appendix titled "Probability and Degree-of-Harm Estimation."

Methodological concern about uneven levels of generality would be included as feedback in the next round of inquiry, along with suggestions of how the problem might be remedied.[6]

Round 2 responses would then be collected and organized by the assessment manager. New predictions would be added and averages of the first-round probability and degree-of-harm estimates would be calculated as feedback for the next round (Round 3). Summaries of the Round 2 predictions made by the other panels would also be included as pertinent background feedback information.

Round 3. The objectives of Round 3 are to identify additional impacts, to elicit probability and degree-of-harm estimates a second time based on the second round averages, and to request reasons why a panelist believes that certain Round 2 averages are too high or low. Two matrices would be provided: one filled out with the Round 2 calculated averages; the other to be used for new Round 3 estimates. If a respondent thinks an averaged rating is significantly off the mark, a higher or lower rating would be assigned (using decimals since the averages employ decimals). The panelists would again be task to identity hitherto unidentified impacts and to critically edit the descriptions of impacts identified thus far.

The request for reasons for probability and parameter ratings that deviate from averaged ratings is an important element of this process of iterative inquiry. The introduction of reasons creates intra-panel interaction, shows how assigned ratings are based on oftentimes complex judgments that synthesize information, provides a basis for subsequent documentation of model inputs, surfaces areas where disagreement and/or uncertainty is an issue, and suggests how the model might be used subsequently to perform "what if" analysis using different sets of assumptions and making corresponding changes in input values.

The assessment manager would then collect and organize Round 3 results, adding new predictions and calculating averages for Round 3 probability and parameter estimates.

Round 4. In Round 4, each panelist would be asked to enter scalar values a third time in light of the new averages. Each panelist would also be encouraged

---

6   It is noted that scalars assigned to the parameter Extent (how widespread the harm is estimated to be among an identified species-population) can be a useful indicator of the level of generality of predictions. If a predicted impact is expected to be widespread within a species-population (receives a rating of 3, say), the prediction in question involves a high level of generality (as compared to a rating of 1, say).

to challenge or otherwise comment on reasons why averaged ratings may be too high or low, and to respond to suggestions for clarifying predicted impacts. The participation of panel participants might be terminated once the assessment manager has tabulated Round 4 results, or a **Round 5** or **Round 6** could be added. Additional rounds would be structured similarly to Round 4.

The probability and parameter scalar estimates used to compute the various harm indices would be the final round averages.

The proposed approach for developing model inputs is considered to be a "best available" method, at least in many or most cases. It is important that the assessment manager assemble documentation for the input values used in model runs, and that documentation for the inputs used are made available to interested parties for review and challenge. Adequate documentation may involve specific requests to panelists to provide source information and/or to elaborate on reasons given for probability and parameter estimates. The overall process is proposed as an organized way of eliciting informed judgments from qualified experts, facilitating interaction among co-participants, providing opportunities for participants and other parties to challenge judgments and assumptions, and documenting model input values.

E. Value Weighting

The Principle of Moral Consideration states that the question of the moral permissibility of harm to a morally considerable entity is a relevant moral question and ought to be asked when the harm in question is expected to be significant. For entities judged to be morally considerable in their own right, harm to one is no more or less a morally *relevant* issue that harm to any other. All morally considerable biotic entities are equally worthy of *moral consideration*. The question examined below is whether equal consideration, thus understood, rules out value weighting in moral deliberation.

1. Inherent Worth and Value Weighting

The principle of *equal* inherent worth is central in Paul Taylor's biocentric ethics. Part of his argument is that there is no non-question-begging way of asserting that what is good about or for human beings is superior to what is inherently good about or good for non-human beings; to make the claim of human superiority is to have already made the tacit assumption that the claim is true. As discussed in Chapter 3, Taylor believes that the principle of equal inherent worth precludes giving greater weight to human interests in moral deliberation. Critics contend that his principle of minimum human wrong involves giving greater weight to certain human interests, and that this is inconsistent with the principle of equal inherent worth.

It is the view here that acknowledgement that morally considerable entities are equally worthy of moral consideration does not rule out value weighting in moral permissibility determinations, provided that value weights are assigned at the level of predicted impacts within the context of particular assessments, not at the level of entity types or harm types in general.

2. Value Weighting: A Suggested Approach

A distinction has been made between the empirical and value dimensions of harm *seriousness*. Judgments about harm magnitude are empirical judgments. A harm judged to have great magnitude—to involve large populations, have a near-term onset, last a long time, lead to other harms, and be uncontrollable and irremediable—is *serious* harm. If the harm to two or more morally considerable entities were judged to be equal in magnitude, there would, *ceteris paribus*, be no non-prejudicial basis for claiming that the harm to one of these entities is any or more less serious than harm to any other.

But harm seriousness also has a value dimension. Harm *qua* harm is a disvalue, but some harms in some contexts may legitimately be judged to have greater disvalue. Even if not killing the last few remaining members of an endangered species were judged to result in less harm than killing them and no laws prohibited their killing, the judgment that something of significant value was at stake would need to be taken into consideration. Greater disvalue may be attributed to the loss of the species than, say, the loss of livestock. Or, in another decision context, greater disvalue may be attributed to the loss of a rare and irreplaceable ecosystem than, say, an increase of local tax revenues. The value judgments on which such attributions are based should not be factored out of decision-making.

Before getting into the discussion of how value weights can feasibly be assigned to predicted impacts in harm assessments, it is instructive to consider reasons for not assigning value weights at all. There are, indeed, a number of considerations that weigh against weighting. *First*, the scaling of the multiple parameters of harm to gauge impact magnitude and the use of this information to generate aggregate harm indices already summarizes a great deal of policy-relevant information. *Second*, the widely shared expectation that human interests should carry more weight in deliberation than non-human interests is mollified by the adoption of a methodology that is careful to avoid bias against humans by taking development benefits into consideration and recognizing that humans can be harmed in more ways and sometimes to a greater degree than non-humans. *Third*, decision-makers in the private sector base decisions on a variety of analytical tools, including cost–benefit and cost-effectiveness analyses incorporating the strategic objectives of the organizations they represent, and would be expected to be interested primarily in unweighted impact indices. *Fourth*, it must be acknowledged that public sector decision makers in a democratic society pay attention to voices expressed in public forums, not analytical models alone and certainly not those that incorporate a particular set of value weights. Value weighting inevitably invites the question of whose weights should be used. Should the weights utilized in an assessment be those judged to be appropriate by a coalition of environmental organizations opposing development, or by a coalition of industries advocating development?

If weighting is used in an assessment to reflect judgments of value significance, it is suggested that the assignment of weights to impacts be employed to answer this question: Would a proposed policy or project judged to be morally permissible without value weights also turn out to be morally permissible under each of several sets of value weights, or an average of these, or the average of weights assigned by a random sample? A proposed policy or project whose permissibility stands up against a variety of weighting schemes would be one whose moral justifiability is strong.

If value weights are used, the challenge is that of settling on a methodologically defensible approach. For a policy or project for which many negative and positive impacts are predicted for many entity types, it would be burdensome and hardly meaningful to attempt to assign weights to *all* such impacts. A more promising approach might involve the following. First, the assessment manager would identify those impacts under each aggregate entity type that have the greatest magnitude based on their previously estimated parameter degrees-of-magnitude and probabilities. The next step would involve listing the items on this "short list" (a total of 25–30, say) in two groups: not-P lost opportunity harms (forgone P "benefits") and not-P avoided harms (avoided P "costs"). Next, value weights are assigned to judge the value significance of each not-P avoided harm and each not-P lost opportunity harm. To reflect the positive value of harm avoidance, the following scalars are then entered: 4 = great value significance (i.e. contributes very significantly to entity well-being and is judged to be a matter of great value significance); 3 = moderate value significance; 2 = marginal value significance. To reflect the negative value of loss of opportunity to benefit, the following scalars are entered: -4 = great value significance (i.e. greatly diminishes entity well-being and is judged to be a matter of great value significance); -3 = moderate value significance; -2 = marginal value significance. By multiplying the computed harm magnitude of each listed impacted by an average of assigned value weights and using this product to replace the computed harm magnitude for each (leaving unchanged the originally computed magnitude of all the other predicted impacts), a value-weighted B/C ratio can be computed for not-P. If the ratio obtained by dividing total not-P avoided harms by total not-P lost opportunity harms is greater than 1.0, not-P (not acting on P) is judged to be morally permissible and P morally impermissible.

Approaches to weighting that focus on entity types or harm types run into problems. If aggregate harm types pertaining to each aggregate entity type are value weighted, the relative value significance of impacts across entity types are not taken into account and all impacts subsumed under a given harm type are given the same weight. If the aggregate harm categories are weighted in general, the cross-entity problem is addressed, but all impacts listed under a harm type will still carry the same weight and the different ways in which various species-populations within an aggregate entity type can be harmed are ignored. If the aggregate entity types are weighted, each impact listed under an entity type is given the same weight and the door is open to unacceptable inter-species bias.

It is acknowledged that weighting on the basis of a subset of predicted impacts having the highest harm magnitude indices does not eliminate the problem of inter-species bias, but it could be expected to minimize such bias, particularly if alternative sets of weightings provided by diverse interest groups (or perhaps an average of these) are used to determine whether a proposed policy or project previously judged to be morally permissible continues to pass the moral permissibility test.

Selected members of the various expert panels might be used as one group to assign value weights. While experts are no more qualified than anybody else to make value judgments in general, they are qualified to make value judgments about factual matters in areas in which they have expertise. An ecologist is not uniquely qualified to judge that extinction of a certain species is a matter of great value significance, but the related judgment that the species is a keystone species linked in a complex causal chain to other species, or that its extinction has cascading effects throughout an ecosystem, are important considerations informing its value significance and the weight it might reasonably be given in moral deliberation.

F. MODEL USES

The harm assessment model is proposed as a methodology for conducting moral permissibility determinations (per the Principle of Moral Permissibility) of proposed policies and projects with far-reaching non-human as well as human consequences. The model can also be used to assess the morally permissibility of proposed restitution measures (per the Principle of Restitution) and initiatives undertaken by concerned parties to prevent and ameliorate human-inflicted harm (per the Principle of Care).

Numerous research organizations in universities, government agencies, and non-profit or non-governmental organizations have the organizational and personnel resources to conduct an assessment along the lines proposed, and it is not hard to imagine an entire impact assessment organized and conducted through the Internet, perhaps through a website set up for this purpose. Regular face-to-face meetings of participants would be an obvious advantage, but electronic exchanges with occasional meetings are feasible. The ability to offer an honorarium would facilitate the recruitment of qualified experts. However, if an assessment were perceived to be an interesting and worthwhile endeavor, compensation may be a minor or unimportant issue.

The model and the suggested approach for developing and validating inputs could be used to evaluate a wide variety of choice alternatives at local, national, or international levels in both the public and private sectors. It could be used by environmental research organizations, organizations committed to creating greater awareness and understating of environmental problems, and/or activist organizations motivated to call attention to and potentially prevent unacceptable practices. It could be employed by non-governmental organizations (NGOs) of various kinds as inputs into the public participation components of government-mandated environmental assessments, or it could be used by public officials as a front-end means of scoping and focusing such assessments.

The model can be used as an educational tool in education. In conjunction with case studies presenting decision alternatives related to large-scale development projects, student teams could be assigned to research available literature, develop model inputs, and evaluate model runs. Adaptation of the model to evaluate proposed oil and gas development in the Alaskan Native Wildlife Refuge (ANWR) is discussed in the Appendix, together with forms and instructions designed to facilitate the development of model inputs (probability and parameter degree-of-harm estimates and value weights).

The model can be used by proponents of development. Given an option that has been judged to be advantageous in light of an organization's policy objectives, it provides a systematic method for exploring the ways in which that option might fruitfully be modified to reduce harmful impacts to non-human life, or for identifying areas in which more detailed studies are needed. Once a harm assessment of a proposed course of action has been made, modifications can be modeled by making relevant changes in inputs and comparing re-computed indices with those of the original (baseline) proposal. "What if" analyses can also be undertaken using alternative value weighting schemes or an average of these. If the model is used to evaluate alternative courses of action (P or Q or R) in the early phases of a planning process, a separate impact assessment is performed for each alternative. By comparing the Project B/C Ratio of each, the alternative expected to lead to the least harm can be identified.

The model can be used to assess risk and to apply the *precautionary principle*: the principle that actions posing serious risks should not be taken unless and until the risks are better understood and effective mitigation measures are in place. Per the Principle of Moral Permissibility, a policy or project ought not to be taken until or unless mitigation measures are sufficient to reduce risk to the extent that the avoided harms of non-implementation outweigh associated lost opportunity harms.

While the model has practical application in the ways suggested, the underlying moral claim is that policy-makers and concerned citizens *morally ought* to ask the questions that are built into the model's structure. They ought to ask whether and how non-human life and life systems could be expected to be harmed by policy and project proposals, and they ought not to act on decisions that cannot be morally justified by the Principle of Moral Permissibility.

G. Toward Reconciliation in Human, Animal, and Environmental Ethics

The proposed ethical framework is consistent with two basic moral principles found in virtually all systems of ethics and law. The Principle of Moral Permissibility presupposes the principle of nonmaleficence, and the Principle of Restitution presupposes the principle that agents of wrongful acts should make proportionate restitution to wronged parties. For this reason, most theorists will presumably find the four life-centered principles to be acceptable within the ethical frameworks they espouse, if appropriate modifications are made pertaining to the scope of entities judged to have moral standing. If the scope of the four principles were confined to humans and sentient animals, few, if any, animal welfare ethicists would take exception; they would agree that all vertebrates potentially harmed by human action ought to be taken into account, that an action expected to cause more harm than its no-action complement is not morally permissible; that permissible restitution ought to be made for vertebrates harmed by an impermissible action; and that it is morally right, although not a duty, to prevent and ameliorate human harm to animals if doing so does not result in greater harm the harm one is seeking to prevent or ameliorate. Likewise, it is presumed that biocentric theorists could embrace all four principles if their scope extends to all living beings, as would many ecocentric theorists if the entities referred to include ecosystems or communities of life. The principles will be found to be sound, even if there is disagreement over the scope of moral considerability.

Not only the principles themselves, but the proposed methodologies for applying them are presumed to be acceptable to theorists and practitioners taking different stances on moral standing. Whether goods and bads are analyzed in terms of preferences, basic needs, or monetary gain and loss, the proposed methodology accommodates these several ways of evaluating impacts. For evaluations of policies and projects involving intensive resource use, large-scale construction, and the discharge of waste materials to the physical environment, the credibility of model inputs is a critical factor. The proposed approach to developing, validating, and documenting model inputs is presumably one that could be adopted regardless of whether predicted impacts are evaluated from a corporate or public policy perspective, or whether the objective is to maximize need satisfaction, preference satisfaction, or net financial gain.

The proposed principles and application methodology steer clear of questions of whether the good of a species and/or ecosystem takes precedence over the good of the individuals comprising that species and/or ecosystem, or whether the good of individuals takes precedence over the collective whole (the species and ecosystem). Questions along these lines are "wedge issues" historically leading to sharp disagreements between ecocentric theorists and wildlife resource managers, on the one hand, and animal welfare theorists and activists, on the other. Such questions are circumvented in an ethic that appeals to the Principle of Permissibility to decide moral permissibility on the basis of the harms involved and eschews the value weighting of entity types. Rather than asking whether or not the good of a species or ecosystem takes precedence over that of its members, or vice versa, attention is directed to actual expected harms, with the stipulation that a course of action is not permissible if its no-action complement is reasonably expected to result in less total harm, all potentially affected individuals, species, and ecosystems taken into account. If priority is given to a "whole" in this decision principle, it is not that of a collective entity, but the "whole" of all potentially affected morally considerable entities. Also, the proposed approach to weighting gives an eco-centrist the opportunity to indicate that consequences seriously disruptive to an ecosystem have greater value significance than, say, diminution of members of a species population, just as it provides the opportunity to a biocentrist to judge otherwise. It has been argued, however, that weights should be assigned at the level of predicted impacts (those that have been judged to have the greatest magnitude), not at the level of entity types in general. It has also been suggested that appropriate use of weighting compares alternative weighting schemes to an unweighted baseline and asks whether a decision alternative (P or not-P, or P or Q or R), initially judged to be permissible, continues to be so under each of several weighting sets. On this approach, no prior commitment is given to "wholes" over "parts," or vice versa.

The assessment methodology focuses on harms but does not exclude considerations of well-being, since the benefits of acting are defined as the harms of not acting. Nevertheless, it may be objected that human quality of life considerations are given insufficient emphasis in the proposed evaluation methodology. Several responses can be given to this objection. *First*, impacts perceived to diminish quality of life can and should be included in the analysis and appropriately categorized using harm terminology. *Second*, the assignment of weights to reflect value judgments takes quality of life considerations into account. *Third*, the proposed methodology is less susceptible to the objection that quality of life considerations are downplayed than utilitarian assessments that narrowly associate human well-being with monetary value or preference satisfaction. The categories of harm utilized in the assessment model include physical pain (the complement of physical pleasure) and emotional distress (the complement of emotional well-being). Resource deprivation is analyzable in terms of needs and preferences, and Functional Impairment is analyzable in terms of health requirements.

The question of non-human moral rights has been addressed in what is thought to be a "bridge building" way. For theorists who limit moral standing to humans, the question may at least be thought to be palatably posed. Rights are defined as negative rights not to be harmed, and the question is posed as an open question. Where harms to non-humans are judged to numerous, extensive, near-at-hand, long-lasting, proliferating, and difficult to control and remedy, the suggestion is that rights protection should at least be entertained. Human rights protections exist because debate and public acceptance has proved to be persuasive. Public debate has resulted in limited protection for selected vertebrates, some endangered species, and some wild places. The plea is for continuing discussion. Posing the question of moral rights in this way defuses the tendency to end the debate before it begins. If rights protection is framed in terms of what is needed to prevent extensive harm whose degree of harmfulness (magnitude) is great and there is growing consensus that the harm is question has important value significance, the anthropocentrist may concede that further legal protections against non-human harm are warranted, if only to safeguard future human well-being. Practical agreement sometimes occurs when there is theoretical disagreement, and there is merit in Norton's suggestion that anthropocentrists and ecocentrists will generally agree practically on sound resource management practices (the "convergence hypothesis")—although notable examples abound where this is not the case (e.g., the wilderness debates discussed in Chapter 4).

While the Principle of Permissibility is aptly characterized as a teleological principle, the overall ethical framework is distinctly deontological. All four life-centered principles are grounded in an attitude of respect for nature, of which virtuous dispositions are an essential component. The previous chapter explored virtues that are paramount in a life-centered ethics and how, in the context of an overall attitude of respect, they can and should be cultivated.

APPENDIX: ANCILLARY CLASSROOM MATERIALS

A. Introduction

To facilitate classroom use of the model and application methodologies outlined in Chapter 6, this appendix includes a case involving proposed oil and gas development in the Arctic National Wildlife Refuge (ANWR), suggestions for setting up and managing an assessment using student teams working over the course of an academic term, forms for developing model inputs, and instructions for downloading the forms and the model programmed in Excel.

Use of the model and its application methodologies in conjunction with a case study provides a potentially rich learning experience for students. Working in teams, students are challenged to critically examine the assessment methodology and to ask the kinds of questions that application of the model requires: What are the expected impacts of a proposed policy or project, all morally considerable biotic entities taken into account? How probable are the predicted impacts? What types of harm are involved? How serious are the harms, taking into consideration their extent, onset, duration, proliferation, controllability, and remediability? What value weights should be assigned to the most serious harms? Is the harm morally permissible? What is the institutional context in which decisions will be made? The pedagogical value of case analysis structured along these lines consists in the opportunity to hone conceptual, analytical, and research skills, to work and collaborate as a team in the performance of defined tasks, and to refine and validate judgments based on best available information in an iterative, multi-round process of inquiry. The instructor will, of course, organize and provide guidance throughout the process.

One student team will have the responsibility of managing the assessment (the assessment management team). The other teams (impact assessment teams), each focusing on an aggregate entity type included in the assessment, will predict impacts and, for each predicted impact, develop probability and parameter degree-of-harm estimates. Once model inputs have been developed, the class as a whole will assign value weights to impacts to permit the computation of value-weighted harm indices.

Tasks related to the development of model inputs are discussed in Section B, together with various matrices that can be used for impact prediction, the estimation of probabilities and parameter degrees-of-harm, and the allocation of value weights to permit the computation of value-weighted harm impact indices. Potential methodological problems are addressed in Section C. Issues related to the scheduling of assessment tasks are discussed in Section D, together with a time chart displaying task start and completion times. Compartmentalization of the model for classroom use is discussed in Section E, along with instruction for downloading the model online. The ANWR case is discussed in Section F, with references to websites that provide supplementary information, reference research reports, and/or contain useful data. The ANWR case follows this discussion.

For instructors electing to include the ANWR case study and the proposed assessment methodology in their courses, it is presupposed that students will have read and discussed the Chapter 6 description of the model: its use of harm terminology, its structure, the suggested approach to developing credible model inputs, and the formulas used to compute harm indices.

B. DEVELOPMENT OF MODEL INPUTS

The instructor will divide the class into student teams at the outset, where one team takes on the responsibilities of the assessment manager and the other teams, each corresponding to one of the aggregate entity types included in the assessment, take on the responsibilities of predicting impacts and scaling their probabilities and parameter degrees-of-harm. The size of the teams will obviously depend on class size and the number of aggregate entity types included in an assessment. If the class has twenty-eight students and six aggregated entity types are included in the assessment, four students might be assigned to each entity assessment team, leaving four students for the assessment management team. (Correspondingly, if the class has forty-five students and eight aggregate entity types are included in the assessment, five students might be assigned to each impact assessment team, leaving five for the assessment management team.) Student interests and academic backgrounds should be taken into account in assigning students to the teams.

1. Impact Prediction

A first important task of the assessment management team is to prepare a development scenario related to oil and gas drilling in the ANWR coastal plain. This will require a close reading of the case and information gleaned from other sources (referenced in Section E), together with some creative imagination. The instructor should critique and "sign off" on the development scenario.

With the drilling scenario in hand, each impact assessment team (corresponding to one of the aggregate entity types included in the assessment) will then complete the questionnaire labeled "Initial Impact Prediction." The following process is suggested for the accomplishment of this task:

- Prediction of impacts by each member of each impact assessment team.
- Team discussion to edit these predictions and to consolidate them for inclusion in the questionnaire labeled "Initial Impact Prediction" (provided in Section F). Several team meetings will probably be needed to add to and pare the list, ensure that each predicted impact identifies the species-populations potentially impacted, and to craft succinct statements of each prediction.
- Incorporation of the edited and consolidated set of predicted impacts in the leftmost column of the questionnaire.
- Team concurrence on appropriate check marks (yes/no answers) called for in the questionnaire: what type of harm each predicted impact is expected to involve, whether the harm is thought to be a direct consequence of development or a causally-related follow-on harm, and whether the predicted impact is positive or negative. The identification of impacts as positive or negative helps inform how they are conceptualized using the harm terminology employed in the assessment, where positive impacts ("benefits") and negative impacts ("costs") are represented, respectively, as not-P lost opportunity harms and not-P avoided harms.
- Submission of the completed questionnaire to the assessment management team.

The form titled "Initial Impact Prediction" and other forms referenced below are provided as a set in Section F. All of these forms can be downloaded to allow the instructor to add space as needed for student inputs and to make other needed modifications.

2. Probability and Degree-of-Harm Estimation

Based on the submissions of the completed questionnaires by the impact assessment teams, the impact assessment team will then prepare the forms used for probability and degree-of-harm estimates by entering predictions in each of the two forms. The two forms (illustrated in Section F) are labeled "Predicted Negative Impacts: Probability and Parameter Degree-of-Harm Estimation" and "Predicted Positive Impacts: Probability and Parameter Degree-of-Harm Estimation." Once the project management team has prepared these forms, each two-form set will then be returned to the impact assessment team that developed the predictions. Next steps include the following:

- Each member of each impact assessment team will then enter probability and parameter scalars (ranging between 1 and 3, as discussed in Chapter 6) in the relevant cells of the two forms. To reduce unnecessary work and possible confusion, the instructor and/or project management should pre-enter N/A in certain cells to indicate instances where a particular harm type does not apply to a harm type (e.g., plants and non-vertebrates do not feel physical pain or emotional distress), or a particular harm parameter does not apply to a harm type (e.g., life termination does not have a duration).
- Additionally, each assessment team member will add new predictions. In this regard, it is suggested that the project management team provide a listing of all the predictions made by the several impact assessment teams as a means of stimulating thinking about causal relationships and additional predictions.
- Each assessment team will then return each individually completed matrix to the assessment management team.
- The assessment team will then compute averages of the scalars entered in each cell and will add any new predictions for the next-round estimate of probabilities and parameter degrees-of harm.

Essentially the same process is followed in successive rounds in which each impact assessment team refines probability and degree-of-harm estimates. When a team concurs that averages for certain cells are too high or low, adjusted estimates are provides, together with reasons for changes.

Final round averages will be used by the project management team as inputs to the model programmed to compute impact indices: harm magnitude for each predicted impact, and total not-P lost opportunity harm and total not-P avoided harm at both the entity-level and the policy/project level. At the policy/project-level, a quotient is obtained by dividing total not-P lost opportunity harm by total not-P avoided harm.

3. Value Weighting

Approaches to value weighting for the purpose of computing value-weighted indices is discussed in detail in Chapter 6. In a classroom setting, the assessment management team will have the initial responsibility of identifying those predicted positive and negative impacts that have the highest computed magnitudes and then constructing the table illustrated in Section F (labeled "Assignment of Value Weights"). As this table shows, the selected highest-magnitude harms are divided into two groups: not-P avoided harms (avoided P "costs") and not-P lost opportunity harms (foregone P "benefits"). Each member of the class will then assign value weights to judge the value significance of each listed impact. For impacts listed as not-P avoided harms, scalars ranging between 4 and 2 are used, where 4 indicates the judgment that the impact on the identified biotic entity is (for the person making the judgment) a matter of high value significance, 3 indicates the judgement that the impact is of moderate value significance, and 2 indicates the judgement that the impact is of marginal value significance. (Positive numbers are used to reflect the positive value of harm avoidance.) For impacts listed as non-P lost opportunity harms, scalars ranging between -4 and -2 are used, where -4 indicates the judgment that the impact is (for the person making the judgment) a matter of great value significance, -3 indicates the judgement that the impact is of moderate value significance, and -2 indicates that the impact is of marginal value significance. (Negative numbers are used to reflect the negative value of loss of opportunity to benefit.) After each class member assigns value weights in this manner, the impact assessment team will calculate average ratings and use these to generate a value-weighted B/C ratio as described in the notes to the table labeled "Assignment of Value Weights."

C. POTENTIAL METHODOLOGICAL PROBLEMS

As discussed in Chapter 6, several potential methodological problems need to be guarded against. A primary responsibility of the assessment management team is to flag methodological problems and to make suggestions for correcting or avoiding them as part of round-to-round instructions and feedback to the impact assessment teams.

1. Harm Terminology

A potential problem can arise if confusion exists over the practice of conceptualizing positive impacts as not-P lost opportunity harms and negative impacts as not-P avoided harms as a means of using harm terminology in an assessment. The instructor should clarify this conceptualization (common in economic cost-benefit analysis) and its employment in the harm assessment methodology.

A positive impact of a proposed policy or project (P) is a predicted condition judged to advantageous or beneficial to a biotic entity. A negative impact of P is a predicted condition judged to be disadvantageous or detrimental. Using the harm terminology of the assessment, a negative impact of P is harmful in a straightforward sense: it is an impact that causes physical damage, resource deprivation, functional impairment, physical pain, emotional distress, and/or life termination in the form of individual death, species extinction, and ecosystem destruction. A positive impact is characterized as one that enables, enhances, or otherwise contributes to structural integrity, resource availability, functional capability, physical pleasure, emotional well-being, and/or life continuation. In these terms, then, a not-P lost opportunity harm is viewed as the loss of opportunity to promote structural integrity, resource availability, functional capability, etc. potentially associated with P implementation, while a not-P avoided harm is viewed as opportunity to avoid conditions that would be expected to cause physical damage, resource deprivation, functional impairment, etc. Not-P lost opportunity harm is the harm of foregoing benefits if P is not implemented; not-P avoided harm is the harm of incurring costs if P is implemented.

2. Generality of Predicted Impacts

Another potential problem can arise when predictions pertaining to one aggregate entity type are very general, referring collectively to numerous species-populations, while predictions pertaining to another aggregate entity type could be comparably generalized but are not, referring instead to several or many comparably impacted populations. The same problem can arise in connection with predicted impacts on sub-groups of the same aggregate entity type. In the context of the assessment methodology employed here, a few generalized predictions relative to numerous particularized predictions can distort computed indices, particularly in regard to value weighting. The assessment management team needs to be alert to the problem of uneven generalization among predictions and offer suggestions (as feedback to the impact assessment teams) to help remedy this potential problem. Scalar ratings assigned to the parameter Extent should be consulted in this regard. A high scalar (e.g. 3) will be assigned to predicted impacts that references numerous species-populations collectively, while a low scalar (e.g., 1) will be given to predicted impact that refer to species-populations in the particular. The problem of uneven generality in the prediction of impacts is discussed in some detail in Chapter 6, along with examples.

3. Impacts on Endangered Species and At-Risk Ecosystems

Assuming that endangered species and at-risk ecosystems are included in the ANWR assessment, the emphasis should be on key indicators of species and ecosystem decline. For at-risk ecosystems, loss of vegetation, number of human inhabitants, miles of road, pipelines, and transmission lines are example indicators. ANWR contains five distinct ecological regions, at least two of which could be put at-risk if oil and gas developments were to occur. The region is also home to several endangered species. A single impact assessment team might be formed to asses impacts on at-risk ecosystems and endangered species. But whether one or two teams are formed, a first task will involve a review of the literature in conservation biology and ecology to identify indicators most relevant to ANWR. The focus should be on cumulative effects and the identification and quantification of key indicators, and should avoid an indiscriminate listing of the potentially numerous predicted listed under the other aggregate entity types.

D. Scheduling of Tasks

For both a twelve-week and a sixteen-week assessment, schedules showing start and completion times for key tasks are provided in Section F. Because the assessment management team depends on the timely submission of satisfactorily completed work by the impact assessment teams, and vice versa, it is important that the various tasks be accomplished on schedule. If grading in a course takes student performance in the case study into consideration, evaluations by each team member of fellow team members and of the performance of other teams may be used as one among other grade determinants. Student understanding that performance in the assessment will affect course grades provides an incentive to do satisfactory work in a timely manner.

E. Programmed Model for Classroom Use

For ease of classroom use, the model is divided into sections: one pertaining to the computation of aggregate entity-level harm impact indices; the other pertaining to the computation of policy/project-level indices. Illustrations of the two matrices are provided in Section F with the Labels "Computations of Entity-Level Indices" and "Computation of Project B/C Ratio."

The model is programmed in Microsoft Excel and can be downloaded from the publisher at www.cognella.com or from the book's author at berry.crawford@wwu.edu.

F. Forms for the Development of Model Inputs

INITIAL IMPACT PREDICTION

AGGREGATE ENTITY TYPE: _____

PREDICTED IMPACTS	Species-Population Impacted	QUESTIONS		
		Positive or negative? Impact?	Direct or Indirect Impact?	Type of Harm? Involved?
(predicted impacts are succintly listed below)	(identify)	(enter P or N)	(enter D of I)	(see Note below)

Note: If the impact is judged to be negative, the identified harm type should be Physical Damage, Resource Deprivation, Functional Impairment, Physical Pain, Emotional Distress, and/or Life Termination. If more than one of these harm types are thought to be relevant, enter those thought to be relevant. If the impact is judged to be positive, the associated harm type should be one or more of the following complements: Physical Integrity, Resource Availability, Functional Capability, Physical Pleasure, Emotional Well-Being, and/or Life Continuation. In the case of positive impacts, ask whether the predicted condition enables, enhances, or otherwise contributes to one or more of these desirable conditions.

AGGREGATE ENTITY TYPE: _____

MODEL INPUTS							
Probability Estimates (scaled 1-3)	Harm Parameter Estimates (scaled 1-3)						
	Extent	Onset	Dura-tion	Prolif-eration	Control-lability	Remed-iability

Harm Type:

Harm Type:

Harm Type:

Note: Using this master matrix, each prediced *positive* impact is listed as a not-P lost opportunity harm (a "benefit" that would be foregone if P were implemented) and associated with a relevant harm type (physical integrity, resource availability, functional capability, physical pleasure, emotional well-being, and/or life continuation).

PREDICTED NEGATIVE IMPACTS: PROBABILITY AND PARAMETER DEGREE-OF-HARM ESTIMATION

AGGREGATE ENTITY TYPE: _____

	MODEL INPUTS						
Probability Estimates (scaled 1-3)	Harm Parameter Estimates (scaled 1-3)						
	Extent	Onset	Dura-tion	Prolif-eration	Control-lability	Remed-iability

Harm Type: _____

Harm Type: _____

Harm Type: _____

Note: Using this master matrix, each prediced *negative* impact is listed as a not-P avoided harm (a "cost" that would be avoided if P were not implemented) and associated

ASSIGNMENT OF VALUE WEIGHTS

PREDICED POSITIVE AND NEGATIVE IMPACTS	ENTITY IMPACTED	IMPACT MAGNITUDE	VALUE SCALAR

Not-P Lost Opportunity Harms (foregone P "benefits")

Not-P Avoided Harms (avoided P "costs")

Notes

Assuming policy or project (P) implementation, twelve predicted negative impacts and twelve predicted positive impacts -- those having the highest computed magnitudes in each group -- are listed above as not-P avoided harms and not-P lost opportunity harms, respectively, and are associated with the relevant entity type impacted.

Value weights are assigned to judge the value significance of each not-P avoided harm and each not-P lost opportunity harm (foregone "benefit"). To reflect the positive value of harm avoidance, the following scalars are used: 4, 3, or 2 to represent the judgment that the impact has great, moderate, or maginal (positive) value significance. To reflect the negative value of loss of opportunity (foregone "benefits"), the following scalars are used: -4, -3, or -2 to represent the judgment that the impact has great, moderate, or marginal (negative) value significance.

By multiplying the computed harm magnitude of each listed impact by an average of assigned value weights and using this product to replace the computed harm magnitude for each (leaving unchanged the computed magnitude of all the other predicted impacts), a value-weighted B/C ratio can be computed for not-P. If the ratio is greater than 1.0 (total avoided harms divided by total lost opportunity harms), not-P is judged to be morally permissible and P morally impermissible.

AGGREGATE ENTITY TYPE: _____ (see Note 1)

Predicted Impacts (see Note 2)	Model Inputs								Computed Harm Indices (See Note 3)	
	Probability (scaled 1-3)	Harm Parameters (scaled 1-3)						Harm Magnitude (each impact)	Total Lost Opportunity Harm	Total Avoided Harm
		Extent	Onset	Duration	Proliferation	Controllability	Remediability			

NOT-P AVOIDED HARM (avoided P "costs")

Physical Damage
Prediction 1
Prediction 2
Prediction 3
(etc.)

Resource Deprivation
(predictions as above)
(matrix format as above to scale probability and parameter estimates)

Functional Impairment
(predictions as above)
(matrix format as above to scale probability and parameter estimates)

Physical Pain
(predictions as above)
(matrix format as above to scale probability and parameter estimates)

Emotional Distress
(predictions as above)
(matrix format as above to scale probability and parameter estimates)

Life Termination
(predictions as above)
(matrix format as above to scale probability and parameter estimates)

NOT-P LOST OPPORTUNITY HARM (foregone P "benefits")

Physical Integrity
Prediction 1
Prediction 2
Prediction 3
(etc.)

Resource Availability
(other predictions listed as above)
(matrix format as above to scale probability and parameter estimates)

Note 1: A matrix is completed for each aggregate entity type included in an assessment. N/A is pre-entered in certain cells to indicate that a harm type is not applicable to a harm type or a harm type.

Note 2: Each predicted impact of a proposed policy or project (P) is stated as a condition expected to affect positively or negatively a specified species-population of an aggregate entity type and is listed under a relevant harm type to characterize the nature of harm involved. For negative impacts, the harm types are: physical damage, resource deprivation, functional impairment, physical pain, emotional distress, and life termination. Positive impacts are characterized as conditions expected to enable or enhance physical integrity, resource availability, functional capability, physical pleasure, emotional well-being, and life continuation. Negative impacts are treated in the model as harms that would be avoided if P is not implemented, and positive impacts are treated as foregone opportunities to benefit if P is not implemented.

Note 3: The several indices are computed as follows:

Harm Magnitude is computed by multiplying the probability estimate (scalar) of each predicted impact by the sum of the scalars assigned to each corresponding harm parameter.

Total Lost Opportunity Harm is computed by summing the computed Harm Magnitude of each predicted impact listed as a not-P lost opportunity harm.

Total Avoided Harm is computed by summing the computed Harm Magnitude of each predicted impact listed as a not-P avoided harm.

COMPUTATION OF PROJECT B/C RATIO

AGGREGATE ENTITY TYPES	TOTAL NOT-P AVOIDED HARM (each entity type)	TOTAL NOT-P LOST OPPORTUNITY HARM (each entity type)	PROJECT B/C RATIO
Humans	☐	☐	
Vertebrate Animals	☐	☐	
Invertebrate Animals	☐	☐	
Plants	☐	☐	
Endangered Species	☐	☐	
At-Risk Ecosystems	☐	☐	
	Total ☐ (all entity types)	Total ☐ (all entity types)	☐

Notes

The model labeled "Computation of Entity Harm Indices" computes Total Not-P Avoided Harm and Total Not-P Lost Opportunity Harm for each aggregate entity type included in an assessment. For each aggregate entity type, the two entity entity-level indices are entered manually in the matrix above.

The model sums these manually-entered totals for each aggregate entity type and divides the sum of the entity-level total avoided harm totals by the sum of the entity-level lost opportunity harm totals to obtain the Project B/C ratio. If total project-level not-P avoided harm divided by total project-level not-P lost opportunity harm is greater than 1.0, not-P is judged to be morally permissible and P morally impermissible. If the ratio is less than 1.0, not-P is judged to be morally impermissible and P morally permissible (assuming no actual rights violations).

See Table 2 of Chapter 6 for an explanation of model terminology and logic.

TWELVE-WEEK TASK COMPLETION SCHEDULE

Week 1
Class discussion of Chapter 6 and Appendix materials
Organization of IAT and AMT teams

Week 2
AMT prepares development scenario for instructor sign-off
IATs begin impact predictions

Week 3
IATs compete impact predictions and submit integrated sets to AMT
AMT enters predictions in matrices used for Round 1 probability and parameter esimates by IMTs

Week 4
IMTs begin Round 1 probability and parameter estimates

Week 5
IMTs complete Round 1 probability and parameter estimates for submission to AMT

Week 6
AMT calculates averages and prepares matrices for Round 2 probability and parameter estimates
IMTs begin Round 2 probability and parameter estimates

Week 7
IATs complete Round 2 probability and parameter estimates for submission to AMT

Week 8
AMT calculates averages and prepares matrices for Round 3 probability and parameter estimates
IATs begin Round 3 probability and parameter estimates

Week 9
IATs complete Round 3 probability and parameter estimates and submits to AMT

Week 10
AMT calculates Round 3 averages for incorporation in the model
AMT distributes computed harm indices to class
AMT prepares matrix of highest magnitude impacts (for value weighting) and distributes to class

Week 11
Class value weighting
AMT calculates averages for value weights and incorates averages in the model
AMT distributes computed value-weighted harm indices to class

Week 12
Class critique of completed assessment

NOTE

IMT = Impact Assessment Team
IATs = Impact Assessment Teams

SIXTEEN-WEEK TASK COMPLETION SCHEDULE

Week 1	Week 2	Week 3	Week 4
Class discussion of Chapter 6	Class discussion of Appendix materials, including ANWR case	AMT preparation of development scenario	IATs begin impact predictions
	Organize IAT and AMT student teams	Instructor "sign off" on scenario	

Week 5	Week 6	Week 7	Week 8
IATs complete impact predictions and submit integrated sets to AMT	AMT enters predictions in matrices used for Round 1 estimation of probability and parameter estimates by IMTs	IMTs begin Round 1 probability and parameter estimates	IMTs complete Round 1 probability and parameter estimates for submission to AMT
			Class discussion of progress to date

Week 9	Week 10	Week 11	Week 12
AMT calculates averages and prepares matrices for Round 2 probability and parameter estimates	IATs begin Round 2 probability and parameter estimates	IATs complete Round 2 probability and parameter estimates for submission to AMT	IATs begin Round 3 probability and parameter estimates
		AMT calculates averages and prepares matrices for Round 3 probability and parameter estimates	Class discussion of progress to date

Week 13	Week 14	Week 15	Week 16
IATs complete Round 3 probability and parameter estimates	IATs complete Round 4 probability and parameter estimates	Class value weighting	Class critique of completed assessment
AMT calculates averages and prepares matrices for Round 3 probability and parameter estimates	AMT calculates Round 4 averages for incorporation in the model	AMT calculates averages for value weights and incorporates averages in the model	
	AMT distributes computed harm indices to class	AMT distributes computed value-weighted indices to class	
	AMT prepares matrix with highest magnitude impacts (for value weighting) and distributes to class	Class selection of a "what if Scenario"	
		AMT modification of input values to model and distribution of results to class	

NOTE

IMT = Impact Management Team
IATs = Impact Assessment Teams

G. The Alaskan Native Wildlife Refuge (ANWR) Case

The ANWR case provides a description of the region—its topography, climate, flora, fauna, human inhabitants, and current public lands status—and the many issues related to potential oil and gas development in the Refuge and the institutional context in which decisions will be made. The complexity and far-reaching implications of this case is considered to be a challenging application of the model. Other cases can, of course, be used in conjunction with the model.

An "ANWR" Google search reveals a plethora of information sources and, not surprisingly, diverse views on the prospect of oil and gas development in the Refuge. Three sites may be particularly useful for purposes of the class assessment: a February 14, 2012 report prepared by the Congressional Research Service titled Arctic National Wildlife Refuge: A Primer for the 112th Congress (available at http://www.fas.org/sgp/crs/misc/RL33872.pdf); the Wikipedia article titled Arctic Refuge drilling controversy (http://en.wikipedia.org/wiki/Arctic_Refuge_drilling_controversy); and (3) the website of the US Fish & Wildlife Service (available at http://arctic.fws.gov). The latter has a section that includes maps and photos, a site index (with tabs listing and describing the Refuge's mammals, birds, and wilderness areas); a section on wildlife and wild landscapes (with tabs providing "A Sense of the Refuge,"[1] a description of the impacts of climate change, and a listing of numerous biological reports and scientific studies); and a section on the Refuge's history and local cultures. The instructor may want to download these and other documents for shared class use.

Many of the organizations referenced in the case study also have websites that students can visit. Some of these are avowedly pro-development, while others are committed to conservation and preservation.

The ANWR case begins below.

---

1 The section of the case study with the heading "A Sense of the Refuge" draws from this fourteen-page description.

DRILLING IN ALASKA'S NATIONAL ARCTIC REFUGE

A Sense of the Refuge

The Alaskan Native Wildlife Refuge (ANWR) is located in northeast Alaska and today consists of about 19.3 million acres, a land area approximating that of South Carolina. Established in 1960 as the Arctic National Wildlife Range, it was renamed the Alaskan Native Wildlife Refuge with the passage in 1971 of the Alaska National Interest Lands Conservation Act. The Refuge has no roads, marked trails, or campgrounds and is managed by the US Fish and Wildlife Service with the mandate to preserve unique wildlife, wilderness, and recreational values. The Refuge has five ecological regions:

- The north coastal marine region, next to the Arctic Ocean, consists of salt marshes, lagoons, barrier islands, beaches, and river deltas. These areas are home to polar bears, fish, and migratory birds.
- The coastal plain region lying to the south is a treeless, flat-to-hilly region where caribou and birds raise young in summer. Polar bears den in the coastal plain in winter and hunt fish in deep pools along shallow rivers after hibernation.
- The alpine zone consists of the vast Brooks Range, the northern-most extension of the Rocky Mountains. Dall sheep, grizzly bears, wolves, and ground squirrels live there.
- The forest-tundra transition has spruce trees interspersed with low tundra plants. Caribou feed in this area through the winter, and moose and wolves roam there year-round.
- The southernmost boreal forest region is a mix of spruce, birch, and aspen trees and is the only extensively forested area in the Refuge. It is the home to moose, lynx, weasels, and numerous song-birds.

Native peoples have lived in the northern and southern portions of the area for thousands of years. Inupiat Eskimos live along the northern coast. They hunt seals and whales, fish from barrier islands and along freshwater rivers, catch birds throughout the spring and summer, and travel inland to hunt caribou, wolves, and Dall sheep. Gwinch'in Athabaskan Indians live to the south. Traditionally, they traveled widely each year in search of food and still establish summer fishing camps along rivers, catch waterfowl and other birds, snare small game, and hunt caribou.

Summer in the Arctic is short and the days are long. On the coastal plain, the sun circles the horizon twenty-four hours a day and does not set from mid-May until late July. For those two intense months, midday and midnight sun blend into one, and plants, animals, and people work hard to garner the resources needed for the long winter season ahead. The winter moon, like the summer sun, circles overhead without setting. Reflections off the expanse of snow illuminate the long nights, and the aurora borealis (the "northern lights) periodically glows in the starry sky.

Plants and animals have adapted to these harsh conditions in a variety of ways. A polar bear mother spends five months in her winter den. Mosquitoes survive winter by replacing the water in their bodies with substances that act like antifreeze in a car. Muskoxen save energy by moving very little and are protected by foot-thick coats. Like plants, lemmings use the blanket of snow as insulation. The base of a snow pack may be +20°F, while the air at its surface may be -30°F. The arctic fox's short legs and small ears help it retain body heat. Of the Refuge's 200 recorded bird species, all but about 25 migrate to warmer regions. Some (e.g., the Arctic Tern) make round-trip trips up to 25,000 miles. Caribou stay active all winter and exhibit the longest migration of any land mammal, up to 2,500 miles annually, traveling in herds between winter grazing ground in the south and summer calving grounds in the north. Plants are the foundation of the food chain in the Arctic Refuge. They are eaten by grazers and the latter are eaten by predators.

Warming as much as 5–7 degrees Fahrenheit has occurred over the past fifty years. If current trends continue—an additional warming in the range of 3.5–7.0 degrees is expected to occur by mid-century—all the glaciers in the Arctic Refuge may disappear by the end of the century. Defenders of Wildlife report that ten Arctic Refuge species—lynx, wolverine, caribou, Dall sheep, Alaska marmot, arctic ground squirrel, singing vole, northern bog lemming, tundra shrew, and barren ground shrew—are "highly vulnerable" to climate change. Three mammals—brown bear, marten, and yaiga vole—are classi-fied as "moderately vulnerable." Species adapted to cold, snow, and ice are particularly vulnerable from snow to freezing rain shifts and the collapse of snow tunnels animals use to reach plant nutrients on the ground. To protect these vulnerable species, environmentalists cite the need to limit activities that disturb wildlife and destroy habitat, to maintain linkages to tundra adjacent to the Refuge, and to accelerate investment in research and monitoring of vulnerable species.

Water is the lifeblood of ANWR. It stings as wind-driven snow in the winter, soaks as gentle rain in summer, and penetrates as thick fog. Fed by springs and river flow during winter, it piles up in fields of ice. In spring, it floods the river corridors, washing gravel bars and nourishing plants. During summer, it courses through rivers and streams and finally reaches the north coast, enriching the ocean with its load of minerals. All along the way, it provides life-sustaining habitats for invertebrates and fish, nesting for birds, and drinking water for animals and humans. Water quantity is limited, especially on the coastal plain, where less than five inches of precipitation falls each year. The plain itself has few lakes, and they are shallow and unevenly distributed. Most of the water available during summer comes from spring snowmelt. It pools on the surface and little percolates through the foot-thick permafrost. Water rights in the area are federally owned and managed by the US Fish and Wildlife Service in cooperation with the State.

When the Refuge was established in 1960, it was already receiving occasional visits by hunters and hikers. Visitation increased gradually throughout the 1970s and 80s. A public use study in 1975 estimated 281 visitors. By 1986, that figure doubled and the number of commercial recreational guides increased from 7 in 1980 to 21 nine years later. Since 1986, visitor numbers have nearly tripled. People generally stay 7–11 days, most often to backpack, float rivers, and hunt.

Legal and Political Context

1959   Signing of the Statehood Act by President Kennedy, giving the State of Alaska the right to choose 103 million acres for use as an economic and tax base.

1964   Signing of the Wilderness Act by President Lyndon Johnson, establishing the National Wilderness Preservation System.

1967   Protest of a federal North Shore oil and gas lease by Alaska Natives, resulting in a freeze on all federal lands in Alaska pending settlement of Native land claims.

1971   Signing of the Alaska Native Claims Settlement Act, giving the Kaktovik Inupiat Corporation surface rights to 92,160 acres of federal lands adjacent to the village and 69,120 acres to be selected within the Arctic Range. The coastal village of Kaktovik is the only settlement in the Arctic Refuge.

1977   Completion of the Trans-Alaska Pipeline System bringing North Shore oil to the mainland.

1980   Signing of the Alaska National Interest Lands Conservation Act (ANILCA) by President Nixon, creating 104 million acres of national parks, wildlife refuges, and wilderness areas in Alaska. The Act expanded the Arctic Refuge to approximately 18 million acres, designated 8 million acres as Wilderness, and designated three rivers as Wild. Section 1002 of ANILCA forbids drilling on the coastal plain (containing the Section 1002 area) without Congressional approval.

1983   Expansion of the Refuge by nearly one million acres in the south when the State decided not to retain control of lands it had selected under the Statehood Act.

1983   Conveyance per the Chandler Lake Land Exchange Agreement of federal subsurface rights on Kaktovik Inupiat Corporation (KIC)lands to the Arctic Slope Regional Corporation, allowing exploratory drilling on KIC lands subject to Congressional approval.

1986   Recommendation by the Republican-led US Fish and Wildlife Service (in a draft management plan) that the 1002 area be opened for oil and gas development to protect the nation's economy and national security. In response, Democratic congressman Morris Udall, chairman of the House Interior Committee, unsuccessfully introduced legislation to turn the 1002 area into a protected wilderness area.

1987   Signing of an agreement by the US and Canada to protect the Porcupine caribou from damage to its habitat and migration routes. Canada's Ivvavik and Vuntut National Parks border ANWR. The agreement requires consultation prior to any final decisions.

1988   Addition of 325,000 acres to the south end of the Refuge, bringing the total area to 19.3 million acres and making it the largest Refuge in the National Wildlife Refuge System.

1989   Exxon Valdez oil spill, effectively derailing a pending bill that would have authorized 1002 drilling.

1990–95   Repeated initiatives in Congress related to 1002 drilling. Various pro-drilling strategies were employed, including threatened filibusters and attempts to add provisions to the Energy Bill, the Defense Appropriations bill, and the budget resolution.

1996   Veto by President Clinton of a bill passed by the Republican controlled Congress to allow 1002 drilling.

1997   Ruling by the US Supreme Court that the barrier islands and lagoons which they enclose are within the boundaries of the Arctic Refuge.

2012   Release in August 2012 by the US Fish and Wildlife Service (USFWS) of its Revised Comprehensive Conservation Plan for ANWR. The plan outlined six management alternatives:
          A: No action
          B: designation of the Brooks Range as a wilderness study area
          C: designation of the Coastal Plain (the 1002 area) as a wildlife sanctuary;
          D: designation of the Brooks Range and the Porcupine Plateau as wilderness study areas;
          E: designation of the Brooks Range, the Coastal Plain, and the Porcupine Plateau as wilderness study areas; and
          F: no new wilderness study areas with revised management guidelines. Public hearings were held at six locations.

2012   Release by USFWS in May 2012 of its Public Comments Report.

In regard to the Public Comment Report, approximately 612,000 communications were recorded by USFWS, of which 1,990 were original statements (30% from Alaska) and 610,275 were form letters. A large number of issues were addressed, including (alphabetically) air quality, USFWS alternatives proposed, archaeological sites, cabins/camps, climate change, cultural and historical resources, environmental justice, fire and fire management, glaciers, indigenous subsistence needs, international treaty obligations, legal and policy context, mineral resources, national values and interests, NEPA process, recreation and visitor use, management (USNWS infrastructure, policies, and operations), socio-economic impacts, water resources, and wildlife.

For communications stating a preference for one of the proposed alternatives, USFWS reports that Alternatives A, C, and E were mentioned most frequently. Numerous responses expressed disapproval of the proposed new wilderness study areas and/or objected to the exclusion of oil development in the 1002 area as one of the alternatives. In regard to exclusion of the 1002 development alternative, the following response from the Office of the Governor illustrates a commonly stated line of opposition: "ANILCA and NEPA require that the Plan address oil and gas exploration and potential oil and gas development and production in the 1002 area. Section 1002 of ANILCA explicitly identifies the oil and gas resources of the coastal plain, and directs the Secretary study the role of oil and gas development in the area and make recommendations regarding it to Congress. ... The statement that there is nothing in the Refuge's purposes ... that requires the Service to consider or propose development and utilization scenarios for natural resources, such as oil and gas, as part of the comprehensive conservation planning process, is inaccurate ... While it is true that the final decision regarding oil and gas development in the Refuge rests with Congress, so does the final decision regarding any further wilderness reviews." Various respondents opposing new wilderness study areas (Brooks Range, Porcupine Plateau, and/or the Coastal Plain) cited the "no more" clause of the 1980 Alaska National Interest Lands Conservation Act (ANILCA).

While numerous comments were made on numerous issues, the following submission regarding visitor use in the Refuge is illustrative: "The CCP draft is greatly remiss in not addressing visitor use. The problems and impacts they relate to are only growing worse and need to be addressed now ... They shouldn't be delayed to some possible future planning process. Crowding on popular rivers needs to be reduced, aircraft landing impacts need to be addressed, group size should be limited (to 8 or 9 people), and use allocation should be based on private user preference."

Estimates of ANWR Oil Reserves

In 1998, the US Geological Survey (USGS) estimated that between 5.7 and 16.0 billion barrels of oil are technically recoverable from ANWR's coastal plain, of which a mean estimate of 7.7 million barrels falls within the 1002 area. The report estimated that 120 billion barrels are technically recoverable from other areas in the US.

A report prepared in 2008 for Alaska Senator Ted Stevens by DOE's Energy Information Administration, which report is based primarily on the 1998 USGS report and the National Energy Modeling System, came to the following conclusions:

- Assuming no regulatory delays, ANWR oil production would begin 10 years after legislation approves oil and gas leasing in the 1002 area, during which time an Environmental Impact Statement would be approved and leases acquired (2–3 years), a single exploratory well would be drilled (2–3 years), a production development plan would be prepared (1–2 years), and feeder pipelines, oil separation and treatment plants, drilling pads, and wells would be constructed (3–4 years).
- If production began in 2018 (2000 + 18 years), production of 780,000 barrels per day would reach a peak in 2027 and decline to 710,000 barrels in 2030 (mean case).
- ANWR production would represent a small fraction of total world production, and would likely be offset in part by somewhat lower production outside the US. [DOE estimates that proved (vs. prospective) world reserves in the range of 1.1–1.3 trillion barrels.]
- ANWR production would reduce oil import dependency to 47.5% (mean case) during the 2022–2026 time frame, but with declining production would increase again to 54% by 2030.
- The opening of ANWR is projected to reduce the price of light crude oil by $0.75 per barrel (2006 dollars).
- The upper limit to ANWR oil production is the transportation capacity of the Trans-Alaska Pipeline System (TAPS). The high ANWR oil production case is projected to come closest in 2026 to reaching TAPS' pipeline

capacity (2.136 barrels per day), when total North Slope oil production peaks at 1.9 million barrels per day.

In 2010, USGS downsized estimates of recoverable oil from the National Petroleum Reserve (east of Prudhoe Bay and west of ANWR), concluding that areas believed to hold oil actually hold natural gas.

Views Supporting 1022 Drilling

A majority of Alaskans support development, including every governor, senator, representative, and legislature for the past 25 years. Alaska residents receive annual dividends ($1,964 per resident in 2000) from a permanent fund dependent primarily on oil and gas revenues.

The Resource Development Council for Alaska, an association of companies from the oil and gas, mining, forest products, tourism, and fisheries industries, is a potent advocate for "the responsible development of the State's natural resources."

In its active and on-going campaign for ANWR development, Arctic Power points out that precedents exist for drilling in wildlife refuges, citing a U.S Fish and Wildlife Service report that 77 of the 567 wildlife refuges in 22 states permit oil and gas-related activities, with actual production occurring in 45 refuges in 15 states.

A state-funded survey revealed that 53 of 68 responding Kaktovik residents "agree that ANWR's coastal plain should be opened to oil and gas exploration." While the survey and tabulation of results is alleged to be problematic, it is evident that some support for drilling exists among some Kaktovik residents.

The Pew Research Poll reported in June 2008 that 50% of Americans favor ANWR drilling.

In response to the USFWS 2012 draft Revised Comprehensive Conservation Plan, the Office of the Governor said this: "Oil and gas development and production in the Refuge may be authorized by Congress at any time, and the current national dialogue regarding the need for jobs, energy security, and deficit reduction makes the likelihood of such an action higher than ever before."

Views Opposing 1002 Drilling

Critics challenge the claim that ANWR oil production will reduce US dependency on foreign oil and lower oil prices. From the above-referenced 2008 DOE report: "The USGS oil resource estimates are based largely on the oil productivity of geologic formations that exist in the neighboring State lands and which continue into ANWR. Thus, the potential ultimate oil recovery and potential yearly production are highly uncertain." Further: "ANWR production is not projected to have a large impact on world oil prices. ... Additional oil production resulting from the opening of ANWR would be only a small portion of total world production, and would likely be offset by production outside the United States."

The Natural Resources Defense Council (NRDC) contends that 1002 drilling would not take place in a compact 2,000-acre space as proponents claim, but require "a spider web of industrial sprawl across the whole of the refuge's coastal plain, including drill sites, airports, roads, and gravel mines. Its actual footprint would be spread across 640,000 acres, or 1,000 square miles."

USGS reports that the 1002 area "has a greater degree of ecological diversity than any other similar sized area of Alaska's north slope" and that "those who have campaigned to establish the Arctic Refuge recognized its wild qualities and [its] unusually diverse assemblage of large animals and smaller, less-appreciated life forms, tied to their physical environments and to each other by natural, undisturbed ecological and evolutionary process."

Numerous Native American groups oppose oil and gas development within the Refuge. The Alaska Inter-Tribal Council (representing 229 Native Alaskan tribes) opposes such development. The Native Alaskan and Canadian Gwinch'in Tribe views ANWR drilling as "a basic Aboriginal human rights issue," noting that "Sixty to 70 percent of our diet comes from the land and caribou is one of the primary animals that we depend on for sustenance." The Inupiat from Point Hope, Alaska passed a resolution in 2005 expressing concern that 1002 drilling would lead to resource exploitation in other wilderness areas. The National Congress of American Indians and the Native American Rights Fund also oppose drilling in the Refuge.

Numerous responses to the USFWS 2012 draft Revised Comprehensive Conservation Plan came from numerous environmental organizations opposing oil development and favoring wilderness conservation, including (listed in order of the number of responses received, many of which were form letters) Defenders of Wildlife, Greenpeace, Sierra Club, Natural Resources Defense Council, Center for Biological Diversity, The Wilderness Society, Alaska

Wilderness League, Save our Environment Action Center, National Wildlife Federation Action Fund, League of Conservation Voters, Audubon Society, Endangered Species Coalition, Wilderness Watch, Pacific Environment, National Wildlife Refuge Association, Gwinch'in Nation, Republicans for Environmental Protection, and Friends of Alaska National Wildlife Refuges.

In response to a League of Conservation Voters survey conducted during the 2008 presidential campaign, candidate Obama said, "I strongly reject drilling in the Arctic National Wildlife Refuge because it would irreversibly damage a protected national wildlife refuge without creating sufficient oil supplies to meaningfully affect the global market price or have a discernible impact on US energy security." John McCain, Obama's rival on the Republican ticket, expressed this sentiment: "As far as ANWR is concerned, I don't want to drill in the Grand Canyon, and I don't want to drill in the Everglades. This is one of the most pristine and beautiful parts of the world."

North Sea Oil Exploration and Development

Following federal approval of an air quality permit and an oil spill clean-up plan, Royal Dutch Shell has embarked on an exploratory drilling program to assess whether an estimated 27 billion barrels of oil and 132 trillion cubic feet of natural gas is recoverable from Alaska's North Sea. Proponents argue that production could cut America's dependence on foreign oil and provide jobs and needed revenue to the Treasury Department. Opponents fear that drilling rig and tanker spills could lead to unmitigated disaster.

The Center for Biological Diversity warns that "All signs point to environmental disaster if an oil spill were to occur in the harsh Arctic waters." The Alaska Wilderness League agrees: "The Arctic is prone to hurricane-force storms, 20-foot ice swells, sea ice up to 25 feet thick, sub-zero temperatures, and months-long darkness. What's more, the Arctic has extremely limited infrastructure (there are no roads or deep water ports and only a handful of small airports) and the nearest Coast Guard station is 1,000 miles away." The Natural Resources Defense Council adds that "Nobody knows how to contain or clean up a spill in the harsh remote seas of the Arctic. If a blowout occurs late in the drilling season, there won't be time to stop it before the winter ice chokes the site, leaving oil to gush uncontrolled for months." Perhaps mitigating this concern, scientists predict that there will be less ice by mid-century, and some are predicting that year-round shipping will be common by that time.

In Washington, politicians are jockeying over whether to ratify "The Law of the Sea Treaty," under which countries abutting oceans will be able to claim up to 200 miles of undersea territory if they can prove it to be an extension of their continental shelves. For the US, that could mean extra territory the size of California. President Obama and former President George W. Bush support the treaty, as does an oddly aligned coalition that includes the Pentagon, oil companies, shipping companies, and various environmental organization that favor the part of the treaty designed to help protect the world's oceans. Although every other Arctic country has ratified the treaty, conservative senators fear that ratification would give too much influence to multinational bodies.

Shell plans to use exploratory drilling ships in two areas of the North Sea: a site west of Barrow named Burger in the Chukchi Sea and a site close to Kaktovik named Hammerhead. Efforts to date have not gone well for Shell. Drilling had to be postponed from July to August of 2012 because of an unexpectedly thick ice pack, concerns have been raised about the durability of one of its underwater oil spill containment vessels, numerous small spills have occurred, and two of its drilling rigs, the Kulluck and Noble Discoverer, are on their way to Asia for dry dock repair. En route for repair, the Noble Discover slipped its mooring and ran aground near one of Alaska's Aleutian Islands. Also, environmentalists are calling for a review of Shell's air quality permit.

Not surprisingly, Alaska's indigenous residents view North Sea drilling as ominous, if not disastrous. The village of Kaktovik passed a resolution in May 2006 authorizing the mayor to take legal and other actions necessary to "defend the community." The resolution referred to Shell Oil as "a hostile and dangerous force" and "called on all North Slope communities to oppose Shell offshore leases ... until the company becomes more respectful of the people." Kaktovik's mayor stated that Shell has failed to work with the villagers on how the company would protect bowhead whales which are part of Native culture, subsistence, and diet.

An increasing number of pro-development advocates see 1002 drilling as a preferred alternative to drilling in the North Sea.

Concluding Note

The future of oil development in the region depends on numerous contingencies: how USFWS structures the alternatives considered in its Revised

Conservation Plan and whether new lands, including Section 1002, are designated as wilderness areas subject to Congressional approval, whether exploratory drilling in the North Sea reveals economically feasible expected recoverable reserves and North Sea development occurs, and whether Congress passes and the President signs a bill authorizing 1002 drilling in the near or longer term.

INDEX

A

B

T

V

W

Z

CPSIA information can be obtained
at www.ICGtesting.com
Printed in the USA
FSOW02n2117300316
18644FS